Core Connections Algebra 2

Second Edition*, Version 4.0, Volume 1

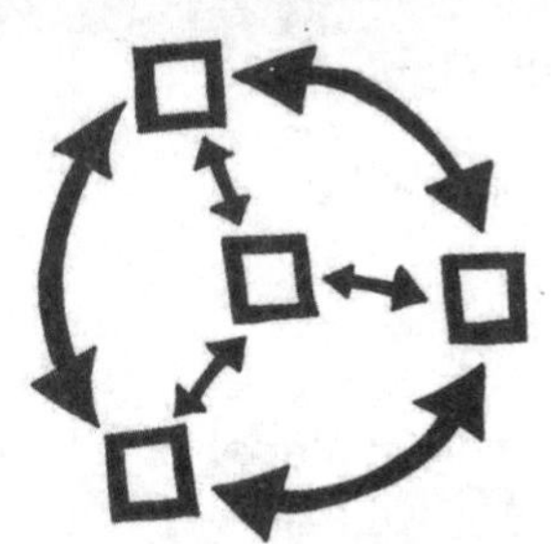

Managing Editors / Authors

Judy Kysh (Both Editions)
San Francisco State University
San Francisco, CA

Michael Kassarjian (2nd Edition)
CPM Educational Program
Encino, CA

Evra Baldinger (First Edition)
University of California, Berkeley
Berkeley, CA

Contributing Authors

Karen Arth
Central High School East
Fresno, CA

Mark Atkinson
North Salem High School
Salem, OR

Carlos Cabana
San Lorenzo High School
San Lorenzo, CA

John Cooper
Del Oro High School
Loomis, CA

Elizabeth Coyner
Christian Brothers High School
Sacramento, CA

Scott Coyner
Christian Brothers High School
Sacramento, CA

Dolores Dean
Holy Family High School
Broomfield, CO

Ernest Derrera
Roosevelt High School
Johnston, CO

Leslie Dietiker
Michigan State University
East Lansing, MI

Misty Nikula
Whatcom Day Acadamy
Bellingham, WA

Bob Petersen
Rosemont High School
Sacramento, CA

Norm Prokup
The College Preparatory School
Oakland, CA

Barbara Shreve
San Lorenzo High School
San Lorenzo, CA

Estelle Woodbury
San Lorenzo High School
San Lorenzo, CA

Karen Wootton
CPM Educational Program
Odenton, MD

Technical Managers

Hannah Coyner
Sacramento, CA

Sarah Maile
Sacramento, CA

Claire Taylor
Sacramento, CA

Program Directors

Leslie Dietiker, Ph.D.
Boston University
Boston, MA

Lori Hamada
CPM Educational Program
Fresno, CA

Brian Hoey
CPM Educational Program
Sacramento, CA

Judy Kysh, Ph.D.
Departments of Education and Mathematics
San Francisco State University, CA

Tom Sallee, Ph.D.
Department of Mathematics
University of California, Davis

*Based on *Algebra 2 Connections*

e-book Manager
Carol Cho
Director of Technology
Martinez, CA

e-book Programmers
Rakesh Khanna
Daniel Kleinsinger
Kevin Stein

e-book Assistants
Debbie Dodd
Shirley Paulsen
Wendy Papciak
Anna Poehlmann
Jordan Wight

Assessment Manager
Karen Wootton
Director of Assessment
Odenton, MD

Assessment Website
Elizabeth Fong
Michael Huang
Daniel Kleinsinger

Illustration
Kevin Coffey
San Francisco, CA

Homework Help Manager
Bob Petersen
CPM Educational Program

Homework Help Website
Carol Cho
Director of Technology

Parent Guide with Extra Practice
Bob Petersen (Managing Editor)
CPM Educational Program
Sacramento, CA

Scott Coyner
Christian Brothers High School
Sacramento, CA

Brian Hoey
Christian Brothers High School
Sacramento, CA

Sarah Maile
CPM Educational Program
Sacramento, CA

Karen Wooton
CPM Educational Program
Odenton, MD

Technical Manager
Rebecca Harlow
Sarah Maile

Technical Assistants
Stephanie Achondo
Eric Baxter
Diego Breedlove
Carrie Cai
Mary Coyner
Bethany Firch
Rebecca Harlow
Leslie Lai
Michael Li
James McCardle
Wendy Papciak
Iris Perez
Eduardo Ramirez
Andrea Smith
Christy Van Beek
Alex Yu
Robert Ainsworth
Rebecca Bobell
Duncan Breedlove
Alex Contreras
Carmen de la Cruz
Elizabeth Fong
Dana Kimball
Keith Lee
Jerry Luo
Nyssa Muheim
Atlanta Parrott
Steven Pham
John Ramos
Rachel Smith
Megan Walters
Erica Andrews
Delenn Breedlove
Elizabeth Burke
Hannah Coyner
Matthew Donahue
Miguel Francisco
Madeline Kimball
Michael Leong
Eli Marable
Alexandra Murphy
Ryan Peabody
Anna Poehlmann
Ali Rivera
Claire Taylor
Sarah Wong

2 3 4 5 6 16 15 14 13 Version 4.0

Printed in the United States of America ISBN: 978-1-60328-113-3

A Note to Students:

Welcome to a new year of math! In this course, you will learn to use new models and methods to think about problems as well as solve them. You will be developing powerful mathematical tools and learning new ways of thinking about and investigating situations. You will be making connections, discovering relationships, figuring out what strategies can be used to solve problems, and explaining your thinking. Learning to think in these ways and communicate about your thinking is useful in mathematical contexts, other subjects in school, and situations outside the classroom. The mathematics you have learned in the past will be valuable for learning in this course. That work, and what you learn in this course, will prepare you for future courses.

In meeting the challenges of this course, you will not be learning alone. You will cooperate with other students as a member of a study team. Being a part of a team means speaking up and interacting with other people. You will explain your ideas, listen to what others have to say, and ask questions if there is something you do not understand. In this course, a single problem can often be solved several ways. You will see problems in different ways than your teammates do. Each of you has something to contribute while you work on the lessons in this course.

Together, your team will complete problems and activities that will help you discover mathematical ideas and develop solution methods. Your teacher will support you as you work, but will not take away your opportunity to think and investigate for yourself. Each topic will be revisited many times and will connect to other topics. If something is not clear to you the first time you work on it, you will have more chances to build your understanding as the course continues.

Learning math this way has an advantage: as long as you actively participate, make sure everyone in your study team is involved, and ask good questions, you will find yourself understanding mathematics at a deeper level than ever before. By the end of this course, you will have a powerful set of mathematical tools to use to solve new problems. With your teammates you will meet mathematical challenges you would not have known how to approach before.

In addition to the support provided by your teacher and your study team, CPM has also created online resources to help you, including help with homework, and a parent guide with extra practice. You will find these resources and more at www.cpm.org.

We wish you well and are confident that you will enjoy this next year of learning!

Sincerely,
The CPM Team

Core Connections Algebra 2
Student Edition

Volume 1

Volume 2

INVESTIGATIONS AND FUNCTIONS

Chapter 1 Investigations and Functions

Welcome to Algebra 2! This chapter will introduce you to the ways you will be working as well as several of the big ideas in this course. You will share your current mathematical knowledge with your study team as you work together to solve problems. Some of these ideas you will revisit later in the course and connect to new mathematical ideas. You will learn to work with a graphing calculator to help you discover qualities of functions and systems of functions.

Guiding Question

Mathematically proficient students construct reasonable arguments and critique the reasoning of others.

As you work through this chapter, ask yourself:

As I investigate functions, am I analyzing the function thoroughly and clearly communicating my reasoning to others?

Chapter Outline

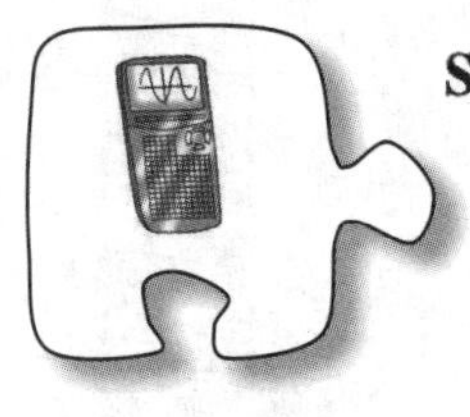

Section 1.1 In this section, you will get to know the members of your study team. You will work with your team to develop skills and techniques for using a graphing calculator to help you explore functions and intersections, and you will present your results to the class.

Section 1.2 Here, you will find multiple ways to represent a geometric relationship, summarize your results, and present your results to the class. You will also analyze the family of exponential functions and investigate a non-linear non-exponential function. You will develop your understanding of what it means to investigate a function.

1.1.1 How can I work with my team to figure it out?

Solving Puzzles in Teams

Welcome to Algebra 2! This first chapter will challenge you to use different problem-solving strategies. You will also be introduced to different tools and resources that you can use throughout the course as you investigate new ideas, solve problems, and share mathematical ideas.

1-1. BUILDING WITH YARN

Work with your team to make each of the shapes you see below out of a single loop of yarn. You may make the shapes in any order. Before you start, review the Team Roles that are described on the next page. Use these roles to help your study team work together today. When you make one of the shapes successfully, call your teacher over to show off your accomplishment.

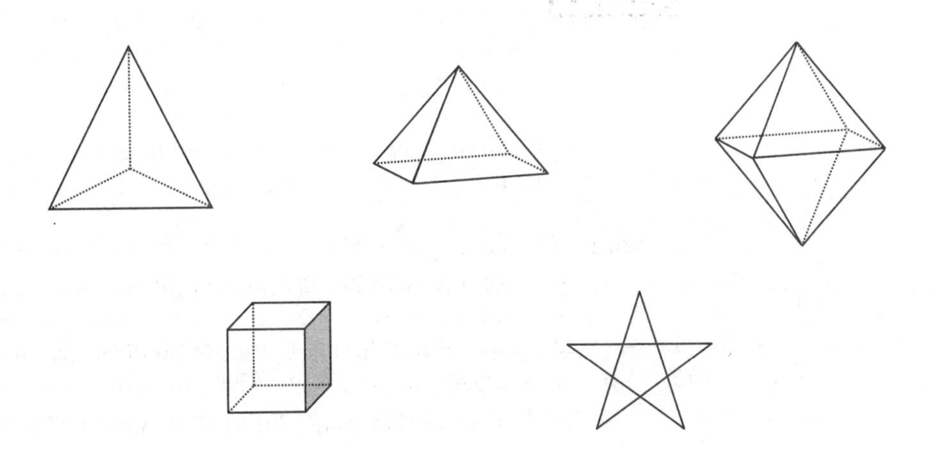

Team Roles

Resource Manager: If your name comes first alphabetically:

- Make sure your team has all of the necessary materials, such as yarn for problem 1-1 or the resource pages for problem 1-2.
- Ask your teacher a question when the *entire* team is stuck. Before raising your hand, you might ask your team, *"Does anyone have an idea? Should I ask the teacher?"*
- Make sure your team cleans up materials by delegating tasks. You could say, *"I will put away the ________ while you _________ ."*

Facilitator: If your name comes second alphabetically:

- Start your team's discussion by reading the question aloud and then asking, *"Which shape should we start with?"* or *"How can we work together to make this shape?"*
- Make sure that all of the team members get any necessary help. You do not need to answer all of the questions yourself. A good Facilitator regularly asks, *"Do we understand what we are supposed to do?"* and *"Who can answer ________'s question?"*

Recorder/Reporter: If your name comes third alphabetically:

- Be sure all team members are able to reach the yarn and have access to the resource pages. Make sure resource pages and work that is being discussed are placed in the center of the table or group of desks in a spot where everyone can see them.
- Be prepared to share your team's strategies and results with the class. You might report, *"We tried ___ , but it didn't work, so we decided to try ___ ."*

Task Manager: If your name comes fourth alphabetically:

- Remind the team to stay on task and not to talk to students in other teams. You can suggest, *"Let's try working on a different shape,"* or *"Are we ready to try the function machines in a different order?"*
- Keep track of time. Give your team reminders, such as, "*I think we need to decide now so that we will have enough time to …*"

1-2. FUNCTION MACHINES

Your teacher will give you a set of four function machines. Your team's job is to get a specific output by putting those machines in a particular order so that one machine's output becomes the next machine's input. As you work, discuss what you know about the kind of output each function produces to help you arrange the machines in an appropriate order. The four functions are reprinted below.

1) $f(x)=\sqrt{x}$ 3) $g(x)=-(x-2)^2$

2) $h(x)=2^x-7$ 4) $k(x)=-\frac{x}{2}-1$

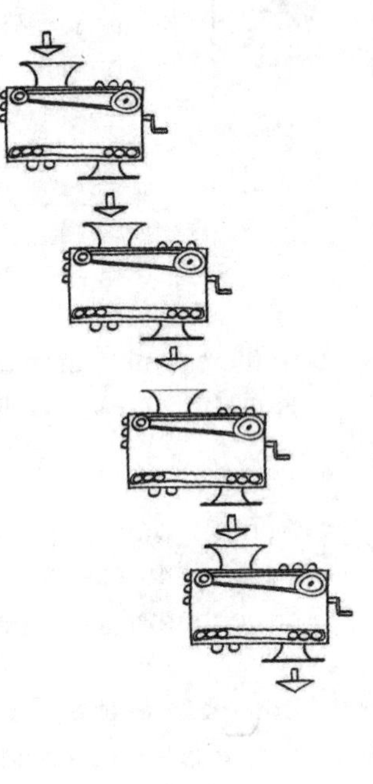

a. In what order should you stack the machines so that when 6 is dropped into the first machine, and all four machines have had their effect, the last machine's output is 11?

b. What order will result in a final output of 131,065 when the first input is 64?

A. $g(x)=-(x-2)^2$

$k(x)=-\frac{x}{2}-1$

$h(x)=2^x-7$

$f(x)=\sqrt{x}$

B.

METHODS AND MEANINGS

MATH NOTES

Functions

A relationship between inputs and outputs is a **function** if there is no more than one output for each input. Functions are often written as y = some expression involving x, where x is the input and y is the output. The following is an example of a function.

$$y=(x-2)^2$$

x	−2	−1	0	1	2	3	4	5
y	16	9	4	1	0	1	4	9

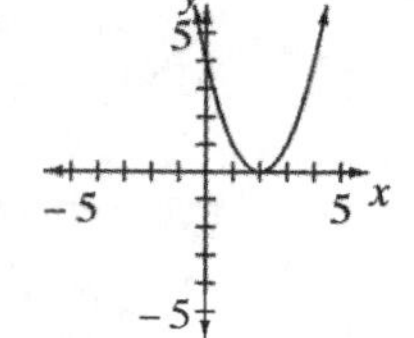

In the example above the value of y depends on x, so y is also called the **dependent variable** and x is called the **independent variable**.

Another way to write a function is with the notation "$f(x)=$" instead of "$y=$". The function named "f" has output $f(x)$. The input is x.

In the example at right, $f(5)=9$. The input is 5 and the output is 9. You read this as, "f of 5 equals 9."

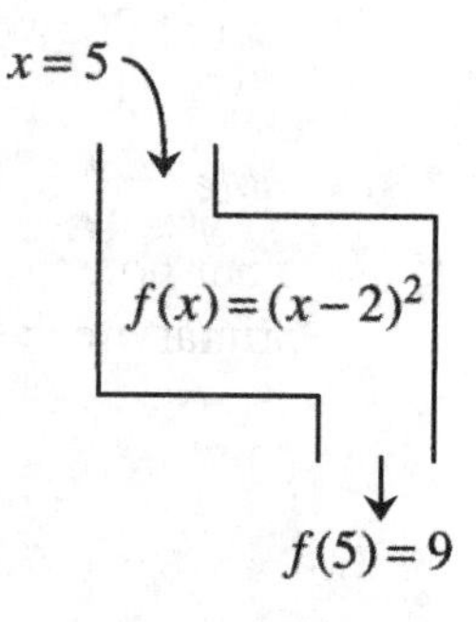

The set of all inputs for which there is an output is called the **domain**. The set of all possible outputs is called the **range**. In the example above, notice that you can input any x-value into the equation and get an output. The domain of this function is "all real numbers" because any number can be an input. The outputs are all greater than or equal to zero, so the range is $y \geq 0$.

$x^2+y^2=1$ is not a function because there are two y-values (outputs) for some x-values, as shown below.

$$x^2+y^2=1$$

x	−1	0	0	1
y	0	−1	1	0

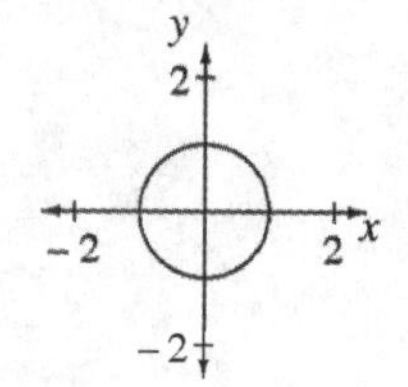

1-3. KEEPING A NOTEBOOK

You will need to keep an organized notebook for this course. Below is one method of keeping a notebook. Ask your teacher if you should follow these guidelines or if there is another system you should follow.

- The notebook should be a sturdy, three-ring, loose-leaf binder with a hard cover.
- The binder should have dividers to separate it into five sections:

TEXT	TESTS AND QUIZZES
HOMEWORK	LINED AND GRAPH PAPER
CLASSWORK/NOTES	

You should put your name inside the front cover of your notebook so it will be returned to you if you lose it. Put your phone number and address (or the school's address, if you prefer) on the inside front cover. It will also help to put your name in large, clear letters on the outside so if someone sees it they can say, *"Hey, Julia, I saw your notebook in the cafeteria under the back table."*

Your notebook will be your biggest asset for this course and will be the primary resource you will use to study, so take good care of it!

1-4. "Find $f(3)$" means to find the output of function $f(x)$ for an input of $x = 3$. For the function $f(x) = \frac{1}{x-2}$, find each of the following values.

a. Find $f(4)$. (This means find the output of the function when $x = 4$.)

b. Find x when $f(x) = 1$. (This means find the input that gives an output of 1.)

1-5. Angelica is working with function machines. She has the two machines $g(x) = \sqrt{x-5}$ and $h(x) = x^2 - 6$. She wants to put them in order so that the output of the first machine becomes the input of the second. She wants to use a beginning input of 6.

a. In what order must she put the machines to get a final output of 5?

b. Is it possible for her to get a final output of –5? If so, show how she could do that. If not, explain why not.

1-6. An average school bus holds 45 people. Sketch a graph showing the relationship between the number of students who need bus transportation and the number of buses required. Be sure to label the axes.

1-7. In this course, you will learn shortcuts that allow you to sketch many different types of graphs quickly and accurately. However, when the directions ask you to *graph an equation* or to *draw a graph*, this means it is not just a sketch you should do quickly. You need to:

- Use graph paper.
- Scale your axes appropriately.
- Label key points.
- Plot points accurately.

On separate sets of axes, graph each of the following equations. If you do not remember any shortcuts for graphing, you can always make an $x \to y$ table.

a. $y = -2x + 7$

b. $y = \frac{3}{5}x + 1$

c. $3x + 2y = 6$

d. $y = x^2$

1-8. The graph for part (d) of problem 1-7 is different from the other three graphs.

a. Explain how the graph is different from the other three graphs.

b. What in the equation of part (d) makes its graph different?

c. What is the graph of part (d) called?

1-9. Write down everything you know about the equation $y = mx + b$. You should include what this general equation represents, as well as what each of the different letters represents. Be as thorough as possible.

1.1.2 How can I use my graphing calculator?

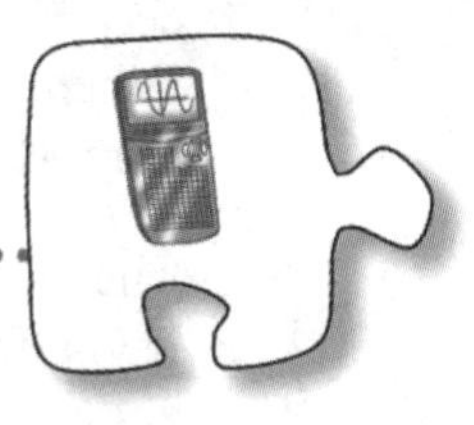

Using a Graphing Calculator to Explore a Function

In Algebra 1 you learned that multiple representations such as situations, tables, graphs, and equations along with their interconnections are useful for learning about functions. A graphing calculator can be a very useful tool for generating different representations quickly. Today, you will use this tool to explore a function. You will describe your function completely to the class.

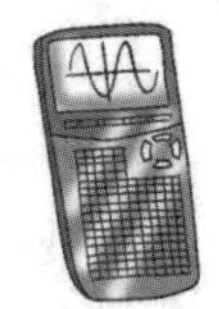

1-10. Your team will use graphing calculators to learn about one of the following functions.

i. $y=2\sqrt{9-x}-4$

ii. $y=\sqrt{100-x^2}$

iii. $y=3\sqrt{x+4}-6$

iv. $y=3\sqrt{4-x}-3$

v. $y=-2\sqrt{25-x^2}+8$

vi. $y=-3\sqrt{x+9}+4$

vii. $y=2\sqrt{25-x^2}-1$

viii. $y=\sqrt{4-x}-1$

Your Task: Describe your team's function in as much detail as possible. Use your graphing calculator to help you generate a table and a complete graph of your function. Remember that drawing a complete graph means:

- Use graph paper.
- Scale your axes appropriately.
- Label key points.
- Plot points accurately.

As you work, keep your graphing calculators in the middle of your workspace, so that you can compare your screens and all team members can see and discuss your results. Be sure to record what you learn as you explore your function. As a team, you will be preparing a report about your function for the class. Consider the Discussion Points below as you work.

Discussion Points

What are the key points on the graph? Where are they exactly?

Can we identify at least five integer inputs that give integer values as outputs?

Are there values of x or y that do not make sense?

How high or low does the graph go?

Did the graphing calculator show an accurate graph?

How can we be sure the graph is complete?

1-11. When your team has completed a table and drawn a complete graph, prepare a report for the whole class.

The class will get the most out of your presentation if you focus on what was particularly interesting about your function or what you learned. Rather than saying, "*We plugged in a 2 and got a 5,*" consider using statements such as, "*We decided to try an input of 2 because we wanted to know what happened to the left of* $x = 3$."

The following sentence starters can help you make a meaningful and interesting presentation.

"At first we were confused by…"

"This makes sense because…"

"We weren't sure about…, so we tried…"

"Something interesting that we noticed about our graph is…"

As you prepare your presentation, your teacher will provide you with poster-making supplies. Reread the task statement of problem 1-10 (labeled "Your Task") and be sure to include all relevant information and ideas in your presentation.

METHODS AND MEANINGS

MATH NOTES

Linear Equations

A **linear equation** is an equation that forms a line when it is graphed. This type of equation may be written in several different forms. Although these forms look different, they are equivalent; that is, their graphs are all the same line.

Standard Form: An equation in $ax + by = c$ form, such as $6x - 3y = 18$.

Slope-Intercept Form: An equation in $y = mx + b$ form, such as $y = 2x - 6$.

You can find the **slope** (also known as the **growth factor**) and the **y-intercept** of a line in $y = mx + b$ form quickly. For the equation $y = 2x - 6$, the slope is 2, while the y-intercept is (0, –6).

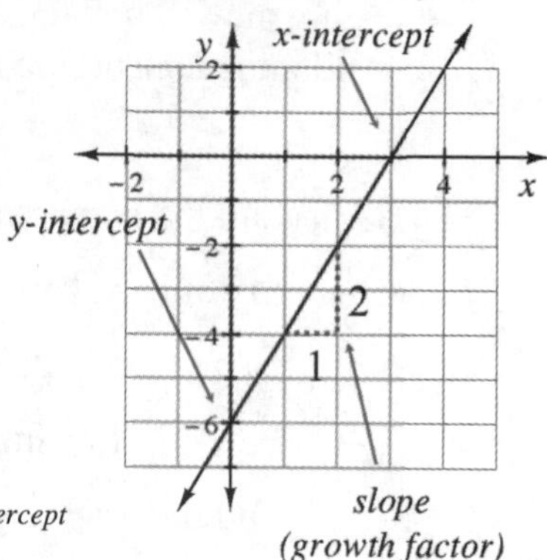

$y = 2x - 6$ ← *y-intercept*; *slope* ↑ (2)

1-12. Junior is saving money in his piggy bank. He starts with 10 cents and adds two pennies each day. Create an $x \rightarrow y$ table and a graph for the function for which x represents the number of days since Junior started saving money and y represents the total money he has saved.

1-13. Use the Zero Product Property and factoring, when necessary, to solve for x. The Math Notes box for Lesson 1.1.4 may be useful, if you need help.

a. $(x+13)(x-7)=0$

b. $(2x+3)(3x-7)=0$

c $x(x-3)=0$

d. $x^2-5x=0$

e. $x^2-2x-35=0$

f. $3x^2+14x-5=0$

1-14. Terri's project for the Math Fair was a magnificent black box that she called a function machine. If you put 3 into her machine, the output would be 8. If you put in 10, the output would be 29; and if you put in 20, it would be 59.

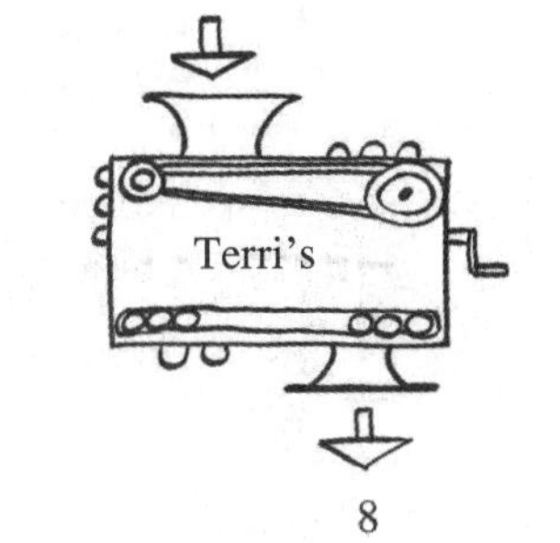

a. What would her machine do to the input 5? What about –1? What about x? Making an input $\rightarrow$ output table may help.

b. Write an equation for Terri's machine.

1-15. Nafeesa graphed a line with a slope of 5 and a y-intercept of (0, –2).

a. Find an equation for her line.

b. Find the value of x when $y=0$.

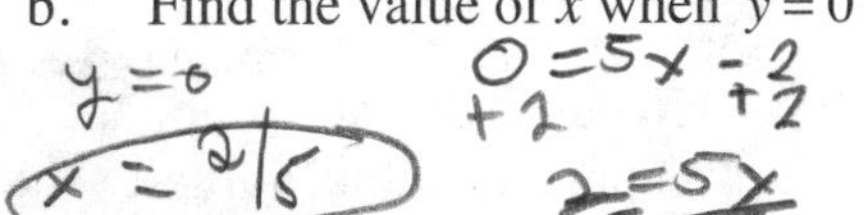

1-16. In each of the following equations, what is y when $x=2$? When $x=0$? Where would the graph of each equation cross the y-axis?

a. $y=3x+15$

b. $y=3-3x$

1-17. Carmichael made a function machine. The inner workings of the machine are visible in the diagram at right. What will the output be in each of the following cases?

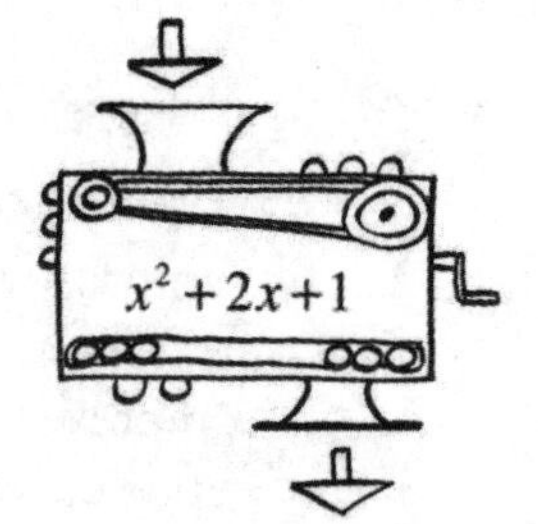

a. If 3 is dropped in?

b. If –4 is dropped in?

c. If –22.872 is dropped in?

1-18. Does the temperature outside depend on the time of day, or does the time of day depend on the temperature outside? This may seem like a silly question, but to sketch a graph that represents this relationship, you first need to decide which axis will represent which quantity.

a. When you graph an equation such as $y = 3x - 5$, which variable (the x or the y) *depends* on the other? Which is not dependent? (That is, which is *in*dependent?) Explain.

b. Which variable is *dependent*: temperature or time of day? Which variable is *independent*?

c. Sketch a graph (with appropriately named axes) that shows the relationship between temperature outside and time of day.

1-19. Jill needs to cut a smaller piece from a 30-foot length of lumber. Create multiple representations ($x \to y$ table, graph, and equation) for the function with x-values that are the length of the piece Jill cuts off and y-values that are the length of the piece that is left over. Which representation best portrays the situation? Why? Explain.

1-20. Make a table and graph the function $f(x) = \frac{1}{2}x^2$. Describe all of the possible input and output values.

1-21. Given $f(x) = -\frac{2}{3}x + 3$ and $g(x) = 2x^2 - 5$, complete parts (a) through (f) below.

a. Calculate $f(3)$.

b. Solve $f(x) = -5$.

c. Calculate $g(-3)$.

d. Solve $g(x) = -7$.

e. Solve $g(x) = 8$.

f. Solve $g(x) = 9$.

1-22. Gerri made a function machine. Below are four pictures of her machine. (Note that these are all pictures of the same function machine.) Find the equation for Gerri's function machine.

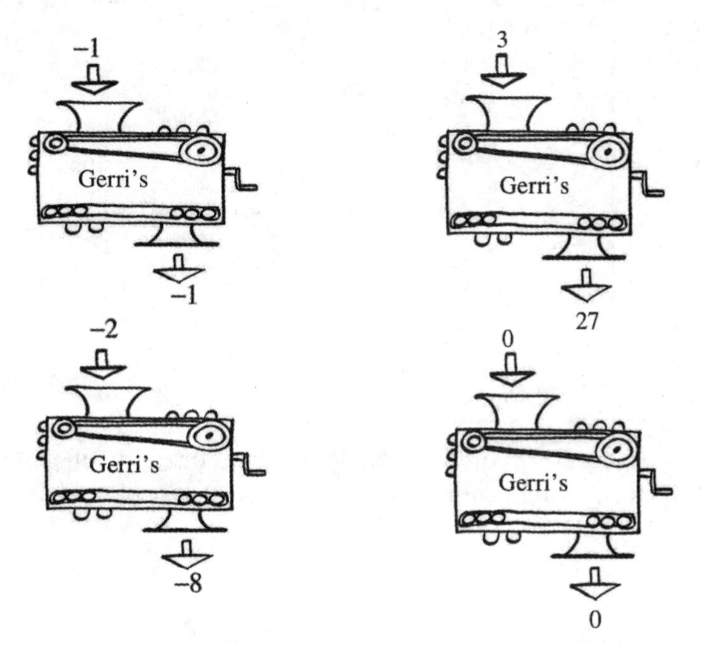

$f(x) = x^3$

$-1^3 = -1$

$3^3 = 27$

$-2^3 = 8$

$0^3 = 0$

1-23. Examine each graph below. Based on the shape of the graph and the labels on the axes, write a sentence to describe the relationship that each graph represents. Then state which axis represents the independent variable and which one represents the dependent variable.

a.

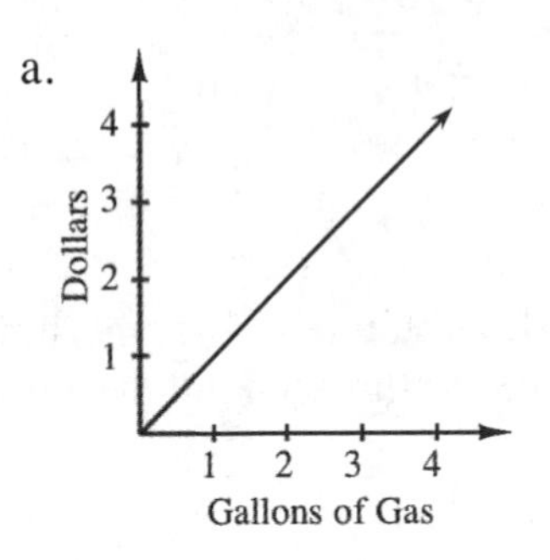

b.

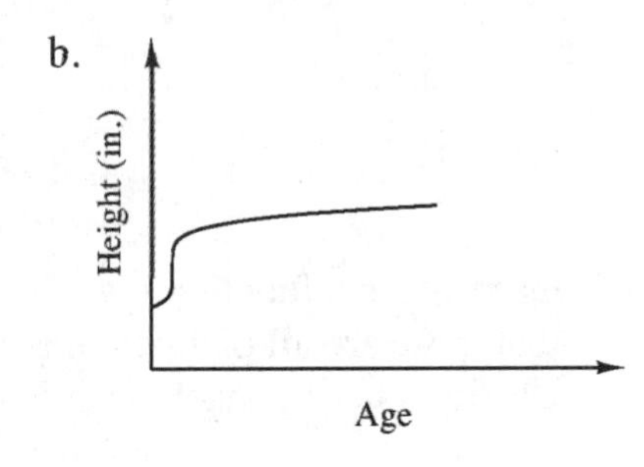

c.

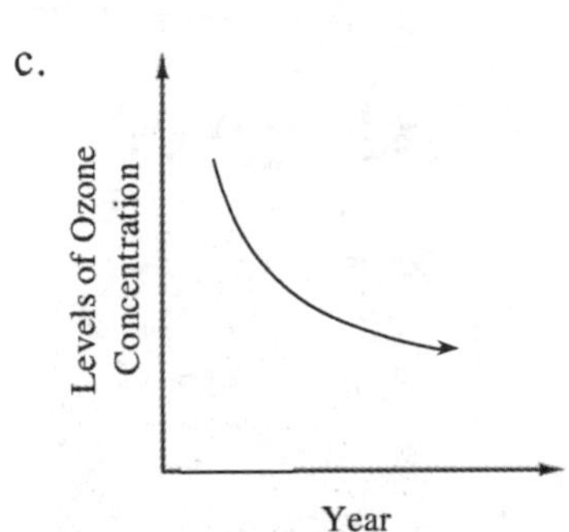

d.

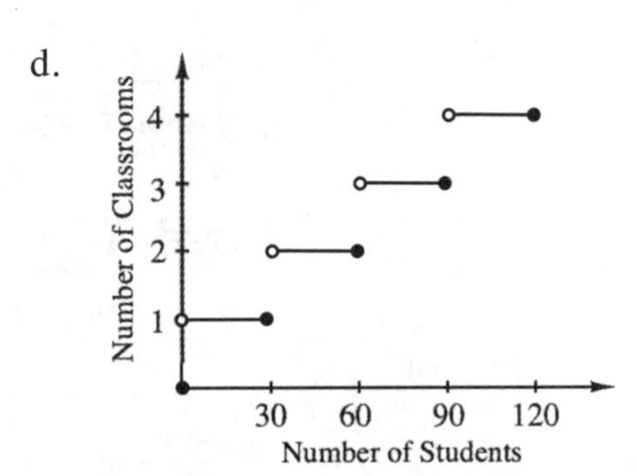

e. What are all of the possible inputs of the graph in part (d)? What are all of the possible outputs?

1-24. Consider triangles ABC and ADE at right. Give a convincing argument why $\Delta ABC \sim \Delta ADE$. Then use what you know about similar triangles to complete each of the following ratios for the triangles.

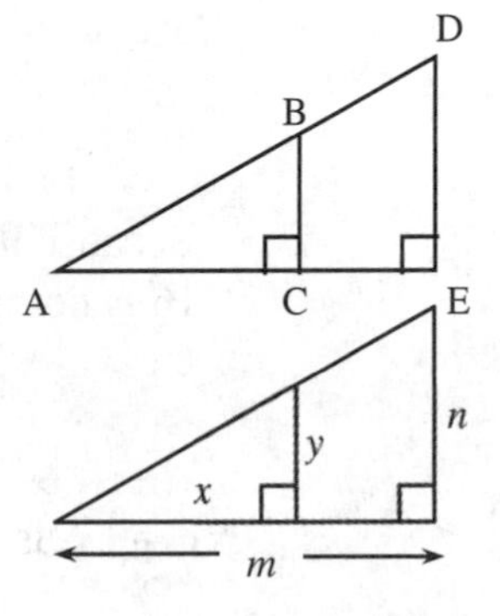

a. 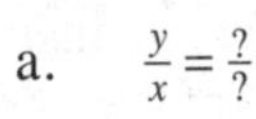

b. $\frac{n}{y} = \frac{?}{?}$

1-25. Note: The stoplight icon to the right of a problem indicates that there is an error in the problem.

Find the error in the solution at right. Explain what the error is and solve the equation correctly. Show how to check your solution to be sure that it is correct.

$$3(x-2)-2(x+7)=2x+17$$
$$3x-6-2x+14=2x+17$$
$$x+8=2x+17$$
$$-9=x$$

1.1.3 Which values are possible?

Domain and Range

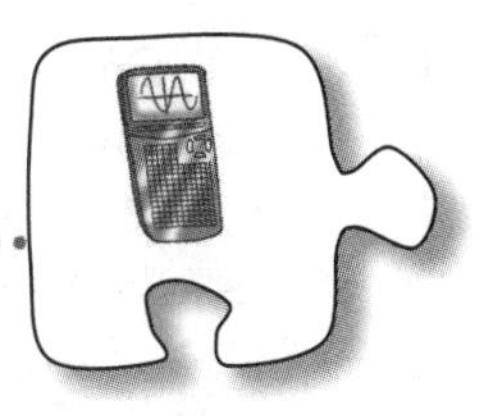

In Lesson 1.1.2 you worked with your graphing calculator to see complete graphs of functions and to determine what information was useful to describe those functions completely. In this lesson you will look at more functions, this time thinking about the input and output values that are possible. You will also learn to use some additional tools on your graphing calculator that will allow you to see a complete graph. As you work with your team, remember to ask each other questions such as:

What values are possible?

Can we see the complete graph?

What other information can we use to describe the function?

1-26. Jerrod and Sonia were working with their team on problem 1-2 to put the function machines in order. These functions are reprinted for you below.

$f(x)=\sqrt{x}$ $\qquad$ $g(x)=-(x-2)^2$

$h(x)=2^x-7$ $\qquad$ $k(x)=-\frac{x}{2}-1$

a. Jerrod first put an input of 6 into the function $g(x)=-(x-2)^2$ and got an output of -16. He wanted to try $f(x)=\sqrt{x}$ as his next function in the order, but he thinks there might be a problem using –16 as an input. Is there a problem? Explain.

b. Because it is not possible to take the square root of –16, it can be said that –16 is not in the **domain** of the function $f(x)$. The **domain** of a function is the collection of numbers that are possible inputs for that function. With your team, find two other numbers that are *not* part of the domain of $f(x)$. Then describe the domain. In other words, what are all of the numbers that *can* be used as inputs for the function $f(x)$?

c. Sonia claimed that $g(x)$ could not possibly be the last function in the order for problem 1-2. She justified her thinking by saying, *"Our final output has to be 11, which is a positive number. The function* $g(x)$ *will always make its output negative, so it can't come last in the order."* Discuss this with your team. Does Sonia's logic make sense? How did she know that the output of $g(x)$ would never be positive?

Problem continues on next page. →

1-26. *Problem continued from previous page.*

d. Because the outputs of the function $g(x)$ do not include certain numbers, it can be said that positive numbers are not part of the **range** of the function $g(x)$. The **range** of a function is the set of all of the possible values that can be outputs. With your team, describe the range of the function $g(x)$. In other words what are all of the values that *can* be outputs of the function?

1-27. Use your graphing calculator to help you draw a complete graph of $y=(x+1)(x-9)$.

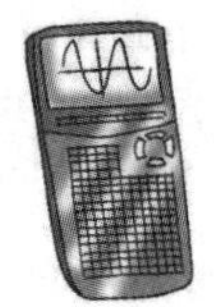

a. Describe the graph completely.

b. What window settings allow you to see the complete graph?

c. How are the settings related to domain and range?

1-28. Use your graphing calculator to draw a complete graph of $y=(x-12)^2+11$.

a. What happens when you use the standard window?

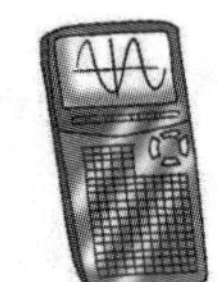

b. What window settings did you use to see enough of the graph to help you visualize and draw a complete graph?

c. What are the domain and range of the function?

1-29. Now you will reverse your thinking to create a graph with a given domain and range.

a. Sketch a function that has a domain of all real numbers between and including –3 and 10 (written $-3 \le x \le 10$) and a range of all real numbers between and including –4 and 6 (written $-4 \le y \le 6$). You do not have to write an equation for your function. Verify your endpoints with your team. Be creative.

b. Sketch a function with a domain of all real numbers and a range of the values 2, 4, 5, and 8 (written $y=2,4,5,8$).

The domain of all real numbers can be written $-\infty < x < \infty$. The symbols $-\infty$ and ∞ represents positive and negative **infinity**. They mean that the domain goes on without ending in the positive and negative direction. Infinity is not a number; it is a concept.

1-30. How can a graphing calculator help you find the solution to a system of equations? Consider this system:

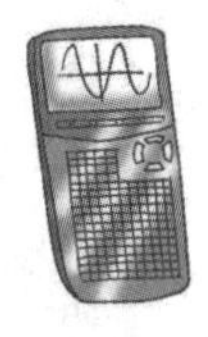

$$5x - y = 35$$
$$3x + y = -3$$

a. First graph the system in a standard window. Can you see the solution on your screen?

b. To find the solution you will need to change the window on your calculator. Discuss with your team what maximum value, minimum value, and scale you should use for the x- and y-axes in order to see the intersection. After you have decided, check your conclusion on the graphing calculator.

c. Use a "trace" function on your calculator to find the solution from the graphs. Then solve the system algebraically.

d. Discuss the two methods with your team. Explain which one your team prefers and why.

1-31. What does the graph of $y = x + \frac{1}{(x+2)^2} - 3$ look like? Graph the equation on your calculator. Use the trace and/or zoom buttons to find the x- and y-intercepts. What is the domain of this function? What is the range?

1-32. Use your graphing calculator to help you sketch the graphs of $y = \frac{1}{x} - 4$ and $y = \frac{1}{x-4}$. Are the graphs the same? Should they be? Explain why or why not.

1-33. LEARNING LOG

Throughout this course, you will be asked to reflect on your understanding of mathematical concepts in a Learning Log. Your Learning Log will contain explanations and examples to help you remember what you have learned throughout the course, as well as questions you are trying to understand and answer. It is important to write each entry of the Learning Log in your own words so that later you can use your Learning Log as a resource to refresh your memory. Your teacher will tell you where to write your Learning Log entries and how to structure them. Remember to label each entry with a title and a date so you can refer to it or add to it later.

In your Learning Log today, describe everything you know about domain and range. Include examples to illustrate your ideas. Title this entry "Domain and Range" and label it with today's date.

METHODS AND MEANINGS

Domain and Range

The set of possible values for the input of a function is called the **domain** of the function. This set consists of every input value for x for which the function is defined.

The **range** of a function is the set of possible values of the output. This set contains every y-value that the function can generate.

Domain and **range** are often written with **inequality notation** as shown in the examples below.

The symbols $-\infty$ and ∞ represents positive and negative **infinity**. They mean that the domain goes on without ending in the positive or negative direction. Infinity is not a number; it is a concept.

If the domain is any number between and including –2 and 7: $-2 \le x \le 7$

If the range is any number greater than but excluding 4: $y > 4$ or $4 < y < \infty$

If the domain is all real numbers except for –3: $x \ne -3$

If the domain is all real numbers: $-\infty < x < \infty$

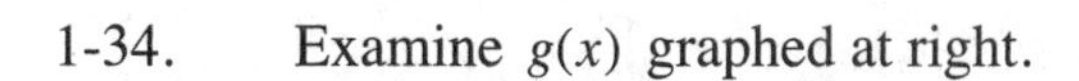

1-34. Examine $g(x)$ graphed at right.

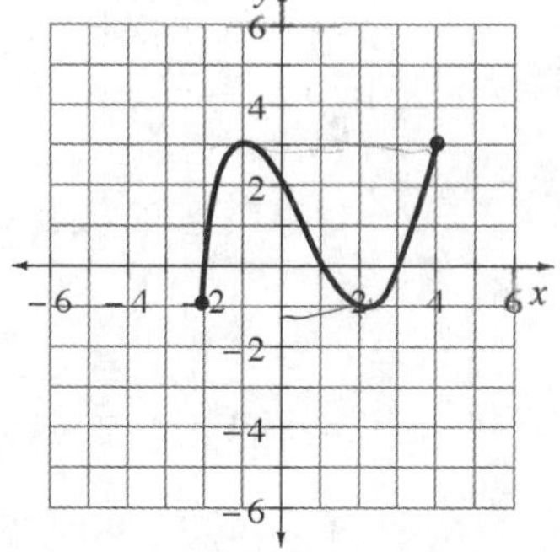

a. Which x-values have points on the graph? That is, describe the domain of $g(x)$.

b. What are the possible outputs for $g(x)$? That is, what is the range?

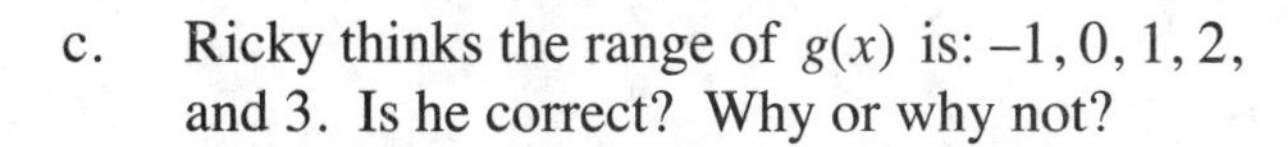

c. Ricky thinks the range of $g(x)$ is: $-1, 0, 1, 2,$ and 3. Is he correct? Why or why not?

d. Draw a graph for another function with the same domain and range as $g(x)$.

1-35. Consider the functions $f(x) = 3x^2 - 5$ and $g(x) = \sqrt{x-5} + 2$.

a. Find $f(5)$.

b. Find $g(5)$.

c. Find $f(4)$.

d. Find $g(4)$.

e. Find $f(x) + g(x)$.

f. Find $g(x) - f(x)$.

g. Describe the domain of $f(x)$.

h. Describe the domain of $g(x)$.

i. Why is the domain of one of these functions more restrictive than the other?

1-36. Nissos and Chelita were arguing over a math problem. Nissos was trying to explain to Chelita that she had made a mistake in finding the x-intercepts of the function $y = x^2 - 10x + 21$. *"No way!"* Chelita exclaimed. *"I know how to find x-intercepts! You make the y equal to zero and solve for x. I know I did this right!"* Here is Chelita's work:

Step 1: $x^2 - 10x + 21 = 0$, so $(x+7)(x+3) = 0$.

Step 2: Therefore, $x + 7 = 0$ or $x + 3 = 0$.

Step 3: So $x = -7$ or $x = -3$.

Nissos tried to explain to Chelita that she had done something wrong. What is Chelita's error? Justify and explain your answer completely.

1-37. As you have found when using a graphing calculator, equations must be solved for y; that is, they must be written in y-form. Rewrite each equation below so that it can be entered into a graphing calculator.

a. $x = 3y + 6$

b. $x = 5y - 10$

c. $x = y^2$

d. $x = 2y^2 - 4$

e. $x = (y - 5)^2$

1-38. Given $f(x) = 2x - 7$, complete parts (a) through (c) below.

a. Compute $f(0)$.

b. Solve $f(x) = 0$.

c. What do the answers to parts (a) and (b) tell you about the graph of $f(x)$?

1-39. Gregory planted a lemon tree in his back yard. When he planted the tree, it was 2 feet tall. He noticed that it has been growing 3 inches every week.

a. Create multiple representations ($x \rightarrow y$ table, graph, and equation) to represent the relationship between the days that have passed and the height of the tree.

b. If the tree continues growing at this rate, when will it be 6 feet tall? How can you see this in each of the representations?

c. State the possible inputs and outputs of the graph.

1-40. Solve each of the following equations. Be sure to check your solutions.

a. $4(x - 1) - 2(3x + 5) = -3x - 1$

b. $3x - 5 = 2.5x + 3 - (x - 4)$

1.1.4 How can I represent intersections?

Points of Intersection in Multiple Representations

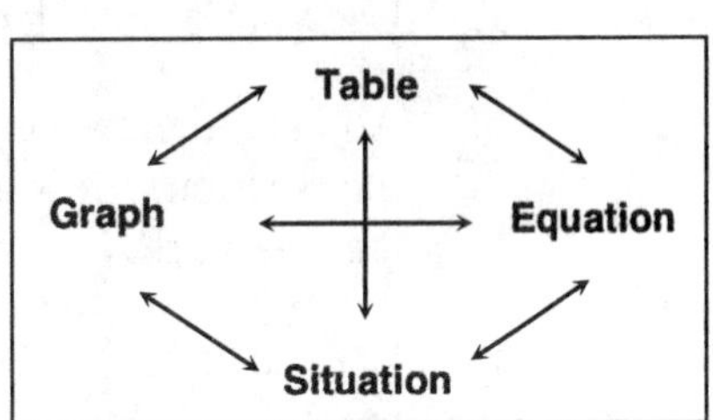

Throughout this course, you will represent functions in several different ways, and you will find connections between the various representations. These connections will give you new ways to investigate functions and to justify your conclusions.

How can these connections help you understand more about systems of equations? In this lesson, you will make connections between ways of representing a system of equations as you use your graphing calculator to find the points of intersection in multiple representations.

1-41. INTERSECTION INVESTIGATION

In Lesson 1.1.3, you used the features of your graphing calculator to find a point of intersection of two graphs. Can you use other representations as well? What about other strategies? Are all strategies equally accurate? Which do you prefer?

Your Task: Work with your team to find *as many ways as you can* (with *and* without your graphing calculator) to determine the points of intersection of the functions $f(x) = 2x^2 - 5x + 6$ and $g(x) = -2x^2 - x + 30$. Be sure to think about tables, graphs, and equations as you work. Be prepared to share each of your methods to the class.

Hint: If you are using a TI83+/84+ calculator, explore the [TABLE], [TBLSET], and [CALC] features on your graphing calculator. For other calculators, your teacher will give you guidance.

Discussion Points

How can we find it using graphs?

How can we find it in tables?

How can we find it using equations?

Further Guidance

1-42. Jason and his team were working on finding the points of intersection of $f(x) = 2x^2 - 5x + 6$ and $g(x) = -2x^2 - x + 30$. He suggested, *"Maybe we could start by looking at the graphs of the functions."*

a. Use your graphing calculator to help you graph $f(x)$ and $g(x)$.

b. Adjust the viewing window so that you can see all of the points of intersection. How accurately can you approximate the coordinates of these points by looking at the graph? Give it a try.

c. Use the "trace" feature to get a more accurate approximation of each of the points.

d. With your team, explore the [CALC] feature of your TI83/84+ graphing calculator. Can you find a way to make the graphing calculator calculate your points of intersection for you? How accurate are your results? Be prepared to share your method to the class.

1-43. Aria was in Jason's team. She had another idea and asked, *"Can't we find the points of intersection by comparing the tables of our two functions?"*

a. What did Aria mean? How can you find points of intersection by looking at tables?

b. Use your graphing calculator to make tables for $f(x)$ and $g(x)$. To do this, you will need to explore the [TABLE] and [TBLSET] features of your TI83/84+ calculator.

c. Find all of the points of intersection in the tables. How accurate are these results?

d. Can you think of any circumstances in which using a table might not be an efficient or accurate strategy for finding points of intersection? Explain.

1-44. Delilah listened to Jason and Aria explain their ideas. She said, *"I thought of another way! We have a method for using the equations to find points of intersection even without the graphing calculator, don't we?"*

a. What method is Delilah referring to?

b. Use Delilah's method to find the points of intersection of these two functions.

Further Guidance section ends here.

1-45. Rhianna says she can draw different functions that have the same *x-intercepts* and the same domain and range. Her teammates say, *"No, that's impossible!"* But Rhianna insists, *"It is possible, we just need to sketch the graphs."*

a. What if the x-intercepts are $(-5, 0)$, $(2, 0)$, and $(6, 0)$, the domain is $-5 \le x \le 7$, and the range is $-4 \le y \le 10$? Is more than one function possible? Give examples to help explain why or why not.

b. What if the x-intercepts are $(-4, 0)$ and $(2, 0)$, the domain is all real numbers, and the range is $y \ge -8$? Is there more than one function possible? Give examples of multiple functions or explain why there can be only one.

METHODS AND MEANINGS

Solving a Quadratic Equation

In a previous course, you learned how to solve **quadratic equations** (equations that can be written in the form $ax^2 + bx + c = 0$). Review two methods for solving quadratic equations below.

Some quadratic equations can be solved by **factoring** and then using the **Zero Product Property**. For example, the quadratic equation $x^2 - 3x - 10 = 0$ can be rewritten by factoring as $(x-5)(x+2) = 0$. The Zero Product Property states that if $ab = 0$, then $a = 0$ or $b = 0$. So if $(x-5)(x+2) = 0$, then $(x-5) = 0$ or $(x+2) = 0$. Therefore, $x = 5$ or $x = -2$.

Another method for solving quadratic equations is using the **Quadratic Formula**. This method is particularly helpful for solving quadratic equations that are difficult or impossible to factor. Before using the Quadratic Formula, the quadratic equation you want to solve must be in standard form (that is, written as $ax^2 + bx + c = 0$).

In this form, a is the coefficient of the x^2-term, b is the coefficient of the x-term, and c is the constant term. The Quadratic Formula is stated at right.

$$x = \frac{-b \pm \sqrt{b^2 - 4ac}}{2a}$$

This formula gives two possible solutions for x. The two solutions are shown by the "$\pm$" symbol. This symbol (read as "plus or minus") is shorthand notation that tells you to evaluate the expression twice: once using addition and once using subtraction. Therefore, Quadratic Formula problems usually must be simplified twice to give:

$$x = \frac{-b + \sqrt{b^2 - 4ac}}{2a} \quad \text{or} \quad x = \frac{-b - \sqrt{b^2 - 4ac}}{2a}$$

Of course if $\sqrt{b^2 - 4ac}$ equals zero, you will get the same result both times.

To solve $x^2 - 3x - 10 = 0$ using the Quadratic Formula, substitute $a = 1$, $b = -3$, and $c = -10$ into the formula, as shown below, then simplify.

$$x = \frac{-(-3) \pm \sqrt{(-3)^2 - 4(1)(-10)}}{2(1)} = \frac{3 \pm \sqrt{49}}{2} = \frac{3+7}{2} \text{ or } \frac{3-7}{2}$$

$$x = 5 \text{ or } x = -2$$

1-46. Use any method to find the point of intersection of $f(x) = 3x - 5$ and $g(x) = -4x + 9$.

1-47. Compute for $f(x) = \frac{1}{x}$.

a. $f(\frac{1}{2})$ b. $f(\frac{1}{10})$ c. $f(0.01)$ d. $f(0.007)$

1-48. Solve each of the following quadratic equations. If you need help, refer to the Math Notes box for this lesson.

a. $x^2 - 8x + 15 = 0$ b. $2x^2 - 5x - 6 = 0$

1-49. Consider the points (–5, 0) and (0, 3).

a. Plot the points and find the distance between them. Give your answer both in simplest radical form and as a decimal approximation.

b. Find the slope of the line that passes through both points.

1-50. Stacie says to Cory, *"Reach into this standard deck of playing cards and pull out a card at random. If it is the queen of hearts, I'll pay you $5.00."* (Note: A standard deck of playing cards contains 52 cards, each of which is unique.)

a. What is the probability that Cory gets Stacie's $5.00?

b. What is the probability that Stacie keeps her $5.00?

1-51. Find the error in the solution at right. Identify the error and solve the equation correctly.

$$4.1x = 9.5x + 23.7$$
$$-4.1x = -4.1x$$
$$5.4x = 23.7$$
$$\frac{5.4x}{5.4} = \frac{23.7}{5.4}$$
$$x = 4.39$$

1-52. Solve each of the following equations.

a. $3.9x - 2.1 = 11.2x + 51.7$ b. $\frac{1}{5}x - 2 = \frac{13}{25} - 0.7x$

1.2.1 How can I represent a function?

Modeling a Geometric Relationship

Mathematics can be used to model physical relationships to help us understand them better. Mathematical models can assume the form of a series of diagrams, a situation, a table, an equation, or a graph. In this course, you will be given situations to explore by gathering and interpreting data. You will learn to generalize your information so that you can make predictions about cases that you did not actually test. In this lesson, you will analyze a geometric relationship and look for connections among its multiple representations.

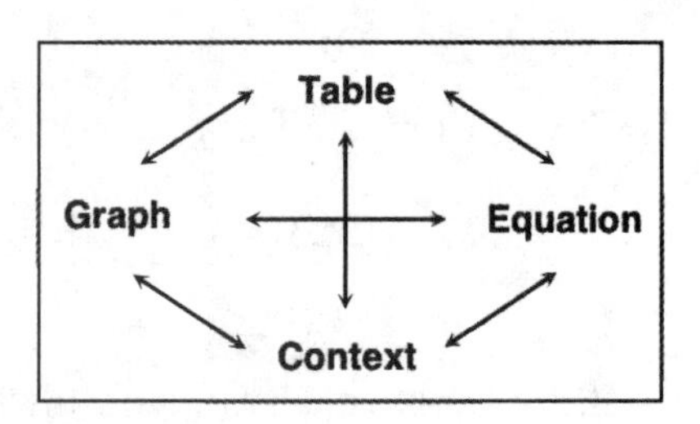

1-53. ANALYZING DATA FROM A GEOMETRIC RELATIONSHIP

Each team will make paper boxes using the instructions given below. Based on the physical models, your team will represent the relationship between the height of the box and its volume in multiple ways.

If it has not been done already, cut a sheet of centimeter grid paper to match the dimensions that your teacher assigns your team. Then, cut the same size square out of each corner, and fold the sides up to form a shallow box (with no lid) as shown below.

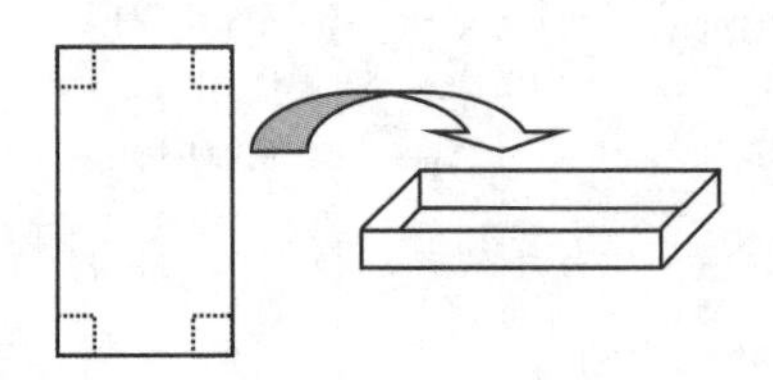

Dimensions	
22 cm × 16 cm	18 cm × 10 cm
22 cm × 14 cm	15 cm × 15 cm
20 cm × 15 cm	15 cm × 10 cm
20 cm × 9 cm	12 cm × 9 cm

Your Task: As a team you will investigate the relationship between the height of a box (the **input**) and its volume (the **output**). You can build as many boxes as necessary to establish this relationship. Be sure to build all of your boxes out of paper of the same size. Record your information using multiple representations – including diagrams, a table, and a graph. Also record any thoughts, observations, and/or general statements that come up in your discussion of the problem.

Discussion Points

How can we collect data for this relationship?

How much data is enough?

What are all the possible inputs for our function?

How are the different representations related?

Further Guidance

1-54. Begin your investigation by building several boxes, taking measurements, and collecting data.

a. As a team, choose a starting input value. Note that this value is the same as *the length of the side of one of the squares cut from the corner of your grid paper* and becomes the height of your box. Now make the first box and determine its volume. Label the box with its important information. Work in the middle of your workspace so that everyone understands what is being measured or calculated, and be sure everyone agrees on the result before recording the information in an input → output table on your own paper.

b. Each team member should now choose a *different* input value and build a new box or draw a diagram using this new value. Calculate the volume of your box. Share your input and output values with the rest of your team and record everyone's data in your input→output table.

c. Use the data in your table to create a graph to represent the situation.

Further Guidance section ends here.

1-55. GENERALIZING

Now you will generalize your results. Generalizing is an important mathematical process. A common way to generalize is to write an equation using algebra.

a. Draw a diagram of one of your boxes. Since this shape is being used to generalize, you want it to represent a relationship between *any* possible input and its output. Therefore, instead of labeling the height with a number, label the height of this box x.

b. Work with your team to calculate the volume (or y-value) for a height of x. It may help you to remember how you calculated the volume when the height was a number and use the same strategy for your new input of x.

1-56. LOOKING FOR CONNECTIONS

Put your $x \rightarrow y$ table, graph, and equation in the middle of your workspace. With your team, discuss the questions below.

As you address each question, remember to give reasons when you can. Also, if you make an observation, discuss how that observation relates to your table, graph, and equation.

a. Is the domain of the relationship limited? That is, are there some input values that would not make sense? Why or why not? How can you tell using the graph? The $x \rightarrow y$ table? Using the equation? Using the boxes themselves (or diagrams of the boxes)?

b. Is the range of the relationship limited? That is, what are all of the possible outputs (volumes)? Are there any outputs that would not make sense? Why or why not?

c. Should you connect the points on your graph with a smooth curve? That is, should your graph be *continuous* or *discrete*? Explain.

d. What is different about your graph for this problem when compared to others you have seen in previous courses? What special points or features does it have?

e. Work with your team to find as many other connections as you can among your geometric models, your table, your equation, and your graph. How can you show or explain each connection?

1-57. What graph do you get when you use the graphing calculator to draw the graph of your equation? Explain the relationship between this and the graph you made on your own paper.

1-58. Organize your findings into a stand-alone poster that shows everything you have learned about all of the representations of your function as well as the connections between the representations. Use colors, arrows, words, and any other useful tools you can think of to make sure that someone reading your poster would understand all of your thinking.

METHODS AND MEANINGS

Triangle Trigonometry

There are three **trigonometric ratios** you can use to solve for the missing side lengths and angle measurements in any right triangle: tangent, sine, and cosine.

In the triangle below, when the sides are described relative to the angle θ (the Greek letter "theta"), the opposite leg is y and the adjacent leg is x. The hypotenuse is h regardless of which acute angle is used.

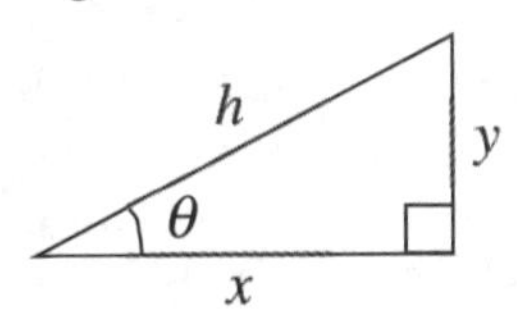

$$\tan\theta = \frac{\text{opposite leg}}{\text{adjacent leg}} = \frac{y}{x}$$

$$\sin\theta = \frac{\text{opposite leg}}{\text{hypotenuse}} = \frac{y}{h}$$

$$\cos\theta = \frac{\text{adjacent leg}}{\text{hypotenuse}} = \frac{x}{h}$$

In general, for any uniquely determined triangle, missing sides and angles can be determined by using the **Law of Sines** or the **Law of Cosines**.

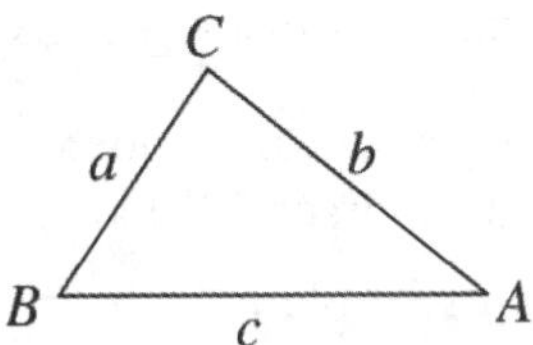

$$\frac{\sin A}{a} = \frac{\sin B}{b} = \frac{\sin C}{c}$$

and

$$c^2 = a^2 + b^2 - 2ab\cos C$$

1-59. Make a table and graph for $h(x) = x^3 - 4$. Find the domain, range, and intercepts.

1-60. For each diagram below, write and solve an equation to find the value of each variable. Give your answer to part (d) in both radical and decimal form. For a reminder of the trigonometry ratios, refer to the Math Notes box for this lesson.

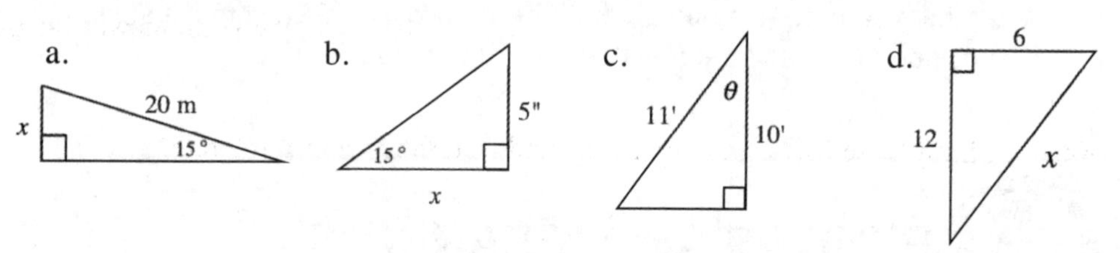

1-61. Consider the equation $4x-6y=12$.

a. Predict what the graph of this equation looks like. Justify your answer.

b. Solve the equation for y and graph the equation.

c. Explain clearly how to find the x- and y-intercepts.

d. Which form of the equation is best for finding the x- and y-intercepts quickly? Why?

e. Find the x- and y-intercepts of $2x-3y=-18$. Then use the intercepts to sketch a graph quickly.

1-62. Name the domain and range for each of the following functions.

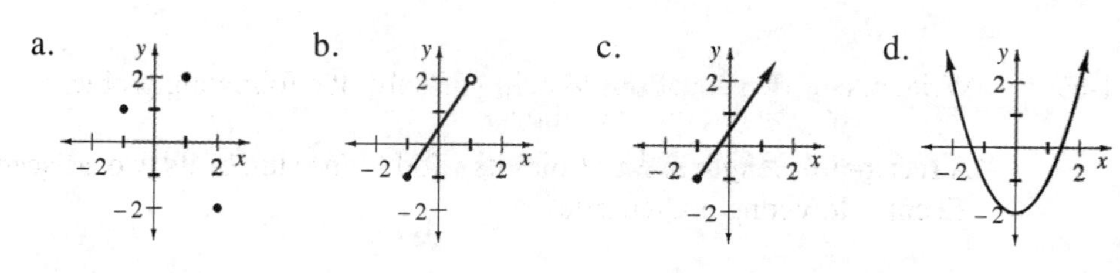

1-63. Find the error in the solution at right. Explain what the error is and solve the equation correctly. Be sure to check your answer.

$$\frac{5}{x}=x-4$$
$$x\cdot\frac{5}{x}=x-4$$
$$5=x-4$$
$$x=9$$

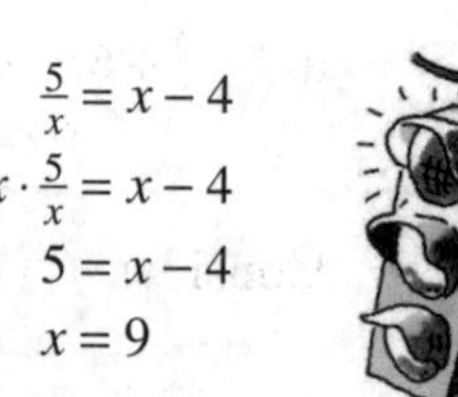

1-64. Solve each of the following equations. Be sure to check your answers.

a. $\frac{6}{x}=x-1$

b. $\frac{9}{x}=x$

1-65. Compute each of the following values for $f(x)=\frac{1}{x-2}$.

a. $f(2.5)$

b. $f(1.75)$

c. $f(2)$

d. Justify your answer for part (c).

1-66. Graph the following functions and find the x- and y-intercepts.

a. $y=2x+3$

b. $f(x)=2x+3$

c. How are the functions in (a) and (b) the same? How are they different?

1-67. A 3-foot indoor children's slide must meet the ground very gradually and make an angle of 155°, as shown in the diagram at right. Find the height of the slide (y) and the length of the floor it will cover (x).

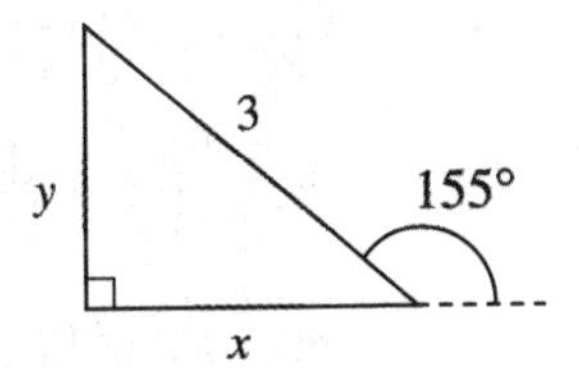

1-68. Find the domain and the range for each of the following functions.

a.

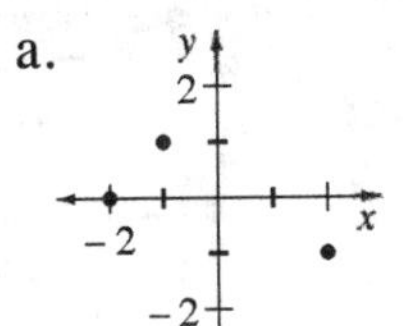

b.

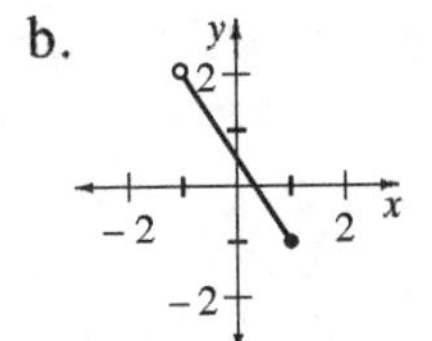

c.

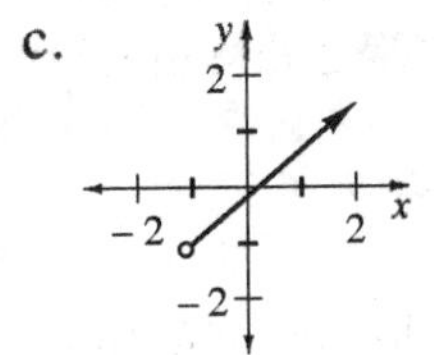

d.

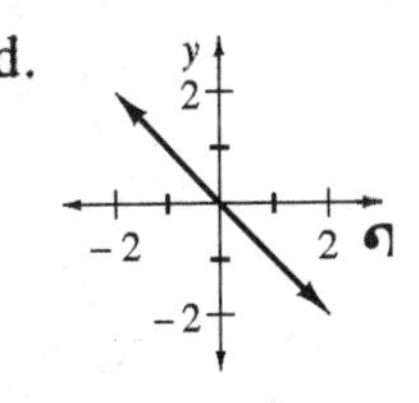

1-69. Write one or two equations to help you solve the following problem.

A rectangle's length is four times its width. The sum of its two adjacent sides is 22 cm. How long is each side?

1-70. Solve each of the following equations.

a. $\frac{3}{x}+6=-45$

b. $\frac{x-2}{5}=\frac{10-x}{8}$

c. $(x+1)(x-3)=0$

1-71. Consider $f(x)=x^2-2x+6$ and $g(x)=2x+11$.

a. Use any method to find the points of intersection of $f(x)$ and $g(x)$.

b. Calculate $f(x)+g(x)$.

c. Calculate $f(x)-g(x)$.

1-72. Rearrange each equation below by solving for x. Write each equation in the form $x =$ ______. (Note that y will be in your answer).

a. $y = \frac{3}{5}x + 1$

b. $3x + 2y = 6$

c. $y = x^2$

d. $y = x^2 - 100$

1-73. Consider circles of different sizes. Create multiple representations of the function ($x \rightarrow y$ table, equation, and graph) with inputs that are the radius of the circle and outputs that are its area.

1-74. Consider the points $(-2, 5)$ and $(5, 2)$ as you complete parts (a) and (b) below.

a. Plot the points and find the distance between them. Give your answer both in simplest radical form and as a decimal approximation.

b. Find the slope of the line that goes through the two points.

1-75. If the number 1 is the output for Carmichael's function machine shown at right, how can you find out what number was dropped in? Find the number(s) that could have been dropped in.

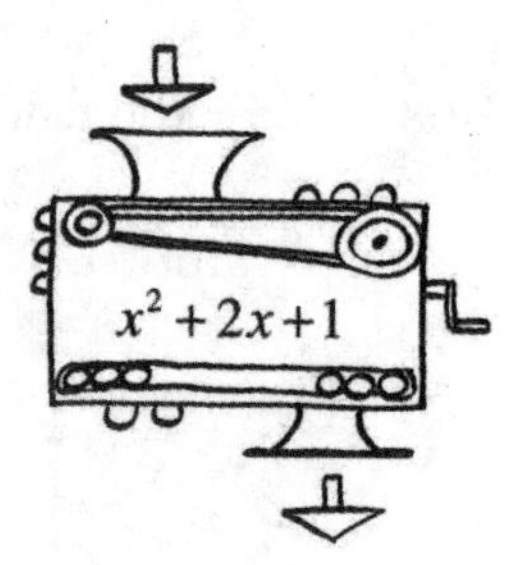

1-76. What value of x allows you to find the y-intercept? Where does the graph of each equation below cross the y-axis? Write each answer as an ordered pair.

a. $y = 3x + 6$

b. $x = 5y - 10$

c. $y = x^2$

d. $y = 2x^2 - 4$

e. $y = (x - 5)^2$

f. $y = 3x^3 - 2x^2 + 13$

1-77. Find the error in the solution at right. Describe the error and solve the equation correctly.

$3x + 2 = 10 - 4(x - 1)$

$3x + 2 = 6(x - 1)$

$3x + 2 = 6x - 6$

$8 = 3x$ so $x = \frac{8}{3}$

1.2.2 How can I investigate a function?

Function Investigation

What does it mean to describe a function completely? In this lesson you will graph and investigate a family of functions with equations of the form $f(x) = \frac{1}{x-h}$. As you work with your team, keep the multiple representations of functions in mind.

1-78. INVESTIGATING A FUNCTION, Part One

Your team will investigate functions of the form $f(x) = \frac{1}{x-h}$, where h can be any number.

As a team, choose a value for h between -10 and 10. For example, if $h = 7$, then $f(x) = \frac{1}{x-7}$.

Your Task: On a piece of graph paper, write down the function you get when you use your value for h. Then make an $x \rightarrow y$ table and draw a complete graph of your function. Is there any more information you need to be sure that you can see the entire shape of your graph? Discuss this question with your team and add any new information you think is necessary.

Discussion Points

How can we be sure that our graph is complete?

How can we get output values that are greater than 1 or less than -1?

Further Guidance

1-79. This function is different from others you have seen in the past. To get a complete graph, you will need to make sure your table includes enough information.

a. Make an $x \rightarrow y$ table with integer x-values from 5 less than your value of h to 5 more than your value of h. For example, if you are working with $h = 7$, you would begin your table at $x = 2$ and end it at $x = 12$. What do you notice about all of your y-values?

b. Is there any x-value that has no y-value for your function? Why does this make sense?

c. Plot all of the points that you have in your table so far.

d. Now you will need to add more values to your table to see what is happening to your function as your input values get close to your value of h. Choose eight input values that are very close to your value of h and on either side of h. For example, if you are working with $h = 7$, you might choose input values such as 6.5, 6.7, 6.9, 6.99, 7.01, 7.1, 7.3, and 7.5. For each new input value, calculate the corresponding output and add the new point to your graph.

e. When you have enough points to be sure that you know the shape of your graph, sketch the curve.

Further Guidance section ends here.

1-80. Now you will continue your investigation of $f(x) = \frac{1}{x-h}$.

a. Each team member should choose a different value of h and make a complete $x \rightarrow y$ table and graph for your new function.

b. Examine all of your team's functions. Together, generate a list of questions that you could ask about the functions your team created. Be as thorough as possible and be prepared to share your questions with the class.

c. The graph of some functions contains an **asymptote**. To learn more about asymptotes, read the Math Notes box at the end of this lesson.

d. As your teacher records each team's questions, copy them into your Learning Log. Title this entry "Function Investigation Questions" and label it with today's date.

1-81. INVESTIGATING A FUNCTION, Part Two: SUMMARY STATEMENTS

Now you are ready for the most important part of your investigation: summary statements! Summary statements are a very important part of this course, so your team will practice making them. A summary statement is a statement about a function *along with a thorough justification*. A strong summary statement should be justified with multiple representations ($x \rightarrow y$ table, graph, equation, and situation, if applicable).

a. Read the example summary statement below about the range of the function $y = x^2$. Discuss it with your team and decide if it is justified completely.

Statement: The function $y = x^2$ has a range of all real numbers greater than or equal to zero ($y \geq 0$). **First justification:** You can see this when you look at the graph, because you can see that the lowest point on the graph is on the x-axis.

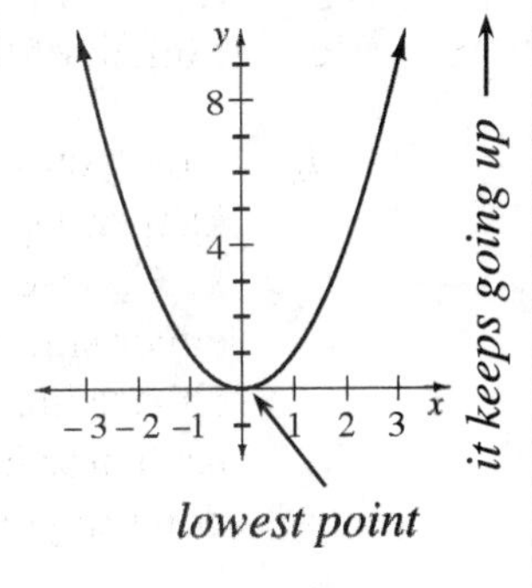

Second justification: You can also see this in the table, because none of the y-values are negative.

x	−3	−2	−1	0	1	2	3
y	9	4	1	0	1	4	9

they will keep getting higher

this is the lowest output

they will keep getting higher

Third justification: It makes sense with the equation, because if you square any number, the answer will be positive. For example, $(-2)^2 = 4$ and $3^2 = 9$.

b. Use your "Function Investigation Questions" Learning Log entry from problem 1-80 to help you make as many summary statements about your functions as you can. Remember to justify each summary statement in as many ways as possible.

1-82. SHARING SUMMARY STATEMENTS

With your team, choose one summary statement that you wrote that you find particularly interesting. Write the summary statement along with its justification so that it can be displayed for the whole class to see. Include sketches of graphs, $x \rightarrow y$ tables, equations, circles, arrows, colors, and any other tools that are helpful.

1-83. What will the graph of $f(x)=\frac{1}{x+25}$ look like?

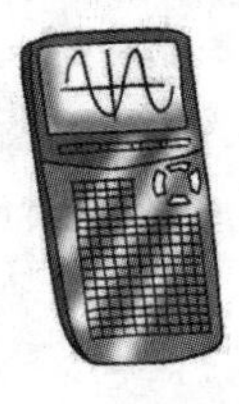

a. Discuss this question with your team and make a sketch of what you predict the graph will look like. Give as many reasons for your prediction as you can.

b. Use your graphing calculator to graph $f(x)=\frac{1}{x+25}$. Do you see what you expected to see? Why or why not?

c. Adjust the viewing window if needed. When you see the full picture of your graph, make a sketch of the graph on your paper. Label any important points.

d. How close was your prediction?

METHODS AND MEANINGS

Graphs with Asymptotes

A mathematically clear and complete definition of an asymptote requires some ideas from calculus, but some examples of graphs with **asymptotes** should help you recognize them when they occur. In the following examples, the dotted lines are the asymptotes, and the equations of the asymptotes are given. In the two lower graphs, the y-axis, $x = 0$, is also an asymptote.

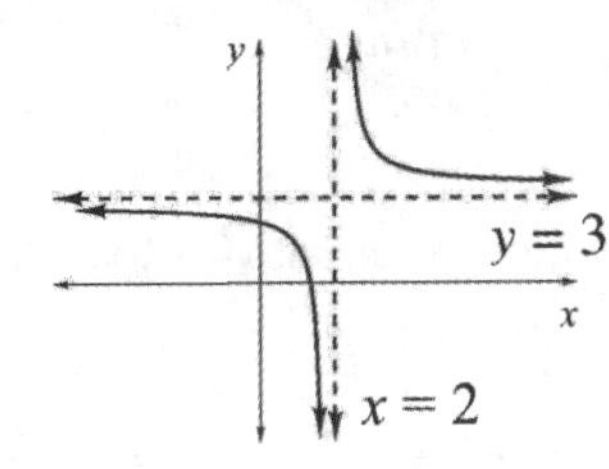

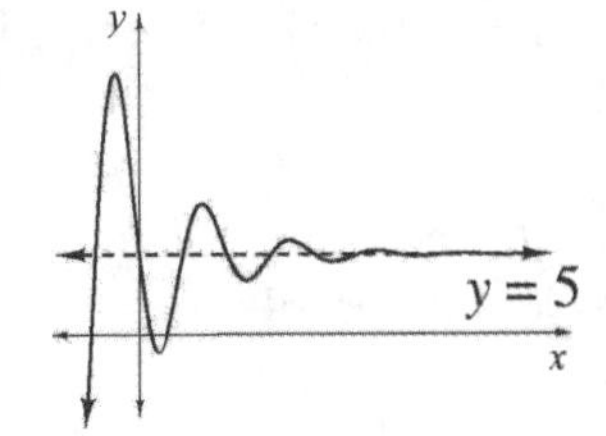

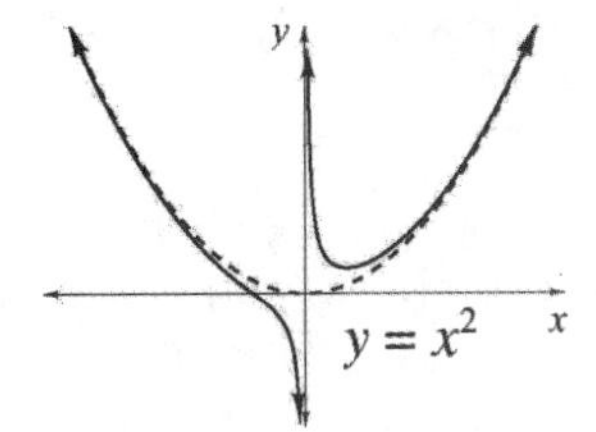

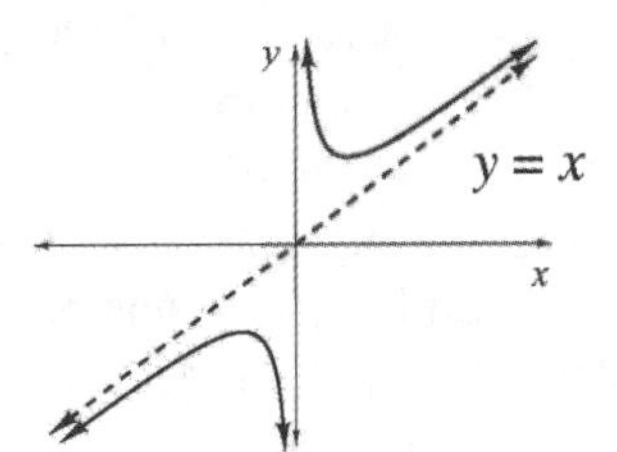

As you can see in the examples above, asymptotes can be diagonal lines or even curves. However, in this course, asymptotes will almost always be horizontal or vertical lines. The graph of a function has a **horizontal asymptote** if as you trace along the graph out to the left or right (that is, as you choose x-coordinates farther and farther away from zero, either toward infinity or toward negative infinity), the distance between the graph of the function and the asymptote gets closer to zero.

A graph has a **vertical asymptote** if, as you choose x-coordinates closer and closer to a certain value, from either the left or right (or both), the y-coordinate gets farther away from zero, either toward infinity or toward negative infinity.

1-84. Use any method to find the points of intersection of $f(x) = 2x^2 - 3x + 4$ and $g(x) = x^2 + 5x - 3$.

1-85. Solve each equation for x.

a. $-2(x+4) = 35 - (7 - 4x)$

b. $\frac{x-4}{7} = \frac{8-3x}{5}$

1-86. Make a complete graph of the function $f(x) = \sqrt{x} - 2$, label its x- and y-intercepts, and describe its domain and range.

1-87. Write and solve an equation or a system of equations to help you solve the following problem.

A cable 84 meters long is cut into two pieces so that one piece is 18 meters longer than the other. Find the length of each piece of cable.

1-88. Carlo got a pet snake as a birthday present. On his birthday, the baby snake was just 26 cm long. He has been watching it closely and has noticed that it has been growing 2 cm each week.

a. Create multiple representations ($x \rightarrow y$ table, graph, and equation) of the function for which the inputs are the weeks since Carlo's birthday and the outputs are the length of the snake.

b. If the snake continues to grow at the same rate, when will it be 1 meter (100 cm) long? How can you see this in each representation?

1-89. What value of y allows you to find the x-intercept? For each of the equations below, find where its graph intersects the x-axis. Write each answer as an ordered pair.

a. $y = 3x + 6$

b. $x = 5y - 10$

c. $y = x^2$

d. $y = 2x^2 - 4$

e. $y = (x - 5)^2$

f. $y = x^3 - 13$

1-90. Make a complete graph of the function $h(x) = 2x^2 + 4x - 6$ and describe its domain and range.

1-91. Solve each equation below for the indicated variable.

a. $y = mx + b$ for x

b. $A = \pi r^2$ for r

c. $V = LHW$ for W

d. $2x + \frac{1}{y} = 3$ for y

1-92. Create multiple representations ($x \to y$ table, graph, and equation) of the function $g(x) = \frac{2}{x}$. Then make at least 3 summary statements.

1-93. Suppose you want to find where the lines $y = 3x + 15$ and $y = 3 - 3x$ cross, and you want to be more accurate than the graphing calculator or graph paper will allow. You can use algebra to find the *point of intersection*.

a. If you remember how to do this, find the point of intersection using algebra and be prepared to explain your method to your team tomorrow in class. If you do not remember, then do parts (b) through (e) below.

b. Since $y = 3x + 15$ and $y = 3 - 3x$, what must be true about $3x + 15$ and $3 - 3x$ when their y-values are the same?

c. Write an equation that does not contain y and solve it for x.

d. Use the x-value you found in part (c) to find the corresponding y-value.

e. Where do the two lines cross?

1-94. The *Salami and More Deli* sells a 5-foot submarine sandwich for parties. It weighs 8 pounds. Assuming that the weight per foot is constant, what would be the length of a 12-pound sandwich?

1-95. If $h(x) = x^2 - 5$, where does the graph of $h(x)$ cross the x-axis? Make a sketch of the graph.

1-96. Graph the following equations.

a. $y - 2x = 3$

b. $y - 3 = x^2$

c. State the x- and y-intercepts for each equation.

d. Where do the two graphs cross? Show how you can find these two points without looking at the graphs.

1-97. Match the law, equation, or formula in Column I with its corresponding name from Column II.

Column I	Column II
a. $x = \frac{-b \pm \sqrt{b^2 - 4ac}}{2a}$	1. Law of Cosines
b. $\frac{\sin A}{a} = \frac{\sin B}{b}$	2. Law of Sines
c. $c^2 = a^2 + b^2$	3. Pythagorean Theorem
d. $c^2 = a^2 + b^2 - 2ab\cos C$	4. Quadratic Formula

1.2.3 What do they have in common?

The Family of Linear Functions

In Lesson 1.2.2, your team investigated functions of the form $f(x)=\frac{1}{x-h}$, where h could be any number. You learned that as you changed h, the graph changed, but the basic shape stayed the same. In this lesson, you will think about functions of the form $f(x)=mx+b$.

1-98. Consider functions of the form $y=mx+b$.

a. What do x and y represent in this function? What do m and b represent? Which ones can you change?

b. With the rest of the class, explore the effects of m and b on the function $y=mx+b$. What effect does m have on the graph? What effect does b have on the graph?

c. For this function, m and b are called **parameters** (as h was for $f(x)=\frac{1}{x-h}$), whereas x and y are called **variables**. With your team, explain the difference between a parameter and a variable.

d. What do all of the functions of the form $y=mx+b$ have in common? Since they all have the same basic relationship between x and y, they can be called a **family of functions**.

1-99. With your team, examine each group of equations below and discuss what you would see if you drew the graphs of the four equations on one set of axes. Write a description of what you imagine you would see. (You do not actually have to draw them.)

a. $x+2y=10$

$y=-\frac{1}{2}x+3$

$-4y=2x+8$

$y=-\frac{1}{2}x$

Same slopes
different
y-intercepts
parallel

b. $5x+y=-3$

$y=-\frac{1}{2}x-3$

$3x-4y=12$

$5y-2x=-15$

Same y-intercepts
(0,3)

1-100. Parts (a) through (f) below are six representations of a relationship between an input and an output. With your team, decide whether each relationship is linear and write a clear summary statement justifying your decision. If the relationship is linear, graph it and find its equation. If it is not linear, describe the growth.

a.

Pieces of Bread	*Grams of Fiber*
0	0
1	5
2	10
3	15
4	20

b. *Killer Fried Chickens charges $7.00 for a basic bucket of chicken and $0.50 for each additional piece. The input is the number of extra pieces of chicken ordered, and the output is the total cost of the order.*

c.

x	y
10	0
5	5
3	7
2	8
1	9
0	10

d.

x	y
10	1
5	2
4	2.5
2	5
1	10
0.5	20

e. *James planted a bush in his yard. The year he planted it, the bush produced 17 flowers. Each year, the branches of the bush split, so the number of flowers doubles. The input is the year after planting, and the output is the number of flowers.*

f.

x	y
0	–7
2	–2
4	3
6	8
8	13

1-101. Work with your team to create one new table and one new situation that display linear relationships. Be sure to justify how you can tell that your table and situation are linear.

1-102. Without using a graph, decide whether the relationship shown in the table at right is linear. Write a clear summary statement justifying your ideas. Be prepared to share your ideas with the class.

x	y
1	0.5
4	–7
10	–22
15	–34.5

1-103. LEARNING LOG

In your Learning Log, explain how you can recognize a linear relationship in a table or the description of a situation. Be sure to include examples. Title this entry "Recognizing Linear Relationships" and label it with today's date.

1-104. Find the slope and intercepts of $3x+4y=12$. Sketch a graph.

1-105. Write an equation for the line that passes through the points (2, 0) and (0, –3). Remember that drawing a diagram (in this case, drawing the graph) can be very helpful.

1-106. Solve each equation below. Give solutions in both radical and decimal form.

a. $x^2+3x-3=0$

b. $3x^2-7x=12$

1-107. Jason loves to download music. *Downloads R Us* sells songs only in packages of three, and it charges \$2.00 for each package of three songs. Jason's favorite group just released their *Greatest Hits* CD, which has 17 songs on it. Jason wants to buy all 17 songs from *Downloads R Us*. How much should Jason expect to pay?

1-108. Make a sketch of a graph showing the relationship between the number of people on your school's campus and the time of day.

1-109. For each graph below, what are the domain and range?

a.
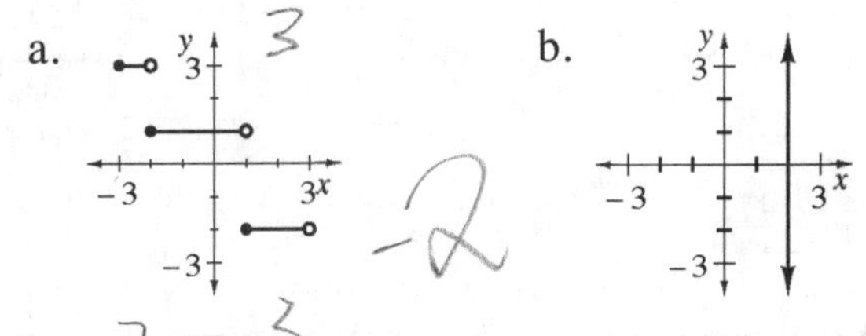

b.
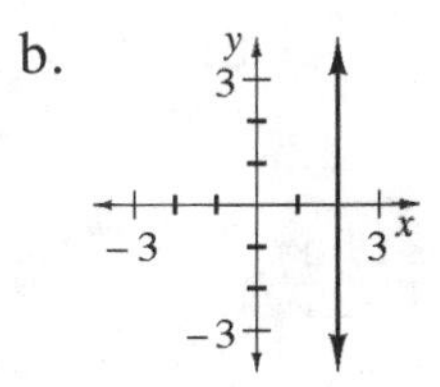

c.
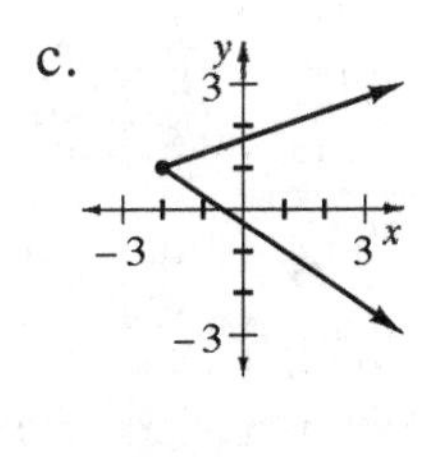

1-110. Uyregor has a collection of six-sided number cubes. He takes one out to roll it.

a. What are all possible outcomes that can come up?

b. What is the probability that a 4 comes up?

c. What is the probability that the number that comes up is less than 5?

1.2.4 What can I learn about it?

Function Investigation Challenge

In this lesson, you will have a chance to show your understanding of investigation as you work with a new function.

1-111. In this activity you will investigate the function $f(x)=\frac{5}{(x^2+1)}-1$.

a. Take a moment to look over your Learning Log entry entitled "Function Investigation Questions." Are there any questions you should add to your list? Discuss this with your team and make any necessary additions to your Learning Log.

b. Now investigate $f(x)=\frac{5}{(x^2+1)}-1$ completely. Be sure to make clear summary statements that are justified using multiple representations.

1-112. Recently, Kalani and Lynette took a trip from Vacaville, California to Los Angeles. The graph at right represents their trip.

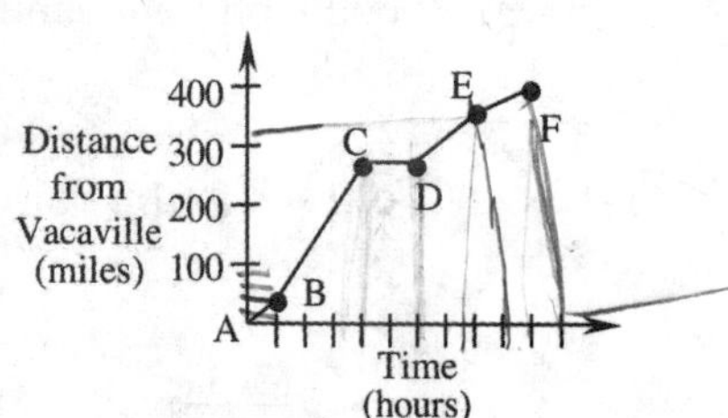

a. Explain what each line segment in the graph represents.

b. About how many miles is it from Vacaville to Los Angeles? How do you know?

c. Using the graph shown above, sketch a graph that would represent their *speed* while traveling. Take your time to think this through carefully and be sure to label the axes.

1-113. Solve each equation below for x.

a. $10-2(2x+1)=4(x-2)$

b. $5-(2x-3)=-8+2x$

1-114. The right triangle shown at right has a height ($m\overline{BC}$) of 12 cm, and its area is 60 square cm. Find $m\measuredangle B$ and the length of the hypotenuse.

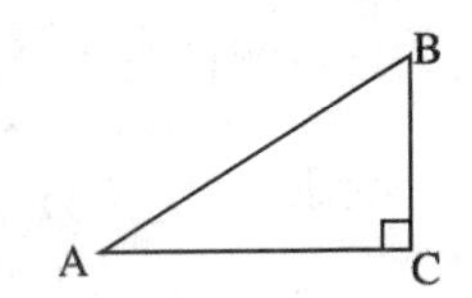

1-115. The longer leg of a right triangle is three inches more than three times the length of the shorter leg. The area of the triangle is 84 square inches. Find the perimeter of the triangle.

1-116. Imagine that you are adding water to the beakers shown below (labeled A, B, and C). Sketch a graph for each beaker to show the relationship between the volume of water added and the height of the water in each beaker. Put all three graphs on one set of axes (you may want to use colored pencils to distinguish the graphs). What are the independent and dependent variables?

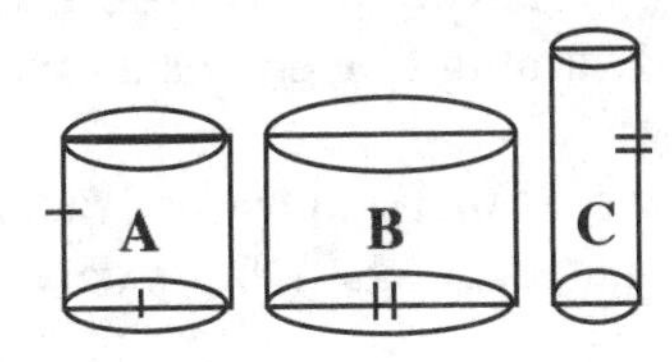

1-117. Sketch a few different equilateral triangles. Create multiple representations ($x \to y$ table, graph, equation) of the function with inputs that are the length of one side of an equilateral triangle and outputs that are its perimeter.

1-118. Have you ever wondered why so many equations are written with the variables x and y? Suppose you are reaching into a bag that contains all the letters of the English alphabet, and you pull out one letter at random to use as a variable in equations.

a. What is the probability that you pull out an x?

b. If you got an x, now what is the probability that you will pull out a y?

Chapter 1 Closure What have I learned?

Reflection and Synthesis

The activities below offer you a chance to reflect about what you have learned during this chapter. As you work, look for concepts that you feel very comfortable with, ideas that you would like to learn more about, and topics you need more help with. Look for connections between ideas as well as connections with material you learned previously.

① TEAM BRAINSTORM

What have you studied in this chapter? What ideas were important in what you learned? With your team, brainstorm a list. Be as detailed as you can. To help get you started, a list of Learning Log entries and Math Notes boxes are below.

What topics, ideas, and words that you learned *before* this course are connected to the new ideas in this chapter? Again, be as detailed as you can.

How long can you make your list? Challenge yourselves. Be prepared to share your team's ideas with the class.

Learning Log Entries

- Lesson 1.1.3 – Domain and Range
- Lesson 1.2.2 – Function Investigation Questions
- Lesson 1.2.3 – Recognizing Linear Relationships

Math Notes

- Lesson 1.1.1 – Functions
- Lesson 1.1.2 – Linear Equations
- Lesson 1.1.3 – Domain and Range
- Lesson 1.1.4 – Solving a Quadratic Equation
- Lesson 1.2.1 – Triangle Trigonometry
- Lesson 1.2.2 – Graphs With Asymptotes

② MAKING CONNECTIONS

The following is a list of the vocabulary used in this chapter. Make sure that you are familiar with all of these words and know what they mean. Refer to the glossary or index for any words that you do not yet understand.

asymptote	dependent variable	domain
equation	function	graph
independent variable	infinity	input
investigate	situation	symmetry
output	range	x-intercept
$x \rightarrow y$ table	y-intercept	

Make a concept map showing all of the connections you can find among the key words and ideas listed above. To show a connection between two words, draw a line between them and explain the connection, as shown in the model below. A word can be connected to any other word as long as you can justify the connection. For each key word or idea, provide an example or sketch that shows the idea.

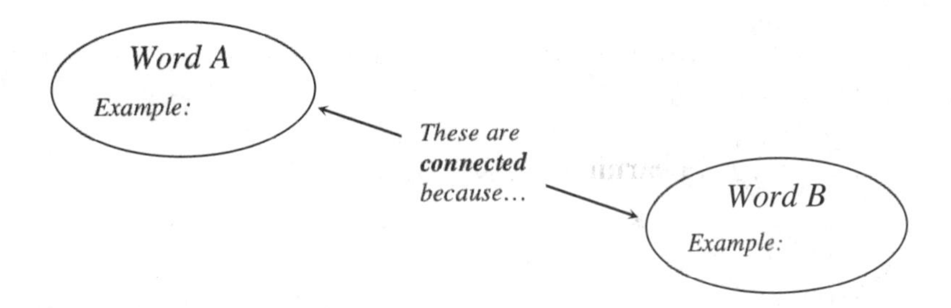

Your teacher may provide you with vocabulary cards to help you get started. If you use the cards to plan your concept map, be sure either to re-draw your concept map on your paper or to glue the vocabulary cards to a poster with all of the connections explained for others to see and understand.

While you are making your map, your team may think of related words or ideas that are not listed above. Be sure to include these ideas on your concept map.

③ PORTFOLIO: EVIDENCE OF MATHEMATICAL PROFICIENCY

Your teacher may have instructed you to take a photograph of the poster you made for Lesson 1.1.2 as evidence of your early understanding about describing functions. If so, include the photograph in your portfolio.

Explain everything you know about $y = x^2 - 4$ and $y = \sqrt{x+4}$.

Your teacher may give you the Chapter 1 Closure Resource Page: Function Investigations Graphic Organizer page to work on (or you can download this from www.cpm.org). A Graphic Organizer is a tool you can use to organize your thoughts and communicate your ideas clearly.

④ WHAT HAVE I LEARNED?

Most of the problems in this section represent typical problems found in this chapter. They serve as a gauge for you. You can use them to determine which types of problems you can do well and which types of problems require further study and practice. Even if your teacher does not assign this section, it is a good idea to try these problems and find out for yourself what you know and what you still need to work on.

Solve each problem as completely as you can. The table at the end of the closure section has answers to these problems. It also tells you where you can find additional help and practice with problems like these.

CL 1-119. Given the functions $f(x) = \sqrt{x+4}$ and $g(x) = x^2 - x$, find the value of each expression below.

a. $f(5)$

b. $g(-1)$

c. x if $f(x) = 10$

d. x if $g(x) = 6$

CL 1-120. Describe the domain and range for each function shown below.

a.

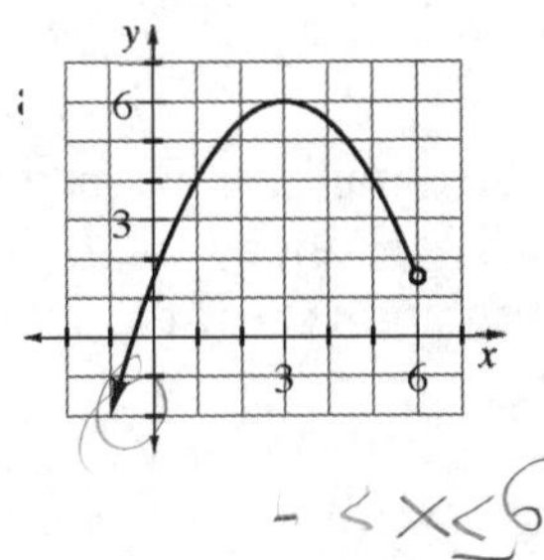

b.

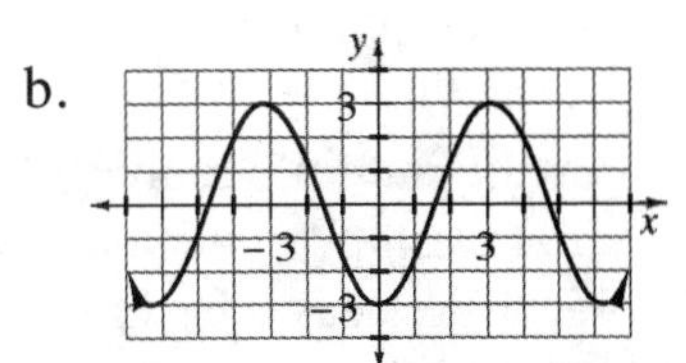

CL 1-121. For each pair of equations below, determine where the graphs intersect.

a. $y = 3x + 15$
$y = 3 - 3x$

b. $y = x^2 - 3x - 8$
$y = 2$

CL 1-122. Graph the function $f(x) = x^2 - 2x - 8$. Identify the domain and range and identify any special points such as the intercepts and vertex.

CL 1-123. Graph each equation below and find the x- and y-intercepts.

a. $y = -\frac{3}{2}x + 8$

b. $2x - 3y = -6$

CL 1-124. Find an equation for each line described below.

a. The line that passes through the point (2, 8) and has a slope of –5.

b. The line that passes through the points (–3, 4) and (5, –4).

c. The line that passes through the points (–2, 4) and (4, –5).

CL 1-125. Solve each equation below.

a. $\frac{x+2}{5} = \frac{10-2x}{3}$

b. $\frac{3}{x} - 1 = 8$

c. $x^2 + 3x = 18$

CL 1-126. Solve for y.

a.

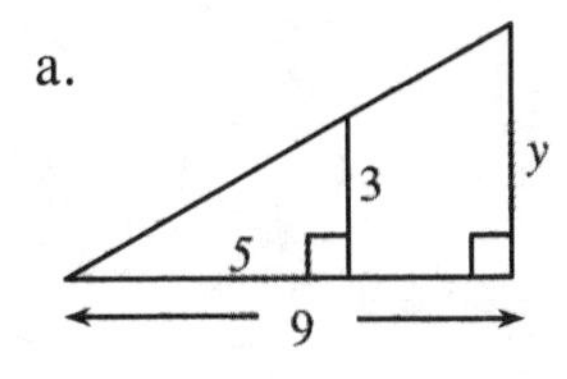

b.

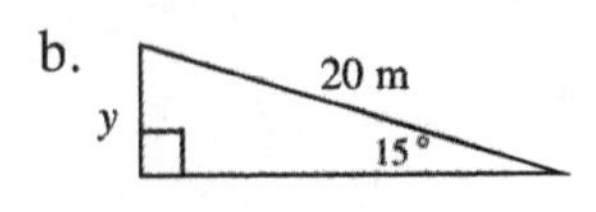

CL 1-127. Micah was given $200 for his birthday. Each week he spends $15 on comic books. In how many weeks will his birthday money be gone?

Create multiple representations ($x \rightarrow y$ table, graph, and equation) for the relationship between the weeks since Micah's birthday and how much money he has left. How does each representation show the solution to the problem?

CL 1-128. Check your answers using the table at the end of this section. Which problems do you feel confident about? Which problems were hard? Have you worked on problems like these in math classes you have taken before? Use the table to make a list of topics with which you need help and a list of topics you need to practice more.

Answers and Support for Closure Activity #4

What Have I Learned?

Note: MN = Math Note, LL = Learning Log

Problem	Solutions	Need Help?	More Practice
CL 1-119.	a. 3 b. 2 c. $x = 96$ d. $x = -2$ or 3	Lesson 1.1.1 MN: 1.1.1	Problems 1-4, 1-5, 1-17, 1-21, and 1-35
CL 1-120.	a. Domain: $-\infty < x < 6$ Range: $-\infty < y \le 6$ b. Domain: all real numbers Range: $-3 \le y \le 3$	Lesson 1.1.3 MN: 1.1.3 LL: 1.1.3	Problems 1-34, 1-35, 1-62, 1-68, and 1-86
CL 1-121.	a. $(-2, 9)$ b. $(5, 2), (-2, 2)$	Lesson 1.1.4 MN: 1.1.4	Problems 1-46, 1-69, 1-71, 1-84, 1-87, and 1-93
CL 1-122.	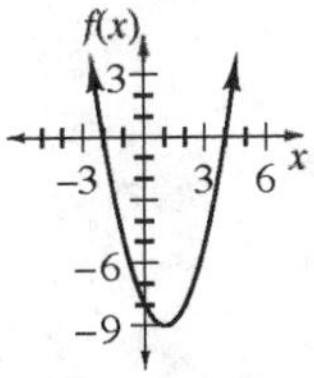 Domain: all real numbers; Range: $y \ge -9$ Intercepts: $(-2, 0), (4, 0)$, and $(0, -8)$ Vertex: $(1, -9)$	Lessons 1.2.2 and 1.2.4 MN: 1.1.3 LL: 1.2.2	Problems 1-20, 1-59, 1-90, and 1-95
CL 1-123.	a. 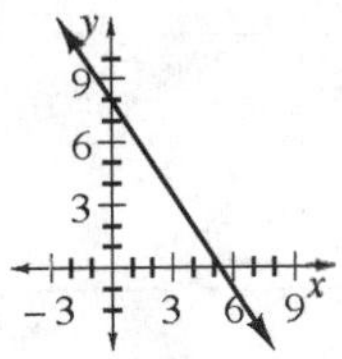 Intercepts: $(5\frac{1}{3}, 0)$ and $(0, 8)$ b. 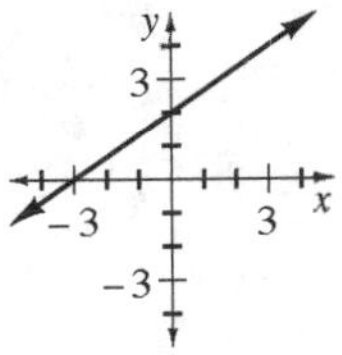 Intercepts: $(-3, 0)$ and $(0, 2)$	MN: 1.1.2	Problems 1-7, 1-61, 1-66, and 1-104

Problem	Solutions	Need Help?	More Practice
CL 1-124.	a. $y=-5x+18$ b. $y=-x+1$ c. $y=-\frac{3}{2}x+1$	MN: 1.1.2	Problem 1-15, 1-49, 1-74, and 1-105
CL 1-125.	a. $x=\frac{44}{13}$ b. $x=\frac{1}{3}$ c. $x=-6$ or 3	Explanations and practice of topics from previous courses are available in the *Core Connections Algebra Parent Guide with Extra Practice,* available free at www.cpm.org.	Problems 1-36, 1-48, 1-52, 1-63, 1-64, 1-70, 1-85, and 1-106
CL 1-126.	a. $y=\frac{27}{5}=5.4$ b. $y\approx 5.18$	MN: 1.2.1	Problems 1-24, 1-60, and 1-67
CL 1-127.	$y=200-15x$, where y represents the total amount of money left and x represents the numbers of weeks that have passed	Lesson 1.1.2	Problems 1-12, 1-19, 1-39, and 1-88

Week	$
0	200
1	185
2	170
3	155
4	140
5	125

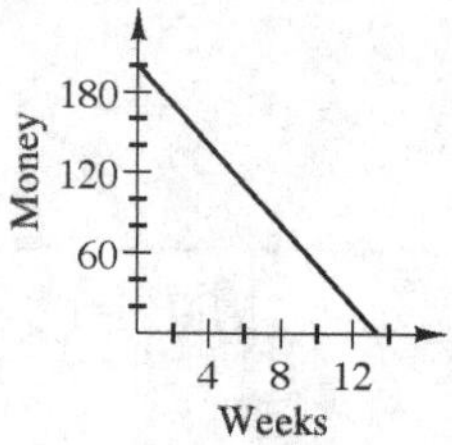

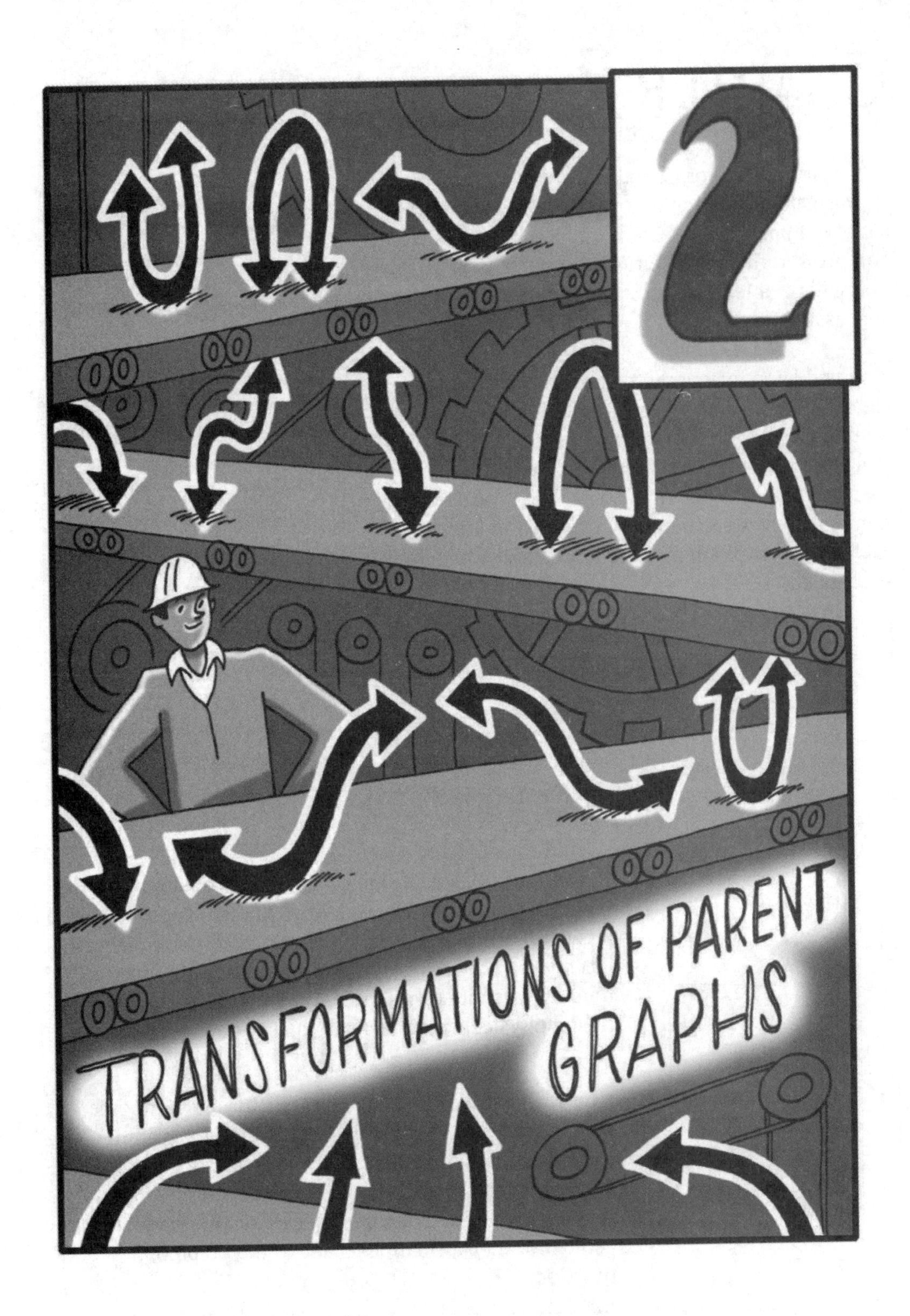
2
TRANSFORMATIONS OF PARENT
GRAPHS

CHAPTER 2 Transformations of Parent Graphs

In the first section of Chapter 2, you will learn how to change the equation of a parabola to make it fit a set of nonlinear data. After you learn how to stretch, compress, reflect, and shift the graph of $f(x)=x^2$, you will be able to create a variety of parabolic shapes and sizes.

You will learn that a graph's transformations are clearly recognizable when its equation is written in graphing form. Understanding this form will help you learn how to rewrite equations so that they are easier to graph. You will also use the quadratic family of functions to model physical situations, such as the arc of a jumping rabbit and the path of a soccer ball.

In Section 2.2, you will apply these same types of transformations to other parent functions.

Guiding Question

Mathematically proficient students model with mathematics.

As you work through this chapter, ask yourself:

How can I model this everyday situation with mathematics?

Chapter Outline

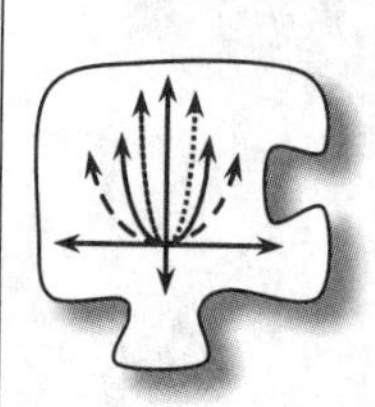

Section 2.1 In this section, you will learn how to shift, stretch, compress, and flip the graph of $f(x)=x^2$. You will write a general equation for the family of quadratic functions. Then you will learn how to graph a quadratic function quickly when it is written in graphing form. You will model physical situations with quadratic functions.

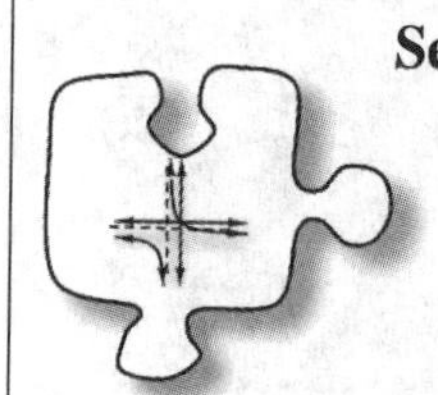

Section 2.2 You will apply the concepts of transformation to other parent functions, and you will learn that transforming each parent function creates a whole family of functions. You will write a general equation for a family of functions. You will learn how the equation predicts the geometric transformations made to the graph of a function.

2.1.1 How can an equation help me predict?

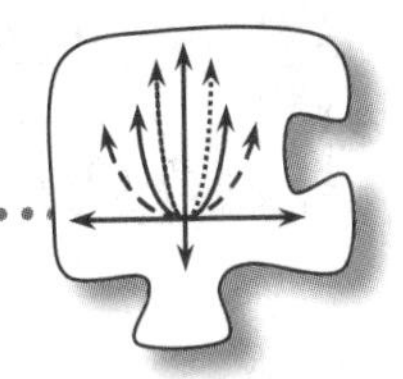

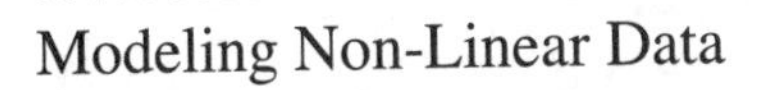

Modeling Non-Linear Data

This chapter will help you develop the power to manipulate functions so that they are useful in a wide variety of situations. Today's lesson focuses on collecting data and finding a function to model the trend in that data. You will then generalize your results and make predictions beyond the range of data you can measure. Discuss the following focus questions with your team while you work:

What will the graph look like?

Should we connect the data points?

How can we find an equation that fits the data?

2-1. SHRINKING TARGETS LAB

What is the relationship between the radius of a disk and its mass? If you double the radius of the disk, does the mass also double?

To answer these questions, your team will use scissors, a scale, and a Lesson 2.1.1 Resource Page. You will measure the weight of at least 8 different circular disks of varying radii (the plural of "radius"). Find your first data point by cutting out the large circle, measuring its radius, and using the scale to weigh it carefully. Repeat this process for circles of different radii.

After your team has collected its data, answer the questions below.

a. Look at your data with your team and predict what you think the graph will look like. Justify your prediction.

b. Enter your data in the graphing calculator and plot it. Sketch the graph of your data on your paper.

c. Consider the shrinking targets situation, what do you predict the x- and y-intercepts should be? What do they represent? Does the graph of your equation have these same intercept(s)? If not, explain completely why not.

Problem continues on next page. →

2-1. *Problem continued from previous page.*

d. What kind of equation do you think will model your data? Will your model predict the intercepts correctly?

e. Work with your team to find an equation that fits your data. Test the accuracy of your team's equation by entering it into your graphing calculator. If necessary, adjust your equation to make its graph fit your data and the x- and y-intercepts better. Once you are satisfied with your model, sketch the graph of your equation on your graph of data points from part (b).

f. What would be the mass of a target with a radius twice as large as the largest one you measured? How do you know?

2-2. What more can be said about the equation you used to model your data from the Shrinking Targets Lab? Consider this as you answer the questions below.

a. What are all of the acceptable input and output values (domain and range) for the activity in Shrinking Targets Lab? Do they match the domain and range of the function you used to model your data? If not, why are they different?

b. In part (a), you may have noticed that your equation only makes sense as a model for your data for part of its domain. Therefore, to accurately describe your model, you can add a condition to your equation, such as, "This equation is a good model when _________."

What condition can you add to describe when your model is valid?

2-3. Look back at the adjustments you made to your equation in problem 2-1 in order to make it fit your data. What did you change in your equation, and what effects did your changes have on its graph? Discuss these questions with your team and be prepared to share your ideas with the class.

METHODS AND MEANINGS

Exponential Functions

An **exponential function** has the general form $y = a \cdot b^x$, where a is the **initial value** (the y-intercept) and b is the **multiplier** (the growth). Be careful: The independent variable x has to be in the exponent. For example, $y = x^2$ is *not* an exponential equation, even though it has an exponent.

For example, in the multiple representations below, the y-intercept is $(0, 4)$ and the growth factor is 3 because the y-value is increasing by multiplying by 3.

$y = 4 \cdot 3^x$

x	y
–3	$\frac{4}{3^3}$ or $\frac{4}{27}$
–2	$\frac{4}{3^2}$ or $\frac{4}{9}$
–1	$\frac{4}{3}$
0	4
1	12
2	36
3	108

×3
×3

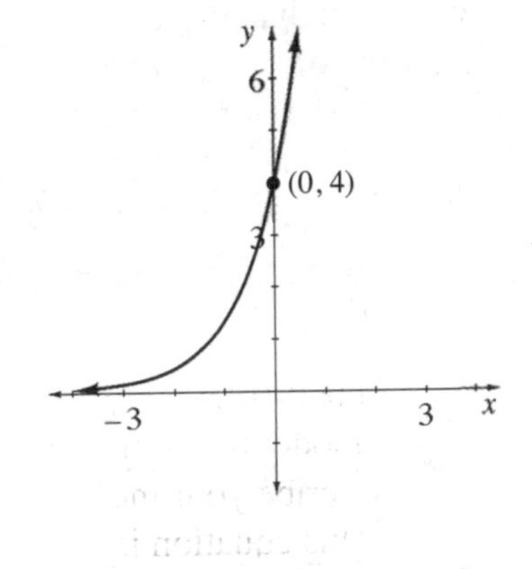

To increase or decrease a quantity by a percentage, use the multiplier for that percentage. For example, the multiplier for an increase of 7% is 100% + 7% = 1.07. The multiplier for a decrease of 7% is
100% – 7% = 0.93.

2-4. Jamilla was moving to a new city. She researched the rates charged by the local utility company for water. She found the listing of charges below. She expects that her family may use up to 1,000 cubic feet of water each month.

- $12.70 monthly service fee
- First 300 cubic feet of water used:
  $3.90 per 100 cubic feet, or fraction thereof
- After the first 300 cubic feet:
  $5.20 per 100 cubic feet, or fraction thereof

a. Sketch a graph of the cost of Jamilla's possible water usage in one month. Be sure to consider what the cost would be for partial units such as 220 or 675 cubic feet of water.

b. Is this graph a function? Why or why not?

c. What are the domain and range of this graph?

2-5. For each equation in parts (a) through (d) below, find the input value that gives the *smallest* possible output. In other words, find the x-value of the *lowest* point on the graph. Then find the input value that gives the *largest* possible output (or the x-value of the *highest* point on the graph).

a. $y = (x-2)^2$ b. $y = x^2 + 2$ c. $y = (x+3)^2$ d. $y = -x^2 + 5$

e. Where on the graphs of each of the above equations would you find the points with the smallest or largest y-values?

2-6. Sketch $y = x^2$, $y = -3x^2$, and $y = -0.25x^2$ on the same set of axes. What does a negative coefficient do to the graph?

2-7. Your results from this problem will be useful in the parabola investigation that you will do in Lesson 2.1.2.

a. Draw the graph of $y=(x-3)^2$. If you are drawing the graph by hand be sure to use the domain $0 \le x \le 6$.

b. How is this graph different from the graph of $y=x^2$?

2-8. Consider the sequence with the initial value 256, followed by 64, 16, ...

a. Write the next three terms of this sequence, then find an equation for the sequence.

b. If you were to keep writing out more and more terms of the sequence, what would happen to the terms?

c. Sketch a graph of the sequence. What happens to the points as you go farther to the right?

d. What is the domain of the sequence? What is the domain of the function with the same equation as this sequence?

2-9. Write the equation for each graph.

a.

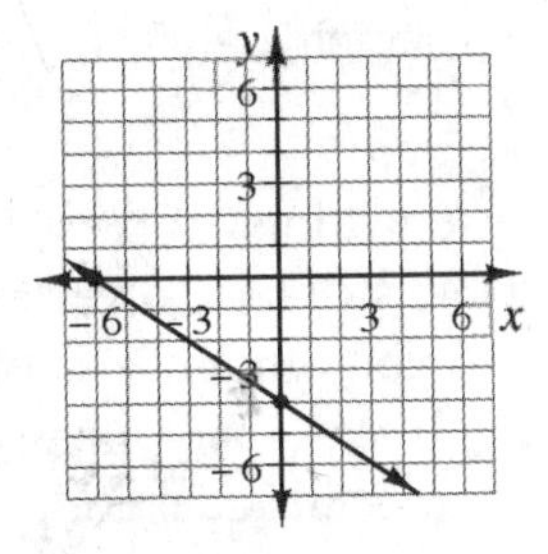

b.

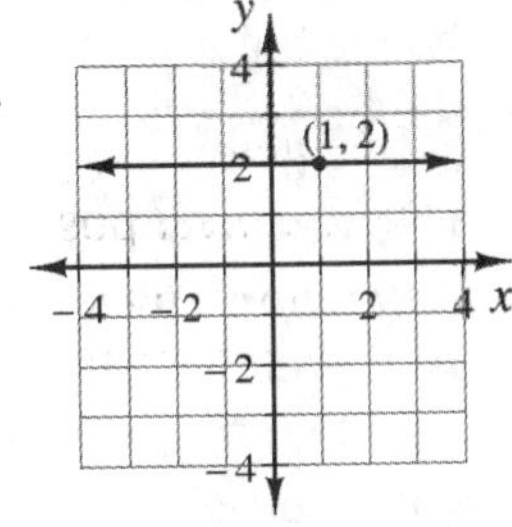

c.

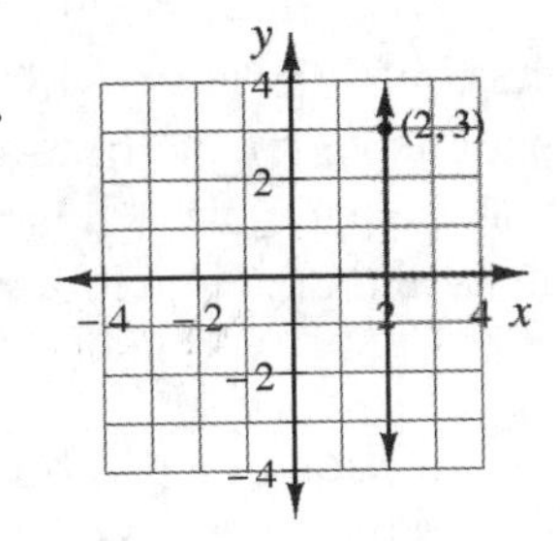

d.

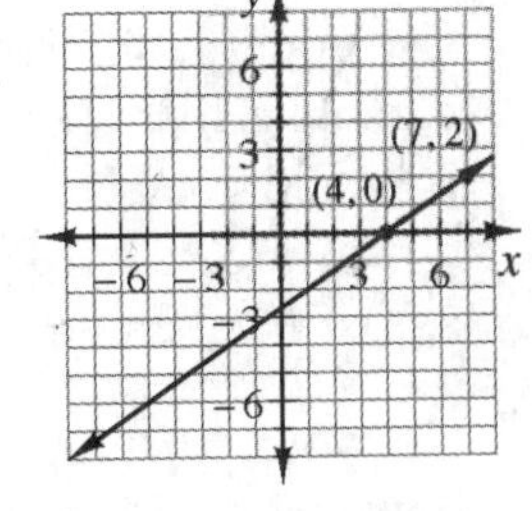

2-10. The slope of $\overline{AB}$ is 5, with points $A(-3,-1)$ and $B(2, n)$. Find the value of n and the distance between points A and B.

2.1.2 How can I shift a parabola?

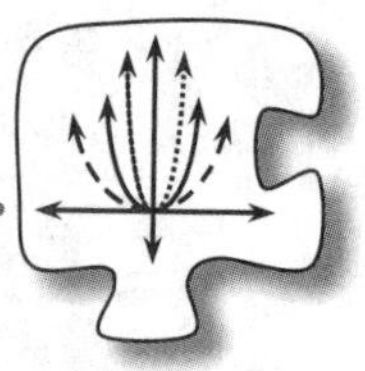

Parabola Investigation

In Algebra 1 you learned about slope and y-intercept, ideas that allow you to write equations and sketch graphs of any line. During this lesson you will work on developing similar tools for parabolas.

2-11. PARABOLA LAB, Part One

What happens to a parabola's graph when you change the numbers in the equation? To get a better sense of the different ways to transform the graph of a parabola, as a team complete the investigation outlined below. As you work, be sure to sketch the graphs you see in your graphing calculator carefully and record the equations you enter.

a. On graph paper, graph the equation $y=(x-2)(x-2)$. Be sure to label any important points on your graph, including the lowest point on the graph, called the **vertex**. (If the graph were to open downward, the vertex would be the highest point on the graph.) Also sketch and write the equation of the line of symmetry of your graph.

b. Use your graphing calculator to find the equations of two parabolas with *different* graphs that also open upward and still have a vertex at $(2, 0)$. Add sketches of these two new graphs to your graph from part (a), along with their equations. As you work, keep track of any ideas you try along with their results, even if they do not answer this question, as they may help you later.

c. Use your graphing calculator to find the equations of two different parabolas that open *downward*, each with its vertex on the x-axis at $x = 2$. How did you change the equation so that the parabola would open downward? Add sketches of these graphs and their equations to your axes. What are their lines of symmetry?

d. Use your graphing calculator to find the equation of a parabola that opens downward with a vertex at $(-4, 0)$. What is the equation of your parabola's line of symmetry?

e. Choose a new point on the x-axis and find at least three equations of parabolas that touch the x-axis only at that one point.

2-12. PARABOLA LAB, Part Two

Polly Parabola had been the manager of the Parabola Department of Functions of America, but she has decided to start her own company called "Professional Parabola Productions." She needs your help. See her memo below.

MEMO

To: Your Study Team
From: Ms. Polly Parabola, CEO
Re: New Parabola Possibilities

I am starting a new company specializing only in parabolas. To win over new customers, I need to be able to show them that we know more about parabolas than any of the other function factories around, especially since every company already sells $y = x^2$.

My customers will need all sorts of parabolas, and we need the knowledge to make them happy. I would love to offer parabolas that are completely new to them.

Please investigate all different kinds of parabolas. Determine all the ways that you can change the equation $y = x^2$ *to change the shape, direction, and location of a parabola on a graph.*

Remember that I'm counting on you! I need you to uncover the parabola secrets that our competitors do not know.

Sincerely,
Ms. Polly Parabola

Your Task: Work with your team to determine all of the ways you can change the graph of a parabola by changing its equation. Be prepared to share your ideas with the class. As other teams contribute ideas to a class discussion, write down any new ideas.

Start by choosing one transformation from the list generated by the class; then find a way to change the equation $y = x^2$ to create this transformation. Whenever you figure out a new transformation, record a clear summary statement before moving on to the next transformation. Be prepared to explain your summary statement to Ms. Polly Parabola.

Discussion Points

What changes can we make to a parabola's graph?

What changes can we make to the equation $y = x^2$?

How do changes in the equation relate to changes in the graph?

Further Guidance

2-13. Graph the parabola $y = x^2$. Be sure to label any important points. When you are sure that your graph is complete and accurate, trace over it in colored pencil.

a. Find a way to change the equation is to make the $y = x^2$ parabola *stretch vertically*. That is, to make the graph look narrower, so the points in the parabola seem to rise away from the vertex more quickly. The new parabola should have the same vertex and orientation (i.e., open up) as $y = x^2$. Record the equations you try, along with their results. Write down the results even when they are wrong – they may come in handy later on.

b. Find a way to change the equation to make the $y = x^2$ parabola *compress vertically*. That is, to make the graph look flatter, so that the points seem to rise away from the vertex less quickly. Record the equations you try, along with their results and your observations.

c. Find a way to change the equation to make the same parabola *open downward*. The new parabola should be congruent (the same shape and size) to $y = x^2$, with the same vertex, except it should open downward so its vertex will be its highest point. Record the equations you try, their results, and your observations.

d. Find a way to change the equation to make the $y = x^2$ parabola *move 5 units down*. Your new parabola should look exactly like $y = x^2$, but the vertex should be at $(0,-5)$. Record the equations you try, along with their results. Include a comment about moving the graph up as well as down.

e. Find a way to change the equation to make the $y = x^2$ parabola *move 3 units to the right*. Your new parabola should look exactly like $y = x^2$, except that the vertex should be at the point $(3, 0)$. If you need an idea to get started, review your work on problem 2-11. Record the equations you try, along with their results. Include a comment about how to move the parabola to the left as well as how to move it to the right.

f. Find a way to change the equation to make the $y = x^2$ parabola *move 3 units to the left*, as in part (e), AND *stretch vertically*, as in part (a). Record the equations you try, along with their results.

Further Guidance section ends here.

2-14. Find a way to change the equation to make the $y = x^2$ parabola *vertically compressed, open down, move six units up, and move two units to the left*. Where is the vertex of your new parabola?

2-15. Now that you are a parabola expert, you can impress Ms. Polly Parabola!

a. Make up your own fancy transformation and show her how you can change your equation to create it.

b. Write a general equation for a parabola that could be shifted or stretched in any direction by any amount. Be prepared to share your ideas with the class.

2-16. Explain the differences between an *accurate sketch* and a *careful graph*.

2-17. If $p(x) = x^2 + 5x - 6$, find:

a. Where $p(x)$ intersects the y-axis.

b. Where $p(x)$ intersects the x-axis.

c. If $q(x) = x^2 + 5x$, find the intercepts of $q(x)$ and compare the graphs of $p(x)$ and $q(x)$.

d. Find $p(x) - q(x)$.

2-18. Solve for z in each equation below.

a. $4^z = 8$

b. $4^{2z/3} = 8^{(z+2)}$

c. $3^z = 81^2$

d. $5^{(z+1)/3} = 25^{1/z}$

2-19. Simplify each of the following expressions. Be sure that your answer has no negative or fractional exponents.

a. $(\frac{1}{81})^{-1/4}$

b. $x^{-2}y^{-4}$

c. $(2x)^{-2}(16x^2y)^{1/2}$

2-20. Daniela, Kieu, and Duyen decide to go to the movies one hot summer afternoon. The theater is having a summer special called Three Go Free. They will get free movie tickets if they each buy a large popcorn and a large soft drink. They take the deal and spend \$22.50 on food, drinks and movie tickets. The next week, they go back again, only this time, they each pay \$8.00 for their ticket, they each get a large soft drink, but they share one large bucket of popcorn. This return trip costs them a total of \$37.50.

a. Find the price of a large soft drink and the price of a large bucket of popcorn.

b. Did you write two equations or did you use another method? If you used another method, write two equations now and solve them. If you already used a system of equations, skip this part.

2-21. Plot each pair of points and find the distance between them. Give answers in both square-root form and as decimal approximations.

a. $(3,-6)$ and $(-2,5)$ b. $(5,-8)$ and $(-3,1)$ c. $(0,5)$ and $(5,0)$

d. Write the distance you found in part (c) in simplified square-root form.

2-22. The amount of profit (in millions) made by Scandal Math, a company that writes math problems based on tabloid articles, can be found by the equation $P(n) = -n^2 + 10n$, where n is the number of textbooks sold (also in millions). Find the maximum profit and the number of textbooks that Scandal Math must sell to realize this maximum profit.

2-23. Your friend is taking an algebra class at a different school where she is not allowed to use a graphing calculator.

a. Explain to her how she can get a good sketch of the graph of the function $y = 2(x+3)^2 - 8$ without using a calculator *and* without having to make an $x \to y$ table. Be sure to explain how to locate the vertex, whether the parabola should open up or down, and how its shape is related to the shape of the graph of $y = x^2$.

b. Your friend also needs to know the x- and y-intercepts. Show her how to find them without having to draw an accurate graph or use a graphing calculator.

2-24. Consider the equations $y = 3(x-1)^2 - 5$ and $y = 3x^2 - 6x - 2$.

a. Verify that they are equivalent by creating a table or graph for each equation.

b. Show algebraically that these two equations are equivalent by starting with one form and showing how to get the other.

c. Notice that the value for a is 3 in both forms of the equation, but that the numbers for b and c are different from the numbers for h and k. Why do you think the value for a would be the same number in both forms of the equation?

2-25. Use what you learned in the parabola investigation to write an equation for each of the parabolas described below.

a. A parabola opening upward, shifted 8 units right, and 5 units down.

b. A parabola with a stretch factor of 10, sitting with its vertex on the x-axis at $x = -6$.

c. A downward-opening parabola with vertex $(-7, -2)$ and a vertical compression of 0.6.

2-26. The point $(3, -7)$ is on a line with a slope of $\frac{2}{3}$. Find another point on the line.

2-27. Simplify each expression without using a calculator. Remember that to simplify expressions with radicals, you can remove perfect square factors such as in this example: $\sqrt{18} = \sqrt{9 \cdot 2} = \sqrt{9} \cdot \sqrt{2} = 3\sqrt{2}$

a. $\sqrt{50}$ b. $\sqrt{72}$ c. $\sqrt{45}$

2-28. Find the value of x.

a.

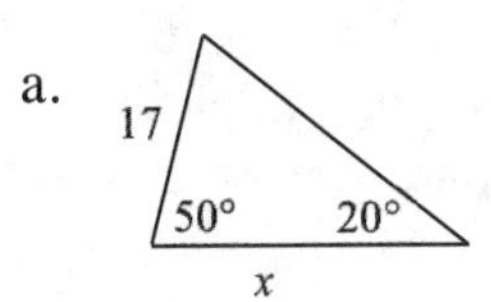

b.

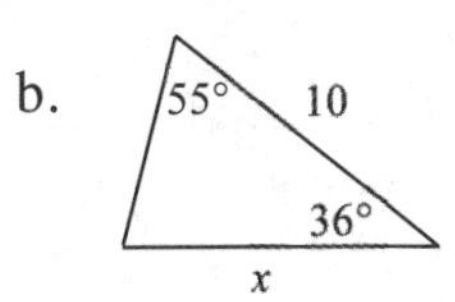

2-29. Suppose your parents spend an average of \$300 each month for your food.

a. In five years, when you are living on your own, how much will you be spending on food each month if you are eating about the same amount and inflation averages about 4% per year?

b. Write an equation that represents your monthly food bill x years from now if both the rate of inflation and your eating habits stay the same.

2.1.3 How can I graph it quickly?

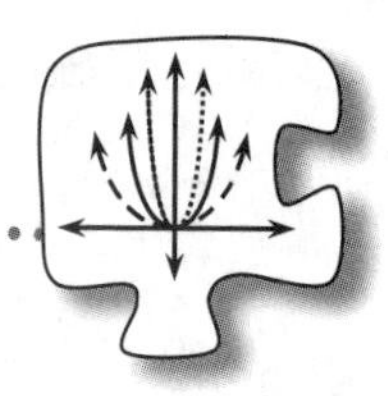

Graphing a Parabola Without a Table

You have developed several tools that enable you to transform graphs of parabolas by altering their equations. In the next few lessons, you will use this knowledge to do more with the equations and graphs of parabolic functions than ever before. In this lesson, you will figure out how to use your growing knowledge of transforming graphs to make a quick and fairly accurate graph of any parabolic function.

2-30. TRANSFORMING GRAPHS

Use your dynamic graphing tool to support a class discussion about the equation $y = a(x - h)^2 + k$. Refer to the bulleted points below.

- Identify which **parameter** (a, h, or k) affects the orientation, vertical shift, horizontal shift, vertical stretch, and vertical compression of the graph compared to the graph of the parent function $y = x^2$.
- What values stretch the graph vertically? Compress the graph horizontally? Why do those values have these impacts?
- What values cause the graph to flip vertically?
- What values cause the graph to shift to the left? To the right? Why?
- What values cause the graph to shift up or down? Why?
- Are there points on your graph that connect to specific parameters in the equation? Explain.

2-31. For each equation below, predict the coordinates of the vertex, the orientation (whether it opens up or down), and whether the graph will be a vertical stretch or a compression of $y = x^2$. Do not use a graphing calculator. Quickly make an accurate graph based on your predictions. How can you make the shape of your graph accurate without using a table? Be prepared to share your strategies with the class.

a. $y = (x + 9)^2$

b. $y = x^2 + 7$

c. $y = 3x^2$

d. $y = \frac{1}{3}(x - 1)^2$

e. $y = -(x - 7)^2 + 6$

f. $y = 2(x + 3)^2 - 8$

g. Now take out your graphing calculator and check your predictions for the equations in parts (a) through (f). Did you make any mistakes? If so, describe the mistake and what you need to do in order to correct it.

2-32. Graph each equation below without making a table or using your graphing calculator. Look for ways to go directly from the equation to the graph. What information did you need to make a graph without using a table? How did you find that information from the equation? Be ready to share your strategies with the class.

a. $y=(x-7)^2-2$

b. $y=0.5(x+3)^2+1$

2-33. In problem 2-32, you figured out that having an equation for a parabola in **graphing form** ($y=a(x-h)^2+k$) allows you to know the vertex, the orientation, and the stretch factor, and that knowing these attributes allows you to graph without having to make a table. How can you make a graph without a table when the equation is given in **standard form** ($y=ax^2+bx+c$)? Consider the equation $y=2x^2+4x-30$.

a. What is the orientation of $y=2x^2+4x-30$? That is, does it open upward or open downward? How could you change the equation to make the graph open the opposite way?

b. What is the stretch factor of $y=2x^2+4x-30$? Justify your answer.

c. Can you identify the vertex of $y=2x^2+4x-30$ by looking at the equation? If not, talk with your team about strategies you could use to find the vertex without using a table or graphing calculator and then apply your new strategy to the problem. If your team is stuck consider doing parts (*i*) through (*iii*) below.

i. What are the *x*-intercepts of the parabola?

ii. Where is the vertex located in relation to the *x*-intercepts? Can you use this relationship to find the *x* coordinate of the vertex?

iii. Use the *x*-coordinate of the vertex to find its *y*-coordinate.

d. Make a quick graph of $y=2x^2+4x-30$ and write its equation in graphing form.

2-34. Rewrite each equation in graphing form and then sketch a graph. Label each sketch so that it is possible to connect it to the equation.

a. $p(x)=x^2-10x+16$

b. $f(x)=x^2+3x-10$

c. $g(x)=x^2-4x-2$

d. $h(x)=-4x^2+4x+8$

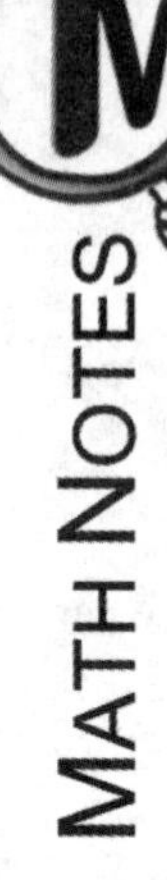

METHODS AND MEANINGS

Forms of Quadratics

There are three main forms of a quadratic function: standard form, factored form, and graphing form. Study the examples below. Assume that $a \neq 0$ and that the meaning of a, b, and c are different for each form below.

Standard form: $f(x) = ax^2 + bx + c$. The y-intercept is $(0, c)$.

Factored form: $f(x) = a(x+b)(x+c)$. The x-intercepts are $(-b, 0)$ and $(-c, 0)$.

Graphing form (vertex form): $f(x) = a(x-h)^2 + k$. The vertex is (h, k).

Similarly, there are three forms of a single-variable quadratic equation.

Standard form: Any quadratic equation written in the form $ax^2 + bx + c = 0$.

Factored form: Any quadratic equation written in the form $a(x+b)(x+c) = 0$.

Perfect Square form: Any quadratic equation written in the form $(ax-b)^2 = c^2$.

Solutions to a quadratic equation can be written in **exact form (radical form)** as in:

$$x = \frac{-3+\sqrt{5}}{2} \text{ or } x = \frac{-3-\sqrt{5}}{2}$$

Solutions can also be estimated and written in **approximate decimal form**:

$$x = -0.38 \text{ or } x = -2.62$$

2-35. Solve each of the following equations *without using the Quadratic Formula*.

a. $y^2 - 6y = 0$

b. $n^2 + 5n + 7 = 7$

c. $2t^2 - 14t + 3 = 3$

d. $\frac{1}{3}x^2 + 3x - 4 = -4$

e. Zero is one of the solutions of each of the above equations. What do all of the above equations have in common that causes them to have zero as a solution?

2-36. Find the vertex of each of the following parabolas by averaging the x-intercepts. Then write each equation in graphing form.

a. $y = (x - 3)(x - 11)$

b. $y = (x + 2)(x - 6)$

c. $y = x^2 - 14x + 40$

d. $y = (x - 2)^2 - 1$

2-37. Did you need to average the x-intercepts to find the vertex in part (d) of the preceding problem?

a. What are the coordinates of the vertex for part (d)?

b. How do these coordinates relate to the equation?

2-38. Scientists can estimate the increase in carbon dioxide in the atmosphere by measuring increases in carbon emissions. In 1998 the annual carbon emission was about eight gigatons (a gigaton is a billion metric tons). Over the last several years, annual carbon emission has been increasing by about one percent.

a. At this rate, how much carbon will be emitted in 2010?

b. Write a function, $C(x)$, to represent the amount of carbon emitted in any year starting with the year 2000.

2-39. Make predictions about how many places the graph of each equation below will touch the x-axis. You may first want to rewrite some of the equations in a more useful form.

a. $y=(x-2)(x-3)$

b. $y=(x+1)^2$

c. $y=x^2+6x+9$

d. $y=x^2+7x+10$

e. $y=x^2+6x+8$

f. $y=-x^2-4x-4$

g. Check your predictions with your calculator.

h. Write a clear explanation describing how you can tell whether the equation of a parabola will touch the x-axis at only one point.

2-40. Simplify each of the following expressions. Be sure that your answer has no negative or fractional exponents.

a. $64^{1/3}$

b. $(4x^2y^5)^{-2}$

c. $(2x^2\cdot y^{-3})(3x^{-1}y^5)$

2-41. Suppose you have a 3 by 3 by 3 cube. It is painted on all six faces and then cut apart into 27 pieces, each a 1 by 1 by 1 cube. If one of the cubes is chosen at random, what is the probability that:

a. Three sides are painted?

b. Two sides are painted?

c. One side is painted?

d. No sides are painted?

2.1.4 How can I rewrite it in graphing form?

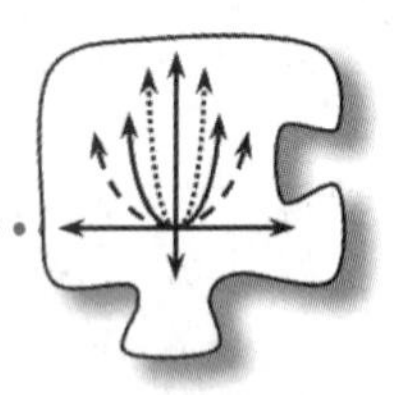

Rewriting in Graphing Form

In Lesson 2.1.3, you used the method of averaging the intercepts to change the equation of a parabola from the standard form $f(x) = ax^2 + bx + c$ to the graphing form $f(x) = a(x - h)^2 + k$ by finding the x-intercepts and averaging them to find the x-value of the vertex. Next you substituted to find the y-value, and then used the coordinates of the vertex for h and k.

What can you say about a parabola that cannot be factored or that does not cross the x-axis? How can you write its equation in graphing form? In a previous course you may have learned how to complete the square for quadratics and this strategy can help you write the graphing form for a parabola.

2-42. In this investigation you will compare two methods of changing a quadratic equation from standard form to graphing form.

a. Write the equation of the parabola $y = x^2 - 2x - 15$ in graphing form using two methods. First, use the method of averaging the intercepts. Then, use the method of completing the square. Find the x-intercept(s), the y-intercept(s), and the vertex of the parabola, and sketch the graph.

b. Write $y = x^2 + 8x + 10$ in graphing form. Find the intercepts and vertex, and sketch the graph. Do both strategies work for this parabola?

c. Can you use both methods to sketch $y = x^2 + 2x + 4$? Do both strategies still work?

d. Discuss the two strategies with your team. Then respond to the following Discussion Points.

Discussion Points

When does the method of averaging the intercepts work better?

When does the method of completing the square work better?

Which method was more efficient and why?

Further Guidance

2-43. Jessica was at home struggling with her homework. She had missed class and could not remember how to **complete the square**. She was supposed to use the method to change $f(x) = x^2 + 8x + 10$ to graphing form. Then her precocious younger sister, Anita, who was playing with algebra tiles, said, "*Hey, I bet I know what they mean.*" Anita's Algebra class had been using tiles to multiply and factor binomials. Anita explained, "$f(x) = x^2 + 8x + 10$ *would look like this,*"

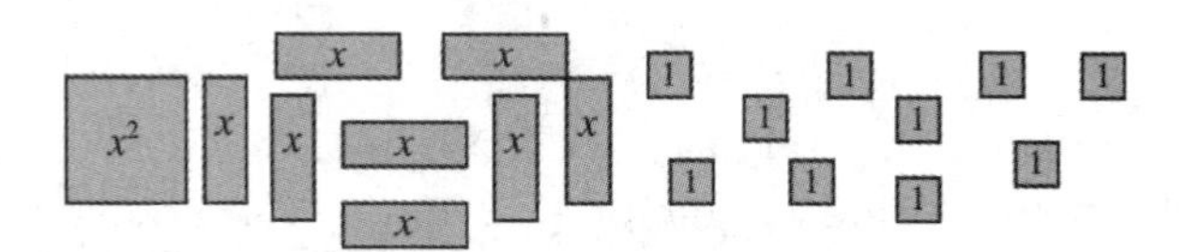

"*Yes,*" said Jessica, "*I took Algebra 1 too, remember?*"

Anita continued, "*And you need to make it into a square!*"

"*OK,*" said Jessica, and she arranged her tiles as shown in the picture below.

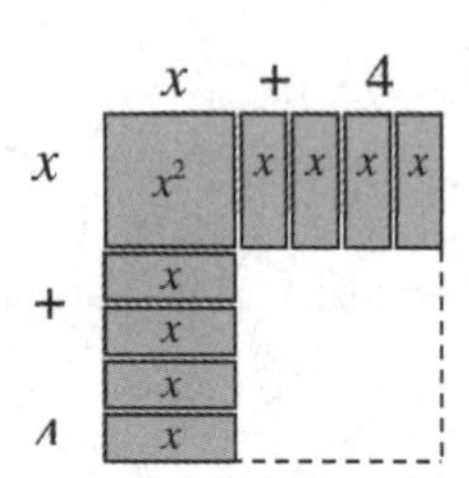

"*Oh,*" said Jessica. "*So I just need 16 small unit tiles to fill in the corner.*"

"*But you only have 10,*" Anita reminded her.

"*Right, I only have ten,*" Jessica replied. She put in the 10 small square tiles then drew the outline of the whole square and said:

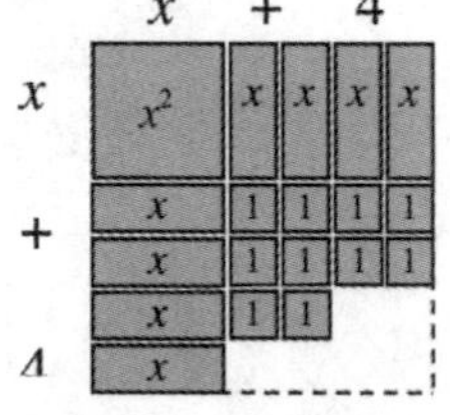

"*Oh, I get it! The* ***complete square*** *is* $(x + 4)^2$ *which is equal to* $x^2 + 4x + 16$. *But my original expression,* $x^2 + 8x + 10$, *has six fewer tiles than that, so what I have is* $(x + 4)^2$, *minus 6.*"

"*Yes,*" said Anita. "*You started with* $x^2 + 8x + 10$, *but now you can rewrite it as* $x^2 + 8x + 10 = (x + 4)^2 - 6$."

Use your graphing calculator to show that $f(x) = x^2 + 8x + 10$ and $f(x) = (x + 4)^2 - 6$ are equivalent functions.

2-44. Help Jessica with a new problem. She needs to complete the square to write $y = x^2 + 4x + 9$ in graphing form. Draw tiles to help her figure out how to make this expression into a square. Does she have too few or too many unit squares this time? Write her equation in graphing form.

2-45. How could you complete the square to change $f(x) = x^2 + 5x + 2$ into graphing form? How would you split the five x-tiles into two equal parts?

Jessica decided to use force! She cut one tile in half, as shown below. Then she added her two unit tiles.

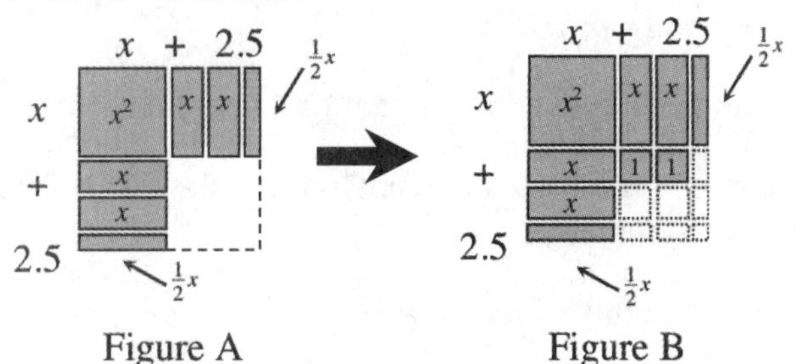

Figure A Figure B

a. How many unit tiles are in the perfect square?

b. Does Jessica have too many or too few tiles in her original expression? How many?

b. Write the graphing form of the function.

c. Now use your work on problems 2-43 through part (b) of problem 2-45 to complete problem 2-42.

Further Guidance section ends here.

2-46. Use the strategy of your choice to write each function below in graphing form.

a. $f(x) = x^2 + 6x + 7$

b. $f(x) = x^2 - 4x + 11$

c. $f(x) = x^2 + 5x + 2$

d. $f(x) = x^2 - 7x + 2$

2-47. How can you use a quadratic equation in graphing form to make a quick sketch of the parabola?

a. What is the vertex and y-intercept of the graph of $y = (x-3)^2 - 25$? Explain how you found the y-intercept.

b. Find the x intercepts of $y = (x-3)^2 - 25$ algebraically. Explain how you found the x-intercepts.

c. Obtain the Lesson 2.1.4 Resource Page and justify each step in solving the equation in part (b) for x when $y = 0$.

d. Find the exact vertex, y-intercept, and x-intercepts of $y = (x+5)^2 - 8 = 0$. Make a sketch of the parabola, then check your sketch with your graphing calculator.

2-48. GENERALIZATION CHALLENGE I

Jeremy had an idea, "*What if we start with the equation in standard form? I bet we can find a way to get the vertex so we don't have to solve the equation or change it to graphing form every time. Let's start with* $y = ax^2 + bx + c$ *and find the x-intercepts for its graph.*"

a. Solve the general quadratic equation to get the x-intercepts.

b. How can you use the x-intercepts to find the line of symmetry? What is the line of symmetry?

c. What is the vertex of the graph of $y = ax^2 + bx + c$?

2-49. GENERALIZATION CHALLENGE II

Jessica had another idea. She said, "*Couldn't we just start with* $y = ax^2 + bx + c$ *and complete the square?*"

Jeremy objected, "*But what do we do about the* ax^2*?*"

a. How can you rewrite the equation so the coefficient of x is one? Do it.

b. What is the square that needs to be completed?

c. What expression has to be added to complete the square?

d. Rewrite the equation in the form $\frac{y}{a} = (x + \_\_)^2 + \_\_\_\_\_$, and multiply by a.

e. What is the vertex? Is the result the same as in problem 2-48? How do you know?

METHODS AND MEANINGS

Finding Graphing Form and Vertex of Parabolas

Starting with the graphing form of a quadratic equation and rewriting it to get standard form is straightforward algebra. But starting with a quadratic equation in standard form and rewriting it to get graphing form is more difficult. You have used two strategies to rewrite standard form in graphing form: **averaging the intercepts** and **completing the square**.

For example, change $y = x^2 + 3x - 10$ to graphing form.

Averaging Intercepts:

x-intercept is where $y = 0$.

Solve $0 = x^2 + 3x - 10$

$0 = (x+5)(x-2)$

The x-intercepts are (–5,0) and (2,0)

Axis of symmetry: $x = \frac{-5+2}{2} = -\frac{3}{2}$

By evaluating for x, find $y = -\frac{49}{4}$

Vertex: $(-\frac{3}{2}, -\frac{49}{4})$

Completing the Square:

Make a perfect square from $x^2 + 3x$:

1.5	$1.5x$	2.25
x	x^2	$1.5x$
	x	1.5

$(x+1.5)^2 = x^2 + 3x + 2.25$

The original expression, $x^2 + 3x - 10$, is 12.25 fewer than $(x+1.5)^2$. So, $y = x^2 + 3x - 10 = (x+1.5)^2 - 12.25$.

Since graphing form is $y = a(x-h)^2 + k$, vertex: $(-1.5, -12.25) = (-\frac{3}{2}, -\frac{49}{4})$

In general, how are h and k in $y = a(x-h)^2 + k$ related to b *and* c in $y = ax^2 + bx + c$? By averaging the two solutions given by the Quadratic Formula, or by completing the square, the axis of symmetry is $y = -\frac{b}{2a}$, and the vertex is $\left(-\frac{b}{2a}, c - \frac{b^2}{4a}\right)$, so $h = -\frac{b}{2a}$ and $k = c - \frac{b^2}{4a}$.

2-50. For each quadratic function below use the method of completing the square or averaging the intercepts to rewrite it in graphing form. Then, state the axis of symmetry and give the vertex of each parabola. Try to use each method at least once.

a. $f(x)=x^2+6x+15$

b. $y=x^2-4x+9$

c. $f(x)=x^2-8x$

d. $y=x^2+7x-2$

2-51. Represent the number you would have to add to an expression of the form x^2+bx to make a complete square.

2-52. How is $y=2^x$ different from $y=-(2^x)$? Sketch the graph of $y=-(2^x)$.

2-53. Throughout this book, key problems have been selected as "checkpoints." Each checkpoint problem is marked with an icon like the one at left. These checkpoint problems are provided so that you can check to be sure you are building skills at the expected level. When you have trouble with checkpoint problems, refer to the review materials and practice problems that are available in the Checkpoint Materials section at the back of your book.

This problem is a checkpoint for finding the distance between two points and finding the equation of a line. It will be referred to as Checkpoint 2A.

For each pair of points, determine the distance between them. Then find the equation for a line through them.

a. $(-2,4)$ and $(4,7)$

b. $(3,4)$ and $(3,-1)$

c. $(-7,20)$ and $(3,-5)$

d. $(1,-2)$ and $(5,-2)$

Check your answers by referring to the Checkpoint 2A materials located at the back of your book.

If you needed help solving these problems correctly, then you need more practice. Review the Checkpoint 2A materials and try the practice problems. Also, consider getting help outside of class time. From this point on, you will be expected to do problems like these quickly and easily.

2-54. The Quadratic Formula can be used to help solve $4x^3 + 23x^2 - 2x = 0$. Show or explain how.

2-55. Find the value of x.

a.

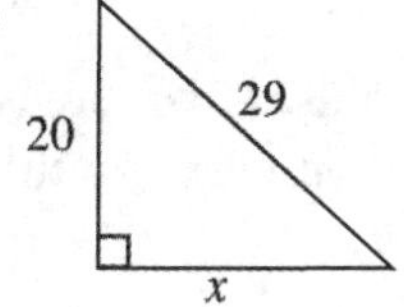

b.

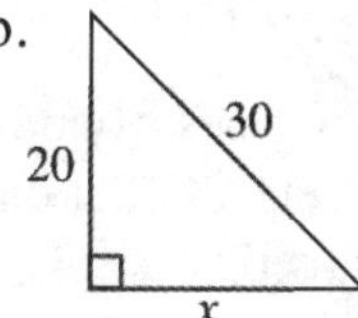

c.

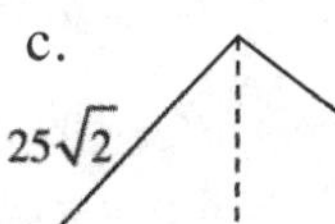

2-56. A dart hits each of these dartboards at random. What is the probability that the dart will land in the unshaded area?

a.

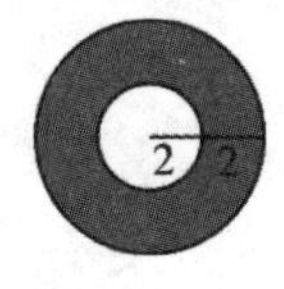

b.

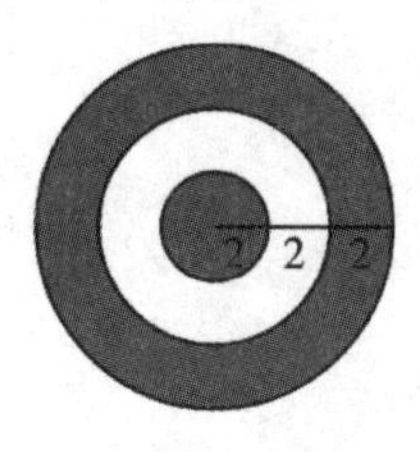

2-57. If $\frac{2}{3}$ of A is $\frac{5}{12}$, and $\frac{4}{3}$ of B is $\frac{8}{9}$, which is larger, A or B?

2-58. Examine the diagram at right. Imagine spinning the rectangle around the y-axis. Think of a rectangular flap attached to the y-axis so that the rectangle will revolve around the y-axis.

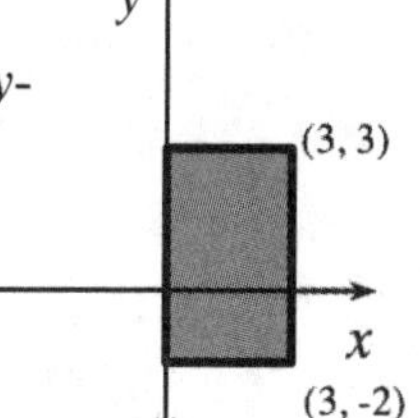

a. Draw the resulting shape.

b. Find the volume of this shape.

2-59. What is a line of symmetry?

a. Draw a figure that has a line of symmetry.

b. Draw a figure that has *two* lines of symmetry.

c. Can you find a basic geometric shape that has an infinite number of lines of symmetry?

2-60. Find the point where $y = 3x - 1$ intersects $2y + 5x = 53$.

2-61. Lettie just got her driver's license. Her friends soon nicknamed her "Leadfoot" because she is always going 80 mph on the freeway even though the speed limit is 65 mph.

a. At this speed, how long will it take her to travel 50 miles?

b. How long would it take her if she drove the 50 miles at 65 mph?

c. Speeding tickets carry fines of about $200 and usually increase the cost of insurance. If Lettie gets a ticket on this trip, then what would be her cost per minute of time saved?

2-62. Solve for the indicated value. Leave your answer in exact form.

a. $x =$ _____

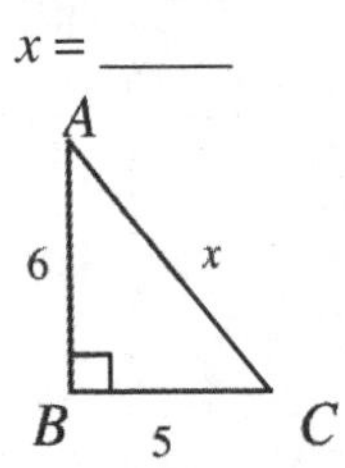

b. $m\angle C =$ _____

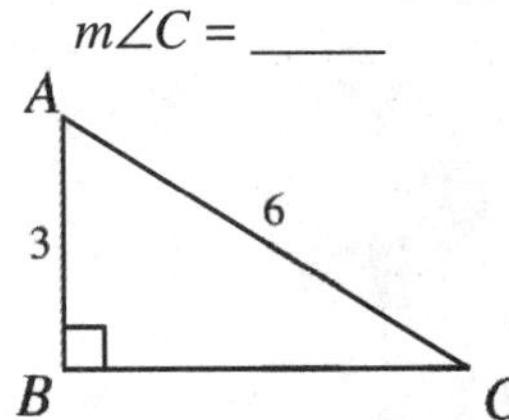

c. $m\angle B =$ _____

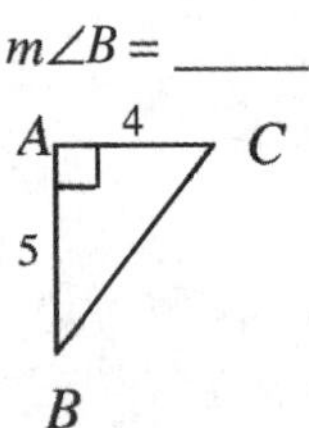

d. $a =$ _____

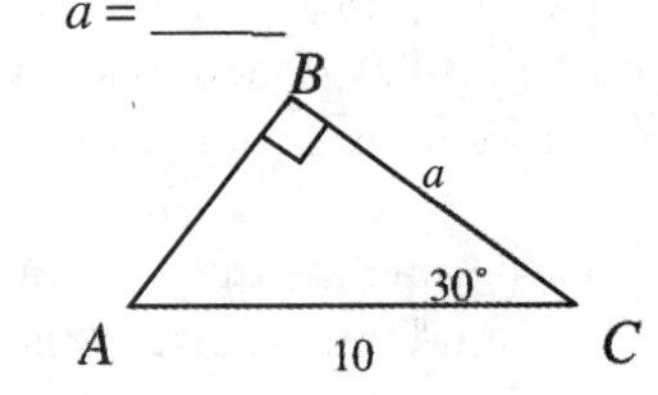

2-63. Below are two situations that can be described using exponential functions. They represent a small sampling of the situations where quantities grow or decay by a constant percentage over equal periods of time. For each situation:

- Find an appropriate unit of time (such as days, weeks, years).
- Find the multiplier that should be used.
- Identify the initial value.
- Write an exponential equation in the form $f(x) = ab^x$ that represents the growth or decay.

a. A house purchased for $120,000 has an annual appreciation of 6%.

b. The number of bacteria present in a colony is 180 at noon, and it increases at a rate of 22% per hour.

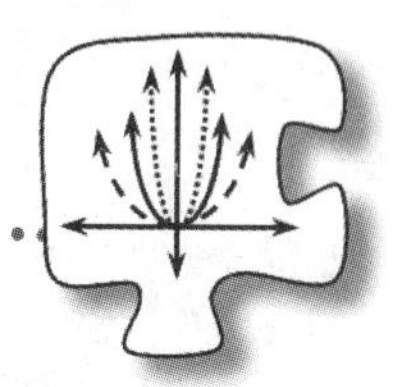

2.1.5 How can I model the data?

Mathematical Modeling with Parabolas

In the past few lessons, you have determined how to move graphs of parabolas around, that is, to transform them, on a set of axes. You have also learned how to write quadratic equations in graphing and in standard form. In this lesson you will put these new skills to work as you use parabolas and their equations to model situations.

2-64. JUMPING JACKRABBITS

The diagram at right shows a jackrabbit jumping over a three-foot-high fence. To just clear the fence, the rabbit must start its jump at a point four feet from the fence.

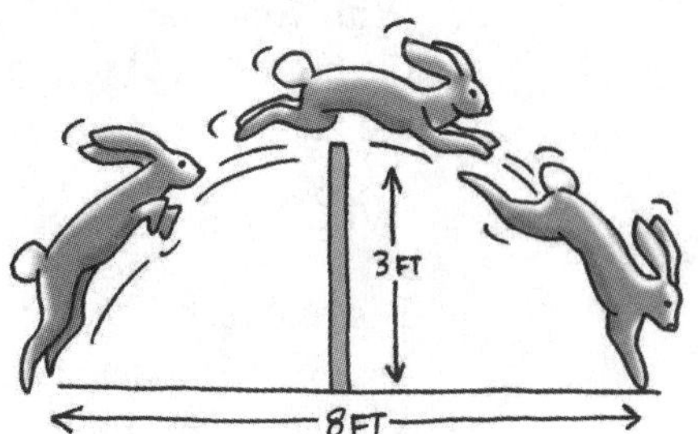

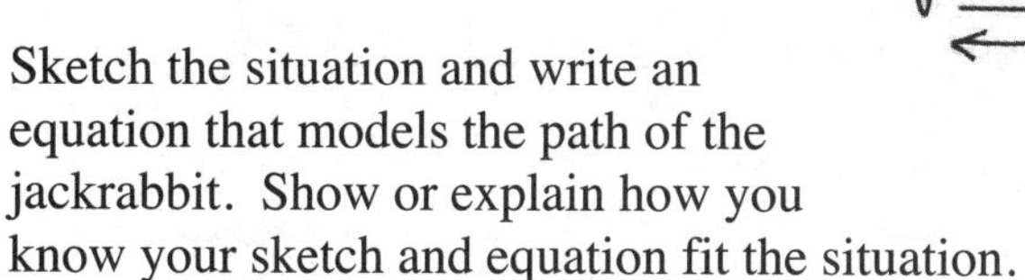

Sketch the situation and write an equation that models the path of the jackrabbit. Show or explain how you know your sketch and equation fit the situation.

Discussion Points

How can we make a graph fit this situation?

What information do we need in order to find an equation?

How can we be sure that our equation fits the situation?

Further Guidance

2-65. Sketch the path of the jackrabbit on your paper. Choose where to place the x- and y-axes in your diagram so that they make sense and make the problem easier. Label as many points as you can on your sketch.

a. What is the shape of the path of the jackrabbit? What kind of equation would best model this situation?

b. What point on your graph can tell you about the values of h and k in the equation? Write the values for h and k into the general equation. Is your equation finished?

c. With your team, find a strategy to find the exact value of a. Will any of the points on your diagram help? Be prepared to share your strategy with the class.

d. What are the domain and range for your model?

e. Did any team in your class get a different equation? If so, write down their equation and show how it can also model the path of the jackrabbit. What choices did that team make differently that resulted in the different equation?

Further Guidance section ends here.

2-66. When Ms. Bibbi kicked a soccer ball, it traveled a horizontal distance of 150 feet and reached a height of 100 feet at its highest point. Sketch the path of the soccer ball and find an equation of the parabola that models it.

2-67. At the skateboard park, the hot new attraction is the *U-Dip,* a cement structure embedded into the ground. The cross-sectional view of the *U-Dip* is a parabola that dips 15 feet below the ground. The width at ground level, its widest part, is 40 feet across. Sketch the cross-sectional view of the *U-Dip*, and find an equation of the parabola that models it.

2-68. LEARNING LOG

With your team, discuss all of the different forms you know for the equation of a parabola. In your Learning Log, write down each form, along with a brief explanation of how that form is useful. Title this entry, "Forms of a Quadratic Function" and label it with today's date.

2-69. FIRE! CALL 9-1-1!

A fireboat in the harbor is helping put out a fire in a warehouse on the pier. The distance from the barrel (end) of the water cannon to the roof of the warehouse is 120 feet, and the water shoots up 50 feet above the barrel of the water cannon.

Sketch a graph and find an equation of the parabola that models the path of the water from the fireboat to the fire. Give the domain and range for which the function makes sense in relation to the fireboat.

2-70. Draw accurate graphs of $y = 2x + 5$, $y = 2x^2 + 5$, and $y = \frac{1}{2}x^2 + 5$ on the same set of axes. Label the intercepts.

a. In the equation $y = 2x + 5$, what does the 2 tell you about the graph?

b. Is the 2 in $y = 2x^2 + 5$ also the slope? Explain.

2-71. Think about how you might sketch a parabola on a graph.

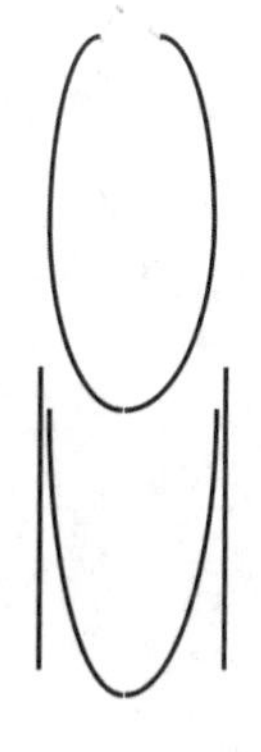

a. Do the sides of a parabola ever curve back in like the figure at right? Explain your reasoning.

b. Do the sides of the parabola approach straight vertical lines as shown in the figure at right? (In other words, do parabolas have asymptotes?) Give a reason for your answer.

2-72. Find the equation of an exponential function that passes through each pair of points.

a. (2,9) and (4,324)

b. (−1,40) and (0,12)

2-73. Find the x- and y-intercepts of the graphs of the two equations below.

a. $y = 2x^2 + 3x - 5$

b. $y = \sqrt{2x - 4}$

2-74. The vertex of a parabola, point (h, k), locates its position on the coordinate graph. The vertex thus serves as a **locator point** for a parabola. Other families of functions that you will be investigating in this course will also have locator points. These points have different names, but the same purpose for each different type of graph. They help you place the graph on the axes.

Sketch graphs for both of the following equations. On each sketch, label the locator point.

a. $y = 3x^2 + 5$

b. $f(x) = -(x - 3)^2 - 7$

2-75. If $g(x) = x^2 - 5$, find the value(s) of x so that:

a. $g(x) = 20$

b. $g(x) = 6$

2.2.1 How can I transform any graph?

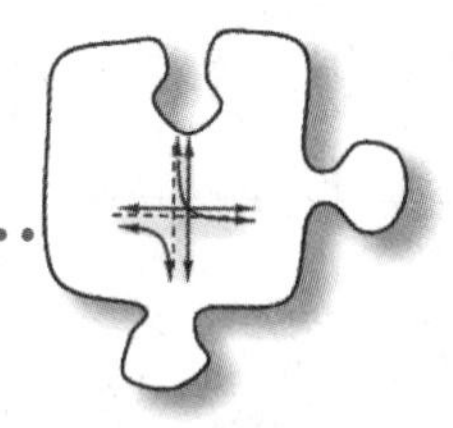

Transforming Other Parent Graphs

You have been learning how to move a parabola around a set of axes, write equations, sketch graphs, and model situations. The graph of $y = x^2$ is called the **parent graph** for the family of parabolas because every other parabola can be seen as a transformation of that one graph.

2-76. In this investigation you will use what you have learned about transforming the graph of $y = x^2$ to transform four other parent graphs. In fact, your team will figure out how to use what you have learned to transform the graph of *any* function!

Your Task: As a team, determine how you can make the graph of any function move left, right, up, and down and how you can stretch it vertically, compress it vertically, and flip it. Each team member should investigate one of the following parent functions: $y = x^3$, $y = \frac{1}{x}$, $y = \sqrt{x}$, $y = |x|$, and $y = b^x$. (If you are investigating $y = b^x$, your teacher will give you a value to use for b.)

- Remember that to investigate completely, you should sketch graphs, identify the domain and range, and label any important points or asymptotes.
- Then graph and write an equation to demonstrate each transformation you find.
- Finally, find a general equation for your family of graphs.

Discussion Points

How can we move a parabola?

How can we use our ideas about moving parabolas to move other functions?

What changes can we make to the equation?

Further Guidance

2-77. First, investigate your parent graph.

a. Graph your equation on a full sheet of graph paper.

b. As a team, place your parent graphs into the middle of your workspace. For each graph, identify the domain and range and label any important points or asymptotes.

2-78. For your parent graph:

a. Find and graph an equation that will shift your parent graph left or right.

b. Find and graph an equation that will shift your parent graph up or down.

c. Find and graph an equation that will stretch or compress your parent graph vertically.

d. Find and graph an equation that will flip your parent graph upside-down.

2-79. One way of writing an equation for a parabola is to use graphing form: $y = a(x - h)^2 + k$. This equation tells you how to shift or stretch the parent graph, $y = x^2$, to get any other parabola.

a. Explain what each parameter (a, h, and k) represents for the graph of a parabola.

b. As a team, write general equations for each given parent equation. Be ready to explain how your general equations work; that is, tell what effect each part has on the orientation (right-side-up or upside-down), relative size (stretched or compressed), horizontal location (left or right shift), and vertical location (up or down shift).

Further Guidance section ends here.

2-80. As a team, organize your work into a large poster that shows clearly:

- Each parent graph you worked with,
- Examples of each transformation you found, and
- Each general equation.

Use tools such as colors, arrows, and shading to show all of the connections you can find. Then add the following problems for other teams to solve:

- Show the graph of a function in your family for which other teams need to find the equation.
- Give an equation of a function in your family that other teams will graph.

2-81. While watering her outdoor plants, Maura noticed that the water coming out of her garden hose followed a parabolic path. Thinking that she might be able to model the path of the water with an equation, she quickly took some measurements. The highest point the water reached was 8 feet, and it landed on the plants 10 feet from where she was standing. Both the nozzle of the hose and the top of the flowers were 4 feet above the ground. Help Maura write an equation that describes the path of the water from the hose to the top of her plants. What domain and range make sense for the model?

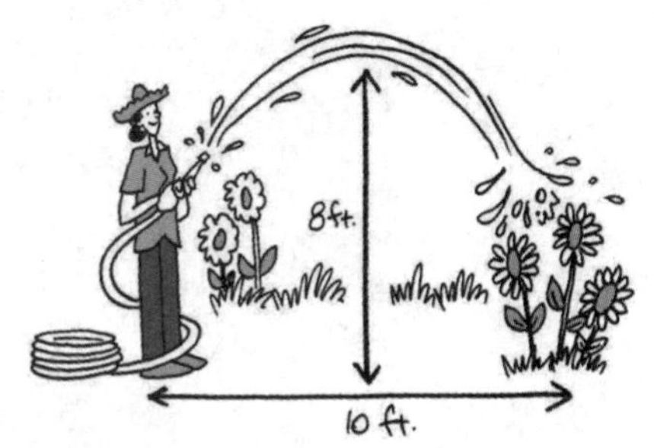

2-82. Draw the graph of $y = 2x^2 + 3x + 1$.

a. Find the x- and y-intercepts.

b. Where is the line of symmetry of this parabola? Write its equation.

c. Find the coordinates of the vertex.

2-83. Change the equation in problem 2-82 so that the parabola has only one x-intercept.

2-84. Simplify each expression. Remember you can simplify radicals by removing perfect square factors (e.g. $\sqrt{12} = \sqrt{4 \cdot 3} = 2\sqrt{3}$).

a. $\sqrt{24}$ b. $\sqrt{18}$ c. $\sqrt{3} + \sqrt{3}$ d. $\sqrt{27} + \sqrt{12}$

2-85. Below are two more situations that can be described using exponential functions. They represent a small sampling of the situations where quantities grow or decay by a constant percentage over equal periods of time. For each situation:

- Find an appropriate unit of time (such as days, weeks, years).
- Find the multiplier that should be used.
- Identify the initial value.
- Write an exponential equation in the form $f(x) = ab^x$ that represents the growth or decay.

a. The value of a car with an initial purchase price of $12,250 depreciates by 11% per year.

b. An investment of $1000 earns 6% annual interest, compounded monthly.

2-86. Rewrite each of the following expressions so that your answer has no negative or fractional exponents.

a. $16^{5/4}$ b. $(x^5y^4)^{1/2}$ c. $(x^2y^{-1})(x^{-3}y)^0$

2-87. Harvey's Expresso Express, a drive-through coffee stop, is famous for its great house coffee, a blend of Colombian and Mocha Java beans. Their archrival, Jojo's Java, sent a spy to steal their ratio for blending beans. The spy returned with a torn part of an old receipt that showed only the total number of pounds and the total cost, 18 pounds for $92.07. At first Jojo was angry, but then he realized that he knew the price per pound of each kind of coffee ($4.89 for Colombian and $5.43 for Mocha Java). Show how he could use equations to figure out how many pounds of each type of beans Harvey's used.

2-88. Lilia wants to have a circular pool put in her backyard. She wants the rest of the yard to be paved with concrete.

a. If her yard is a 50 ft. by 30 ft. rectangle, what is the radius of the largest pool that will fit in her yard?

b. If the concrete is to be 8 inches thick, and costs \$2.39 per cubic foot, what is the cost of putting in the concrete? No concrete will be used in the pool. (Reminder: Volume = (Base Area) $\cdot$ Depth).

2-89. Consider a line with a slope of 3 and a y-intercept at $(0, 2)$.

a. Sketch the graph of this line.

b. Write the equation of the line.

c. Find the initial term and the next three terms of the sequence $t(n) = 3n - 1$. Plot the terms on a new set of axes next to your graph from part (a) above.

d. Explain the similarities and differences between the graphs and equations in parts (a) through (c). Are both continuous?

2-90. The Gross National Product (GNP) of the United States in 1960 was $1.665 \cdot 10^{12}$ dollars. Until 1989 it increased at a rate of 3.17% per year. Use this information to answer each of the questions below.

a. What was the GNP in 1989?

b. Write an equation to represent the GNP t years after 1960, assuming that the rate of growth remained constant.

c. Do you think the rate of growth really remains constant? Explain.

2-91. Write each expression in simpler radical form.

a. $\sqrt{x} + \sqrt{y} + 5\sqrt{x} + 2\sqrt{y}$

b. $(2\sqrt{8})^2$

c. $\frac{\sqrt{50}}{\sqrt{2}}$

d. $\sqrt{\frac{3}{4}}$

2-92. Multiply each of the following expressions.

a. $2x^2(3x+4x^2y)$

b. $(x^3y^2)^4(x^2y)$

2-93. Sketch a graph and draw the line of symmetry for the equation $y=2(x-4)^2-3$. What is the equation of the line of symmetry?

2-94. People who live in isolated or rural areas often have their own tanks that hold propane gas to run appliances like stoves, washers, and water heaters. Some of these tanks are made in the shape of a cylinder with two hemispheres on the ends, as shown in the picture at right. (Recall that a hemisphere is half of a sphere, and the volume of a sphere is found by using $V=\frac{4}{3}\pi r^3$.)

The Inland Propane Gas Tank Company wants to make tanks with this shape, and to offer models in different sizes. The cylindrical portion of each of the different tanks will be 4 meters long. However, the radius, r, will vary among the different models.

a. One of the tank models has a radius of 1 meter. What is its volume?

b. If the radius is doubled, will the volume double? Explain. Then calculate the volume of the larger tank with $r=2$ m.

c. Write an equation that will let the Inland Propane Gas Tank Company determine the volume of a tank with any size radius.

2-95. Write a possible equation for each of these graphs. Assume that one mark on each axis is one unit. When you are in class, check your equations on a graphing calculator and compare your results with your teammates.

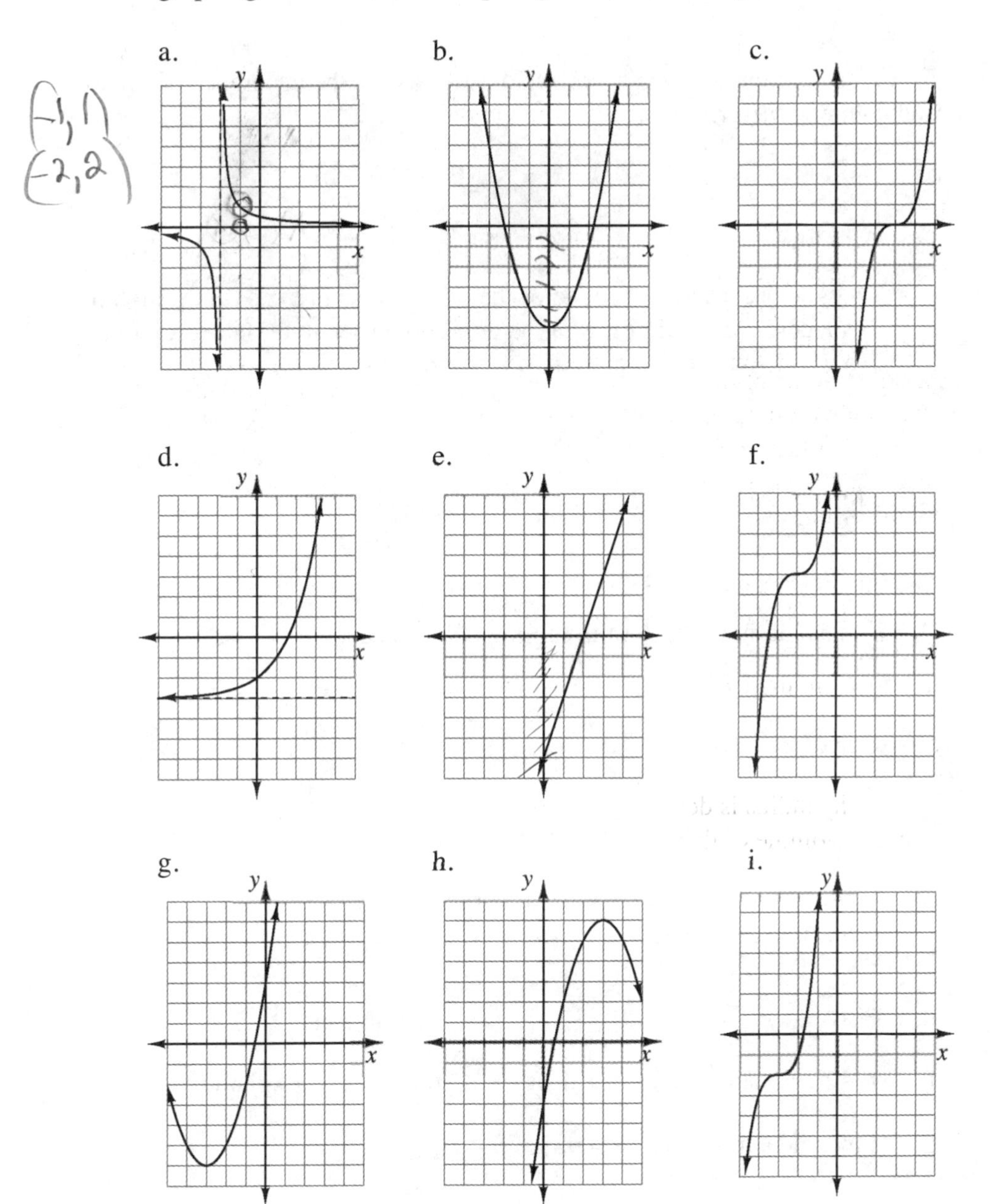

2-96. By mistake, Jim graphed $y = x^3 - 4x$ instead of $y = x^3 - 4x + 6$. What should he do to his graph to get the correct one?

2-97. Simplify each radical expression.

a. $(3\sqrt{2})^2$ b. $\sqrt{\frac{9}{4}}$ c. $\sqrt{\frac{1}{3}}$ d. $(3+\sqrt{2})^2$

2-98. Factor each of the following expressions. Look for the difference of squares and common factors.

a. $4x^2-9y^2$ b. $8x^3-2x^7$

c. x^4-81y^4 d. $8x^3+2x^7$

e. Did you use a shortcut to factor the expressions in parts (a) through (c)? If so, describe it. If not, what pattern do you see in these expressions? How can you use that pattern to factor quickly?

2-99. Solve for x: $ax+by^3=c+7$.

2-100. Write an equation for each of the following sequences.

a. 20, 14, 8, … b. –6, –24, –96, …

2-101. Given $f(x)=x^3+1$ and $g(x)=(x+1)^2$:

a. Sketch the graphs of the two functions.

b. Solve $f(x)=9$. c. Solve $g(x)=0$.

d. Solve $f(x)=-12$. e. Solve $g(x)=-12$.

f. For how many values of x does $f(x)$ equal $g(x)$? Explain.

g. Find and simplify an expression for $f(x)-g(x)$.

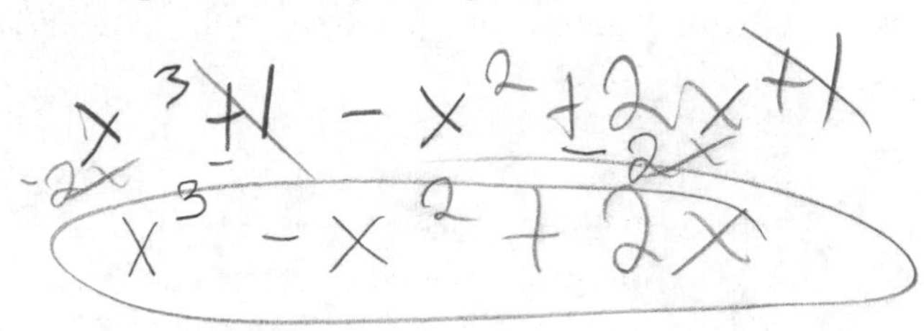

2.2.2 What is the significance of (h, k)?

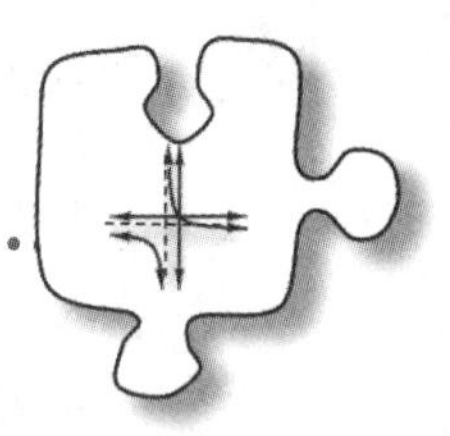

Describing (h, k) for Each Family of Functions

In Lesson 2.2.1, you learned that you could apply your knowledge of transforming parabolas to transform several other parent functions. In this lesson, you will consolidate your knowledge of each of the parent functions that you know and you will identify the importance of the point (h, k) for each parent function and its family.

2-102. Think about the parent graph for parabolas, $y = x^2$.

a. Write the equation of a parabola that will be the same as the parent graph, but shifted four units to the right.

b. Does the strategy you used to move parabolas horizontally also work for other parent graphs? Justify your answer.

c. You have learned that the general equation for a parabola is $y = a(x-h)^2 + k$. To move the graph of $y = x^2$ h units to the *right*, you replaced x^2 with $(x-h)^2$. Work with your team to justify why replacing x with $(x-h)$ moves a graph to the right. Think about multiple representations as you discuss this and be prepared to share your ideas with the class.

2-103. With your team, brainstorm a list of all of the families of functions that you have learned about so far in your study of algebra.

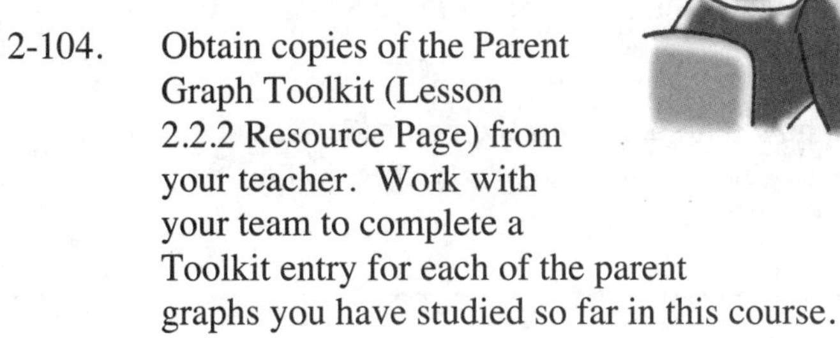

2-104. Obtain copies of the Parent Graph Toolkit (Lesson 2.2.2 Resource Page) from your teacher. Work with your team to complete a Toolkit entry for each of the parent graphs you have studied so far in this course.

2-105. What is the equation of the parent graph of a line? Use what you have learned about transforming parent graphs to write the general equation of a transformed line.

a. Use this general equation of a line to write the equation of a line with slope $\frac{4}{5}$ that passes through the point $(3, 9)$.

b. A line passes through the points $(-1, 5)$ and $(8, -2)$. Substitute each of these into the general equation to create a system of equations. Now solve this system to find the slope. Is this how you have found slope in the past?

2-106. LEARNING LOG

What can the point (h, k) tell you about the how to graph a function from its equation? How can it help you write the equation for a function given its graph? Discuss these questions with your team and then answer them in a Learning Log entry. Be sure to include examples to help you illustrate your ideas. Title this entry "How to use (h, k)" and label it with today's date.

MATH NOTES

Point-Slope Equations for Lines

If you think of $y = x$ as a parent equation, then the general equation for the family of lines can be written as

$$y = a(x - h) + k.$$

When this equation is rewritten as $y - k = a(x - h)$ it is often called the **point-slope** form of the equation for a line that contains the point (h, k) and has slope a.

For example, if you know a line contains the point $(7, -8)$ and has slope -4 then the equation can be written $y - (-8) = -4(x - 7)$ or $y + 8 = -4(x - 7)$.

2-107. Use the point (h, k) to help you write a possible equation for each graph shown below.

a.

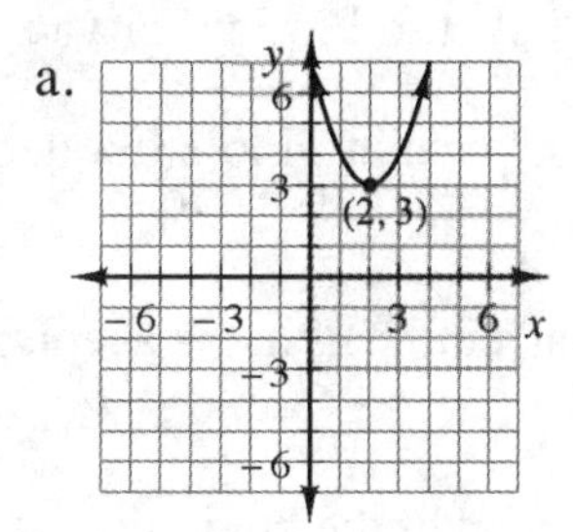

b.

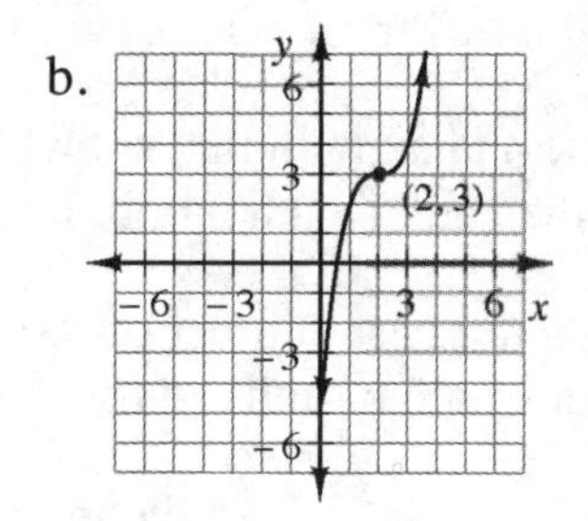

c.

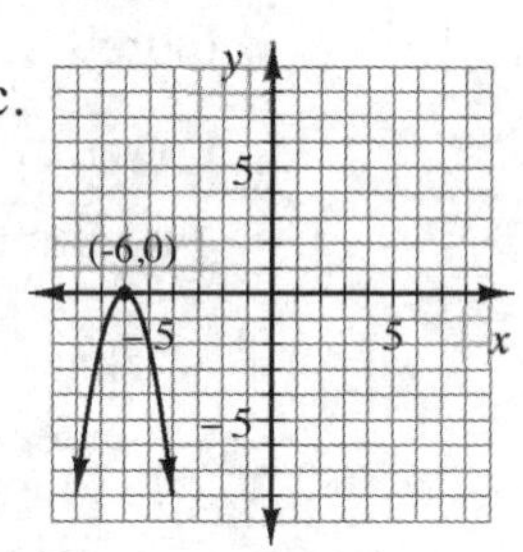

2-108. Find the domain and range for each of the graphs in the previous problem.

2-109. For each of the following equations, describe how d transforms the parent graph.

a. $y = dx^3$

b. $y = x^2 - d$

c. $y = (x - d)^2 + 7$

d. $y = \frac{1}{x} + d$

2-110. Find the equation of an exponential function that passes through each pair of points.

a. (3,0.05) and (5,0.0125)

b. (1,16) and (4,128)

2-111. Rewrite each of the following expressions so that your answers have no negative or fractional exponents.

a. $5^{-2} \cdot 4^{1/2}$

b. $\frac{3xy^2z^{-2}}{(xy)^{-1}z^2}$

c. $(3m^2)^3(2mn)^{-1}(8n^3)^{2/3}$

d. $(5x^2y^3z)^{1/3}$

2-112. Tino is a businessman who flies to sales conferences regularly. He flies from Seattle to Kansas City once each month and from Seattle to Los Angeles once every 3 months (March, June, September, and December). The flight to Kansas City adds 1500 miles each way to his frequent flier account, while flying to Los Angeles adds 950 miles each way to his account. In January last year, he started with 12,000 miles in his account. In June and December he withdrew 25000 miles from his account for a ticket to Florida for vacation.

a. Make a table and a graph that shows the balance in Tino's frequent flier account at the end of each month last year.

b. What was the highest number of miles that Tino had in his account during the year? In which month did this occur?

c. How many miles did Tino have in his account at the beginning of this year?

d. If Tino continues this same pattern of flying will he have enough miles to go on both of his usual vacations this year? Why or why not?

2-113. Solve each equation for x (that is, put it in $x =$ ___ form).

a. $y = 2(x-17)^2$

b. $y + 7 = \sqrt[3]{x+5}$

2-114. Where do the following pairs of lines intersect?

a. $y = 5x - 2$
$y = 3x + 18$

b. $y = x - 4$
$2x + 3y = 17$

2-115. Write each expression below in simplest radical form.

a. $\sqrt{75} + \sqrt{27}$

b. $\sqrt{x} + 2\sqrt{x}$

c. $(\sqrt{12})^2$

d. $(3\sqrt{12})^2$

2-116. If $g(x) = x^2 - 5$, find:

a. $g\left(\frac{1}{2}\right)$

b. $g(h+1)$

2-117. Graph these two lines on the same set of axes: $y=2x$ and $y=-\frac{1}{2}x+6$.

a. Find the x- and y-intercepts for each equation.

b. Shade the region bounded by the two lines and the x-axis.

c. What are the domain and range of the region? How did you find these values?

d. Find the area of this region. Round your answer to the nearest tenth.

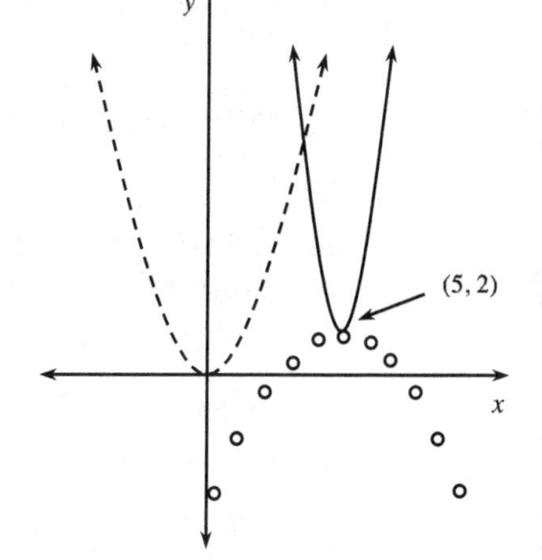

2-118. The graph of $y=x^2$ is shown as a dashed curve at right. Estimate the equations of the two other parabolas.

2-119. Find the x- and y-intercepts and the vertex of $y=x^2+2x-80$. Then sketch the graph and write the equation in graphing form.

2-120. Is -578 a term in the sequence defined by $t(n)=-5n+7$? Justify your answer.

2.2.3 How can I move a function?

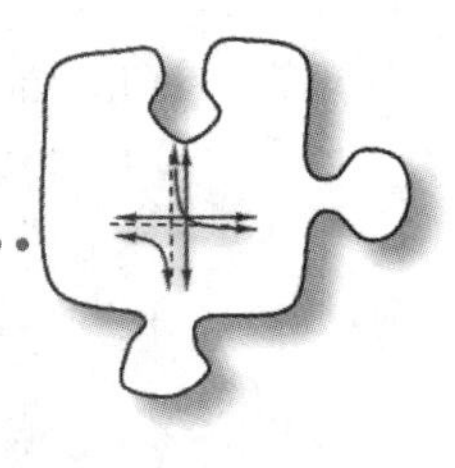

Transformations of Functions

In your Geometry course you transformed figures just like you transformed parent graphs in this course. Today you will look more at geometric transformations and you will explore what happens when you take the opposite of x before applying the operations of the function. That is, you will investigate $f(-x)$.

2-121. In Geometry, you called the transformation of figures "translations," "reflections," "rotations," and "dilations." Refer to your Parent Graph Toolkit from problem 2-104 and/or your Learning Log entry in problem 2-106 as you complete parts (a) through (d) below.

a. What kind of a geometric transformation have you made when you replace $f(x)$ with $f(x)+k$? Be as specific as you can.

b. What kind of geometric transformation occurs when you replace $f(x)$ with $-f(x)$? Be as specific as you can.

c. What kind of transformation is $f(x-h)$?

d. What kind of transformation is $a \cdot f(x)$? Be specific.

2-122. Investigate the transformation $y=f(-x)$ as directed below.

a. For each of the parent graphs you have investigated so far, investigate what happens to the graph when you replace x with $-x$. For each parent function, draw the original and the new graph on the same set of axes in different colors.

b. For each parent equation, substitute $-x$ for x and algebraically simplify the result.

c. Describe the geometric transformation that occurs when you replace $f(x)$ with $f(-x)$.

2-123. Functions can be categorized as **even** or **odd functions**. With your team sort the functions you investigated in problem 2-122 into the following three groups:

EVEN FUNCTIONS: All functions where $f(-x) = f(x)$.

ODD FUNCTIONS: All functions where $f(-x) = -f(x)$.

FUNCTIONS THAT ARE NEITHER EVEN nor ODD.

2-124. LEARNING LOG

How will the graph of a function change when $-x$ replaces x in the function $f(x)$? How can you tell from its graph whether a function will be even? How can you tell from its equation whether a function will be even? Discuss these questions with your team and then answer them in a Learning Log entry. Be sure to include examples. Title this entry "Reflections and Even Functions" and label it with today's date.

MATH NOTES

METHODS AND MEANINGS

General Equations for Families

If $y = f(x)$ is an equation for a parent graph, then the general equation for the family of functions with similar characteristics as $f(x)$ can be written as:

$$y = a \cdot f(x-h)+k$$

Where (h,k) is the point corresponding to (0, 0) in the parent graph and, relative to the parent graph, the function has been:

- Vertically stretched if the absolute value of a is greater than 1.
- Vertically compressed if the absolute value of a is less than 1.
- Reflected across the x-axis if a is less than 0.

So far in this chapter you have worked with the following families of functions:

Parent	Family	General Equation
$y = x$	Line	$y = a(x-h)+k$
$y = \|x\|$	Absolute Value	$y = a\|x-h\|+k$
$y = x^2$	Parabola	$y = a(x-h)^2+k$
$y = x^3$	Cubic	$y = a(x-h)^3+k$
$y = \frac{1}{x}$	Hyperbola	$y = a(\frac{1}{x-h})+k$
$y = \sqrt{x}$	Square Root	$y = a\sqrt{x-h}+k$
$y = b^x$	Exponential	$y = ab^{(x-h)}+k$

2-125. Decide whether each of the following functions is even, odd, or neither. Show or explain your reasoning.

a. $y = \frac{2}{3}x+1$

b. $y = (x+2)^2$

c. $y = |x| - x^2$

2-126. For each of the following functions sketch the graph of the original and of $y = f(-x)$.

a. $f(x) = 2|x-4|+3$

b. $f(x) = \dfrac{1}{x+4}$

c. Is either of these functions odd or even? Justify your answer.

2-127. A parabola has vertex $(2, 3)$ and contains the point $(0, 0)$. Find an equation that represents this parabola.

2-128. For each equation below, find the x- and y-intercepts and the locator point (h, k), then write the equations in graphing form.

a. $y = 7 + 2x^2 + 4x - 5$

b. $x^2 = 2x + x(2x-4) + y$

2-129. Consider the system of equations at right:

$$3y - 4x = -1$$
$$9y + 2x = 4$$

a. What is the parent of each equation?

b. Solve this system algebraically.

c. Find where the two graphs intersect.

d. Explain the relationship between parts (b) and (c) above.

2-130. Write an equation for each of the following sequences.

a. $10, 2.5, 0.625, \ldots$

b. $-2, -8, -14, \ldots$

2-131. Find the intercepts, the locator point (h, k), the domain, and the range for each of the following functions.

a. $y = |x-4|-2$

b. $y = -|x+1|+3$

2.2.4 How can I transform circles?

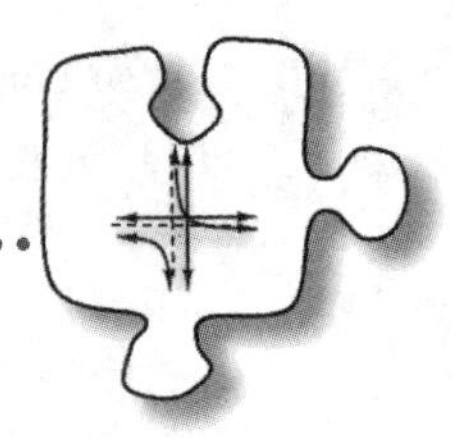

Transforming Non-Functions

In this lesson, you consider two new parent equations that are different from the ones you have seen in the past because they are not functions. You will investigate them and apply the knowledge you have gained in this chapter to transform them. You will identify ways in which these new equations are different from the functions with which you have been working.

2-132. Begin by fully investigating $x = y^2$ and $x^2 + y^2 = 25$ as follows.

a. Without using your graphing calculator, make a table and a graph for each equation.

b. Marabel and Lissa were working on this problem. Marabel was making a table for $x = y^2$. For an x-value of 4, she found a y-value of 2. Lissa was watching and said, *"Wait! When x is 4, there is also another possible value for y."* What did Lissa mean? Look back at your tables and decide if there are more points you could add.

c. Now describe $x = y^2$ and $x^2 + y^2 = 25$ completely. This includes finding the domain and range of each equation, finding the important points such as intercepts, and describing what happens to y as x increases.

d. How are these relationships different from others you have been working with?

2-133. Rewrite $x = y^2$ and $x^2 + y^2 = 25$ so that you can graph them with your graphing calculator. When you have rewritten both equations, try graphing them using your calculator. Do they look like the graphs you made in problem 2-132?

2-134. TRANSFORMATIONS OF NON-FUNCTIONS

In order to graph the equation of the circle on your graphing calculator, you had to express the non-function as two functions. Now apply your knowledge of transforming functions to learn about transforming circles.

Your Task: As a team, transform the graphs of $y = \pm\sqrt{25 - x^2}$ horizontally and vertically. Then find a general equation for this family of circles using h, and k. Be prepared to share your findings and your strategies with the class.

Discussion Points

How did we change the equation in other families so that the graph moves vertically? So that it moves horizontally?

How can we rewrite the two functions for a circle the same way?

2-135. Write your general equations for a circle in standard form by rewriting the equation $y = \pm\sqrt{-(x-h)^2 + 25} + k$ to isolate 25 on one side of the equation. What information does the locator point (h, k) give about the graph of the circle?

2-136. A circle has a special characteristic, its radius, which defines its size.

a. Refer back to the graph of $x^2 + y^2 = 25$. What is the radius? How is the radius of the circle related to the equation?

b. What would be the equation of a circle that has its center at $(5, -7)$ with radius 10? With radius 12?

c. Now generalize the connection between the radius and the equation of a circle. Write a general equation for a circle with any center (h, k) and radius r.

d. Given the equation $(x-3)^2 + (y+7)^2 = 169$, how can you find the radius of the circle?

2-137. Consider the equation $(x-4)^2+(y+1)^2=16$.

a. What is the shape of the graph? How can you tell?

b. What information can you learn about the graph just by looking at the equation?

c. Sketch a graph of $(x-4)^2+(y+1)^2=16$.

2-138. Look at your work from problem 2-133. The non-function $x=y^2$ had a graph that is called a "sleeping parabola."

a. How could you transform the equation $y=\pm\sqrt{x}$ to move the graph horizontally and vertically? How could you transform the equation to stretch or compress the graph, or to "flip" it vertically?

b. Write a general equation for transforming the sleeping parabola family $y=\pm\sqrt{x}$ by using a, h, and k.

c. Write the equation for a sleeping parabola in standard form by isolating x on one side of the equation.

2-139. Write the equation $y=x^2+7x-8$ in graphing form.

2-140. You are standing outside the school, waiting to cross the street, when you hear booming music coming from an approaching car.

a. Sketch a graph that shows the relationship between how far away from you the car is and the loudness of the music.

b. Which is the dependent variable and which is the independent variable?

2-141. The Green Streak Taxi Company charges a \$3.00 base fee plus \$2.50 per mile. The cab driver sets his meter at \$3.00 and the meter adds \$0.25 each one-tenth of a mile. Draw a graph to represent this fare structure. Describe the domain and range of your graph.

2-142. Write an equation for a function that is odd, and explain how you can tell it is odd from its graph, its table and its equation.

2-143. Explain the difference between the graphs of $y = \frac{1}{x}$ and $y = 4(\frac{1}{x+5}) + 7$.

2-144. Multiply the expressions in parts (a) through (c) to remove the parentheses.

a. $(x-1)(x+1)$

b. $2x(x+1)(x+1)$

c. $(x-1)(x+1)(x-2)$

d. Find the x- and y-intercepts of $y = x^3 - 2x^2 - x + 2$. The factors in part (c) should be useful.

2-145. Solve the following systems of equations. In other words, find values of a and b that make each system true. Be sure to show your work or explain your thinking clearly.

a. $2 = a \cdot b^0$
$\frac{1}{2} = a \cdot b^2$

b. $\frac{1}{2} = a \cdot b^0$
$2 = a \cdot b^2$

2-146. A parabola has vertex $(3, 5)$ and contains the point $(0, 0)$.

a. If this parabola is a function, find its equation.

b. Suppose this parabola is not a function, but is a "sleeping" parabola. Find its equation.

2-147. Sketch the graph of $y = 2(x-1)^2 + 4$.

a. Now rewrite the equation $y = 2(x-1)^2 + 4$ without parentheses. Remember the Order of Operations!

b. What would the difference be between the graphs of the two equations above? This is sort of a trick question, but explain your reasoning.

c. What is the parent function of $y = 2(x-1)^2 + 4$?

d. What is the parent function of $y = 2x^2 - 4x + 6$?

2-148. Consider the equation $(x-5)^2+(y-8)^2=49$.

a. What can you tell about the graph just by looking at the equation?

b. Sketch a graph of $(x-5)^2+(y-8)^2=49$.

2-149. A line passes through the points $(0, 2)$ and $(1, 0)$.

a. Find the slope of the line.

b. Find the slope of a line parallel to the given line.

c. Find the slope of a line perpendicular to the given line.

d. Find the product of the slopes you found in parts (b) and (c).

e. Make a conjecture about the product of the slopes of any two perpendicular lines. Test your conjecture by creating more examples.

2-150. Give the equations of two functions, $f(x)$ and $g(x)$, so that $f(x)$ and $g(x)$ intersect at exactly:

a. One point. b. Two points. c. No points.

2-151. Find the x- and y-intercepts for the following parabolas.

a. $y=(x+12)^2-144$ b. $y=(x-8)^2-4$

2-152. This problem is a checkpoint for solving linear systems in two variables. It will be referred to as Checkpoint 2B.

Solve the system of linear equations at right.

$$5x-4y=7$$
$$2y+6x=22$$

Check your answers by referring to the Checkpoint 2B materials located at the back of your book.

If you needed help solving these problems correctly, then you need more practice. Review the Checkpoint 2B materials and try the practice problems. Also, consider getting help outside of class time. From this point on, you will be expected to do problems like these quickly and easily.

2.2.5 Can I combine functions?

Transforming Piecewise-Defined Functions

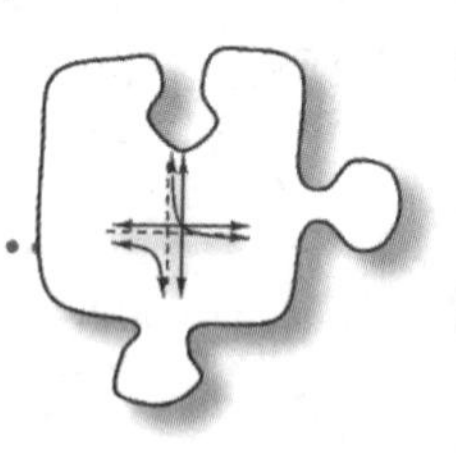

Often the equation for a single familiar function describes a part of a situation, but then is not a good description for the rest of the situation. A step graph is one kind of **piecewise-defined function**. The graphs of these situations are functions, but a single equation is not sufficient to describe them. Describing them requires two (or more) different equations for different inputs. Today you will build new functions by using pieces of familiar functions. Phone plans and water rates are situations that can be modeled using step functions.

2-153. The Horizon Phone Company offers a basic monthly voice phone plan where you pay $40.00 for the first 450 minutes and then $0.45 per minute after that. The graph at right shows how the plan works.

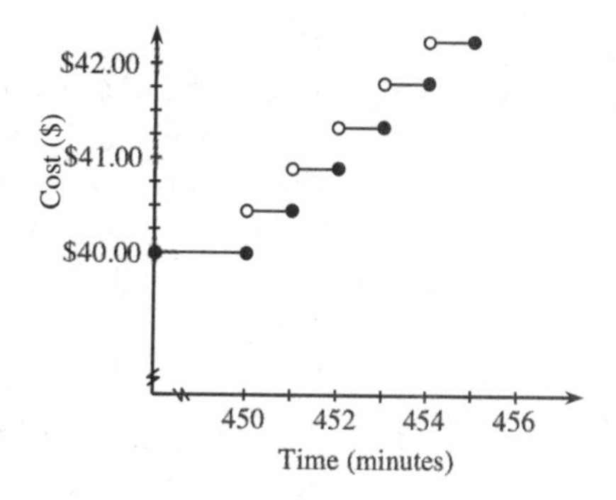

a. This is a piecewise-defined function with many pieces. Describe each piece and the domain and range for the function overall. Then describe the domain and range for the first few pieces.

b. Write an equation for each part of the domain.

2-154. With your team, create a piecewise-defined function with at least three "pieces." The function does not need to be a step-function with horizontal line segments, but it needs to meet the definition of a function. Make a table and a graph for your function, and write an equation for each part. Be sure to state the domain for each part, as well as the domain for the whole function.

2-155. Here is another piecewise-defined function, $F(x)$, defined in the domain $-4 \le x \le 7$ by the graph below.

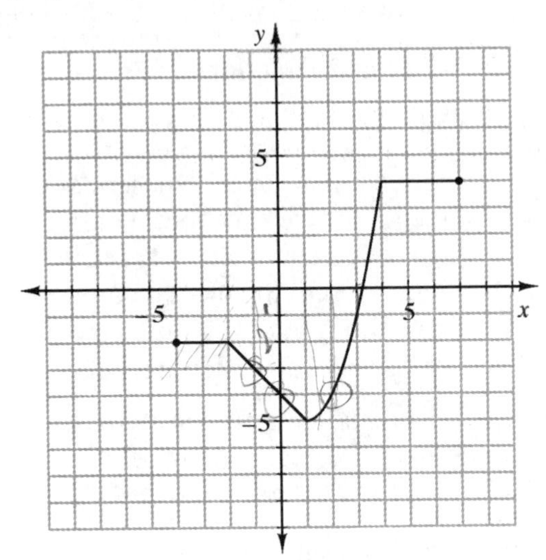

a. Because there is no single equation that represents the whole graph, it is often useful to make a more complete table than you might usually make. On your paper, fill in a table for the function like the one below.

x	−4	−3	−2	−1	0	1	2	3	4	5	6	7
$F(x)$	-2	-2	-2	-3	-4	-5	-4	-1	4	4	4	4

b. Use the graph and the table that you made to write equations for each part of the piecewise-defined function. Be sure to state the domain for each part.

2-156. TEAM TRANSFORMATION CHALLENGE

Obtain the Lesson 2.2.5A Resource Page. Use the resource page to show the graph, the table, and the equations for each of the following transformations of the piecewise-defined function in problem 2-155.

a. $y = -F(x)$

b. $y = \frac{1}{2}F(x)$

c. $y = F(x) + 4$

d. $y = F(x-4)$

2-157. GRAPHS OF ODD AND EVEN FUNCTIONS

Your goal in this investigation is to determine whether a function is odd or even by looking at its graph.

a. Use your graphing calculator to graph the following functions, and make a quick sketch of each graph on your paper. Be sure to label each graph.

$f(x) = x^2$ $\qquad f(x) = (x+5)^2$ $\qquad f(x) = x^2 + 5$

$f(x) = x^3$ $\qquad f(x) = (x+5)^3$ $\qquad f(x) = x^3 + 5$

$f(x) = \frac{1}{x}$ $\qquad f(x) = -2.5x$

b. Determine which of the functions above are odd, even, or neither. Can you find an efficient way to do this with your graphing calculator?

c. How can you tell by looking at the graph whether a function is odd, even, or neither?

d. Classify the function at right as odd, even, or neither. Explain.

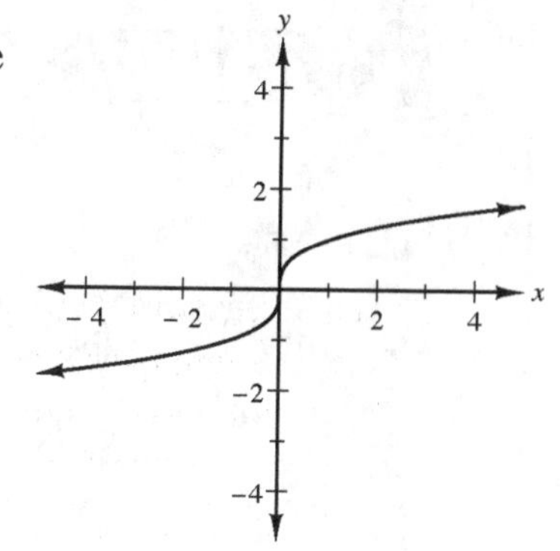

2-158. Write an equation for an even function of your own. Now write another function of your own that is odd. Show that your functions meet the even/odd criteria. The functions you use do not have to be parent functions.

2-159. Write an equation for a function that is neither even nor odd. Show that it is neither.

2-160. AN ADDITIONAL CHALLENGE

In general, a transformation for the parent function $F(x)$ in problem 2-155 can be represented by $y = aF(x-h) + k$. With your team, choose your own values for a, h, and k and show the table, graph, and equations for your transformed $F(x)$.

2-161. LEARNING LOG

In the last few lessons, you have developed the ability to create a family of functions by transforming *any* parent function. Does the function you start with (the parent) affect how you will transform it? If so, how? If not, why not? Are there any parent graphs that are hard for you to transform? Why or why not? Write a Learning Log entry answering these questions. Title it "Transform Any Function" and label it with today's date.

METHODS AND MEANINGS

Even and Odd Functions

When a function $f(-x) = f(x)$, the function f is called an **even function**. For example, for the function $f(x) = x^2$:

$$f(-x) = (-x)^2 = x^2 = f(x)$$

Thus, $f(x) = x^2$ is an even function.

When $f(-x) = -f(x)$, the function f is called an **odd function**. For example for the function $f(x) = x^3$:

$$f(-x) = (-x)^3 = -x^3 = -f(x).$$

Therefore, $f(x) = x^3$ is an odd function.

2-162. Write a set of equations for the piecewise-defined function shown on the graph at right. Be sure to include the domain for each part of the function.

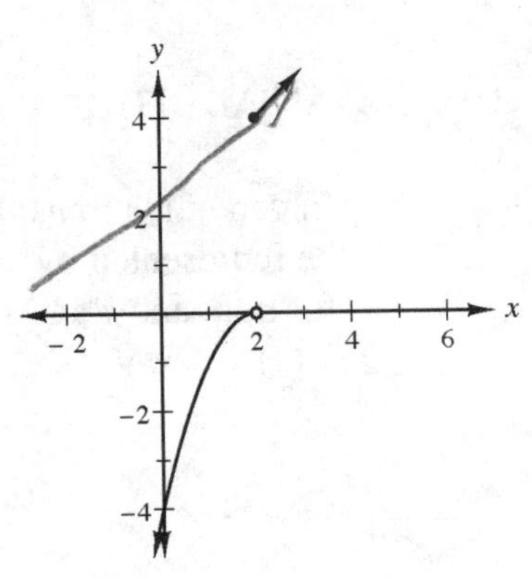

2-163. Write an equation for a function that is even. Then explain how you can tell it is even from its graph, its table, and its equation.

2-164. Use your knowledge of absolute value functions to find the equation of the graph at right.

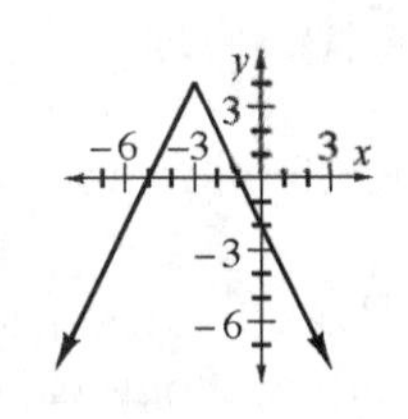

2-165. Write an equation for each of the circles shown in the graphs below.

a.

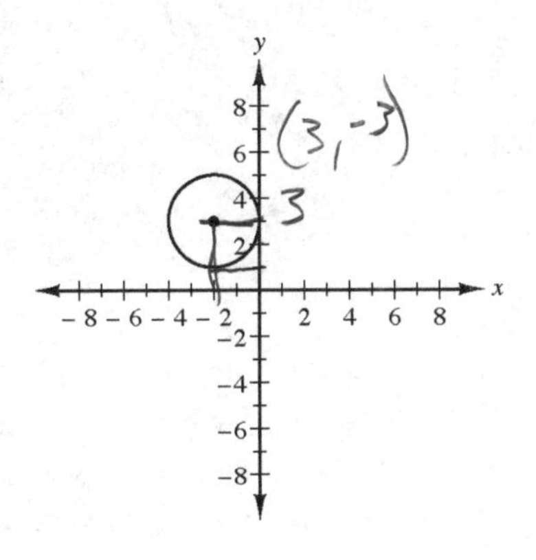

b.

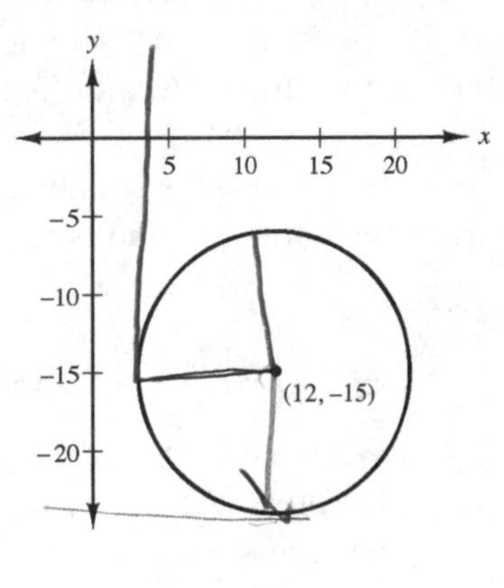

2-166. Use the technique of completing the square to express $y = x^2 - 5x + 7$ in graphing form and state the vertex.

2-167. Shortcut Shuneel claims he has a shortcut for finding the vertex of a parabola. While using his shortcut on $y = 2x^2 + 3x + 1$, he ended up with $y = 2(x + \frac{3}{4})^2 - \frac{7}{2}$. Is Shuneel's new equation correct? Why or why not?

2-168. Remember function machines? Each of the following pictures shows how the same machine changes the given x-value into a corresponding $f(x)$ value. Find the equation for this machine.

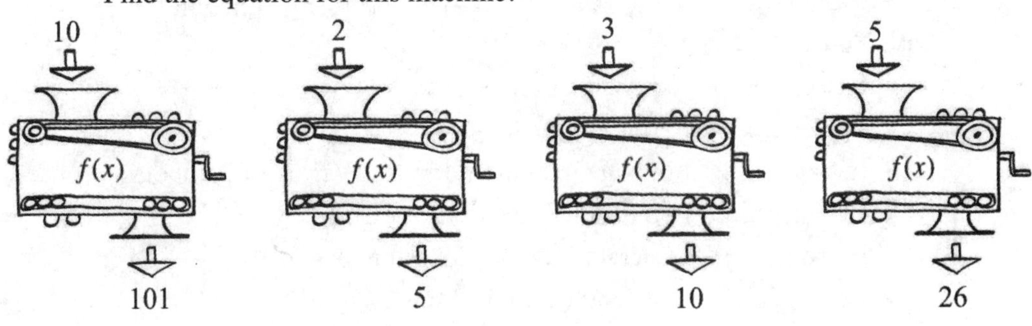

2-169. If $x^2 + kx + 18$ is factorable, what are the possible values of k?

Chapter 2 Closure What have I learned?

Reflection and Synthesis

The activities below offer you a chance to reflect about what you have learned during this chapter. As you work, look for concepts that you feel very comfortable with, ideas that you would like to learn more about, and topics you need more help with. Look for connections between ideas as well as connections with material you learned previously.

① TEAM BRAINSTORM

What have you studied in this chapter? What ideas were important in what you learned? With your team, brainstorm a list. Be as detailed as you can. To help get you started, a list of Learning Log entries and Math Notes boxes are below.

What topics, ideas, and words that you learned *before* this chapter are connected to the new ideas in this chapter? Again, be as detailed as you can.

Next consider the Standards for Mathematical Practice that follow Activity ③: Portfolio. What Mathematical Practices did you use in this chapter? When did you use them? Give specific examples. How long can you make your list? Challenge yourselves. Be prepared to share your team's ideas with the class.

Learning Log Entries

- Lesson 2.1.5 – Forms of a Quadratic Function
- Lesson 2.2.2 – How to use (h, k)
- Lesson 2.2.3 – Reflections and Even Functions
- Lesson 2.2.5 – Transform Any Function

Math Notes

- Lesson 2.1.1 – Exponential Functions
- Lesson 2.1.3 – Forms of Quadratics
- Lesson 2.1.4 – Finding Graphing Form and Vertex of Parabolas
- Lesson 2.2.2 – Point-Slope Equations for Lines
- Lesson 2.2.3 – General Equations for Families
- Lesson 2.2.5 – Even and Odd Functions

② MAKING CONNECTIONS

Below is a list of the vocabulary used in this chapter. Make sure that you are familiar with all of these words and know what they mean. Refer to the glossary or index for any words that you do not yet understand.

compress	dilate	domain
even function	function	general equation
graphing form	(h, k)	horizontal shift
odd function	parameter	parent graph
piecewise-defined function	range	reflection
standard form	step function	stretch factor
transformation	translation	variable
vertex	vertex form	vertical shift

Make a concept map showing all of the connections you can find among the key words and ideas listed above. To show a connection between two words, draw a line between them and explain the connection. A word can be connected to any other word as long as you can justify the connection.

While you are making your map, your team may think of related words or ideas that are not listed here. Be sure to include these ideas on your concept map.

③ PORTFOLIO: EVIDENCE OF MATHEMATICAL PROFICIENCY

This section gives you an opportunity to show growth in your understanding of key mathematical ideas over time as you complete this course. Several options are presented below. Follow your teacher's directions for which options you should complete.

- Explain everything that you know about $y = x^2 - 4$ and $y = \sqrt{x+4}$.

- Your teacher may give you the Chapter 2 Closure Resource Page: Transformations Graphic Organizer to complete. Use it to organize and show everything that you know about transforming the parent graph(s) your teacher gives you.

- The function $g(x)$ is graphed at right. Graph each of the following functions.

  $y = 2g(x) + 3$ $\qquad\qquad$ $y = -g(x-1)$

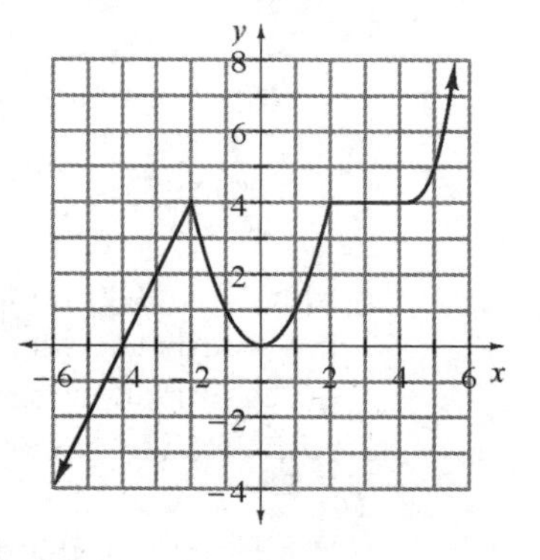

- In Section 2.1, you generalized about how to write equations in graphing form by completing the square. For example, you learned how to complete the square by analyzing actual squares that represented the algebraic quantities you were working with, such as in the expression represented by the tiles at right. Then you generalized the process to complete the square for expressions involving negative and fractional terms, which are not easy to represent with tiles. Consider this as you answer the questions below.

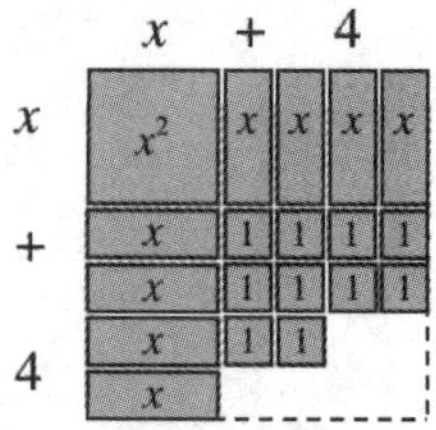

  i. In general, what can you do to complete the square for a quadratic function, no matter what the x term is?

  ii. Use the general strategy you described in part (*i*) above to complete the square for the quadratic equation $f(x) = x^2 - 4.5x + 17$

- Consider the Standards for Mathematical Practice that follow. What Mathematical Practices did you use in this chapter? When did you use them? Give specific examples.

BECOMING MATHEMATICALLY PROFICIENT
The Common Core State Standards For Mathematical Practice

This book focuses on helping you use some very specific Mathematical Practices. The Mathematical Practices describe ways in which mathematically proficient students engage with mathematics everyday.

Make sense of problems and persevere in solving them:

Making sense of problems and persevering in solving them means that you can solve problems that are full of different kinds of mathematics. These types of problems are not routine, simple, or typical. Instead, they combine lots of math ideas and everyday situations. You have to stick with challenging problems, try different strategies, use multiple representations, and use a different method to check your results.

Reason abstractly and quantitatively:

Throughout this course, everyday situations are used to introduce you to new math ideas. Seeing mathematical ideas within a context helps you make sense of the ideas. Once you learn about a math idea in a practical way, you can "**reason abstractly**" by thinking about the concept more generally, representing it with symbols, and manipulating the symbols. **Reasoning quantitatively** is using numbers and symbols to represent an everyday situation, taking into account the units involved, and considering the meaning of the quantities as you compute them.

Construct viable arguments and critique the reasoning of others:

To **construct a viable argument** is to present your solution steps in a logical sequence and to justify your steps with conclusions, relying on number sense, facts and definitions, and previously established results. You communicate clearly, consider the real-life context, and provide clarification when others ask. In this course, you regularly share information, opinions, and expertise with your study team. You **critique the reasoning of others** when you analyze the approach of others, build on each other's ideas, compare the effectiveness of two strategies, and decide what makes sense and under what conditions.

Model with mathematics:

When you **model with mathematics**, you take a complex situation and use mathematics to represent it, often by making assumptions and approximations to simplify the situation. Modeling allows you to analyze and describe the situation and to make predictions. For example, you model when you use multiple representations, including equations, tables, graphs, or diagrams to describe a situation. In situations involving the variability of data, you model when you describe the data with equations. Although a model may not be perfect, it can still be very useful for describing data and making predictions. When you interpret the results, you may need to go back and improve your model by revising your assumptions and approximations.

Use appropriate tools strategically:

To **use appropriate tools strategically** means that you analyze the task and decide which tools may help you model the situation or find a solution. Some of the tools available to you include diagrams, graph paper, calculators, computer software, databases, and websites. You understand the limitations of various tools. A result can be check or estimated by strategically choosing a different tool.

Attend to precision:

To **attend to precision** means that when solving problems, you need to pay close attention to the details. For example, you need to be aware of the units, or how many digits your answer requires, or how to choose a scale and label your graph. You may need to convert the units to be consistent. At times, you need to go back and check whether a numerical solution makes sense in the context of the problem.

You need to **attend to precision** when you communicate your ideas to others. Using the appropriate vocabulary and mathematical language can help make your ideas and reasoning more understandable to others.

Look for and make use of structure:

To **looking for and making use of structure** is a guiding principal of this course. When you are involved in analyzing the structure and in the actual development of mathematical concepts, you gain a deeper, more conceptual understanding than when you are simply told what the structure is and how to do problems. You often use this practice to bring closure to an investigation.

There are many concepts that you learn by looking at the underlying structure of a mathematical idea and thinking about how it connects to other ideas you have already learned. For example, you understand the underlying structure of an equation such as $y = a(x-h)^2 + b$ which allows you to graph it without a table.

Look for and express regularity in repeated reasoning:

To **look for and express regularity in repeated reasoning** means that when you are investigating a new mathematical concept, you notice if calculations are repeated in a pattern. Then you look for a way to generalize the method for use in other situations, or you look for shortcuts. For example, the pattern of growth you notice in a geometric sequence results in being able to write a general exponential equation that highlights the growth and starting point.

④ WHAT HAVE I LEARNED?

Most of the problems in this section represent typical problems found in this chapter. They serve as a gauge for you. You can use them to determine which types of problems you can do well and which types of problems require further study and practice. Even if your teacher does not assign this section, it is a good idea to try these problems and find out for yourself what you know and what you still need to work on.

Solve each problem as completely as you can. The table at the end of the closure section has answers to these problems. It also tells you where you can find additional help and practice with problems like these.

CL 2-170. Chucky and Angelica were reviewing equations of parabolas for their upcoming math test. They disagreed on what the equation would look like for a parabola whose vertex was at $(-4, 3)$.

a. Help them write an equation for a parabola that opens upward from its vertex at $(-4, 3)$. What is the equation of its line of symmetry?

b. Chucky wants the same parabola to open down and Angelica wants it to be compressed. Show them how to change your original equation to meet both of their desires. Does the line of symmetry change?

c. Move your parabola from part (b) 7 units to the right and 8 units down and stretch it vertically so that it is thinner than the original parabola. What is the equation of the parabola? What is the equation of its line of symmetry?

CL 2-171. For each equation, give the locator point (h, k) and the equation of any asymptotes, and then draw the graph.

a. $f(x) = -|x+2| - 1$

b. $y = \frac{1}{x} + 2$

c. $y = \frac{1}{x+5} - 2$

d. $y = -x^3 + 5$

CL 2-172. For each of the functions in problem 2-171 sketch the graph of $y = f(-x)$.

CL 2-173. Gloria the grasshopper is working on her hops. She is trying to jump as high and as far as she can. Her best jump so far was 28 cm long, and she reached a height of 20 cm. Sketch a graph and write an equation of the parabola that describes the path of her jump.

CL 2-174. Use what you know about transforming parent graphs to write an equation for each of the graphs described below.

a. A parabola stretched by a factor of 0.25, opening downward and shifted 12 units down and 3 units left.

b. A cubic with a stretch factor of 2 and a locator point at (–6, 1).

c. A hyperbola, $y=\frac{1}{x}$, but with asymptotes at $y=-6$ and $x=2$.

CL 2-175. Find the equation of the exponential functions with a horizontal asymptote at $y=0$ through the following pairs of points.

a. $(2,99)$ and $(6,8019)$

b. $(-1,50)$ and $(2,25.6)$

CL 2-176. Write an equation for each of the following sequences.

a. $10,7,4,\ldots$

b. $-2,-8,-32,\ldots$

CL 2-177. For each of the equations below, complete the following:

- Find the *x*- and *y*-intercepts.
- Find the vertex.
- Sketch a graph of each parabola on its own set of axes.
- Write the equation in graphing form.

a. $y=x^2+8x+12$

b. $y=(x-4)(x+2)$

c. $y=x^2-6x-9$

d. $y=x^2+5x+1$

CL 2-178. Factor each of the following expressions.

a. $2x^2+7x-4$

b. $8x^2+24x+10$

CL 2-179. Dinner at David's costs \$8.95 today and has been increasing an average of 7% per year.

a. What will it cost in 10 years?

b. What did it cost 10 years ago?

CL 2-180. If $g(x) = (x+1)^2$, complete each part below.

a. $g(5)$

b. $g(2m+4)$

c. x if $g(x) = 9$

CL 2-181. Solve each equation for y.

a. $4 - 2(x+y) = 9$

b. $x = 2(y-1)^2 + 2$

CL 2-182. Check your answers using the table at the end of this section. Which problems do you feel confident about? Which problems were hard? Have you worked on problems like these in math classes you have taken before? Use the table to make a list of topics you need help on and a list of topics you need to practice more.

Answers and Support for Closure Activity #4

What Have I Learned?

Note: MN = Math Note, LL = Learning Log

Problem	Solution	Need Help?	More Practice
CL 2-170.	a. Answers may vary but should be in the form of $y = a(x+4)^2 + 3$, where a is any positive number. $x = -4$ b. $y = a(x+4)^2 + 3$, where a is between 0 and –1; Line of symmetry does not change. c. $y = a(x-3)^2 - 5$, where a is less than –1. $x = 3$	Lessons 2.1.2, and 2.1.3 MN: 2.1.3 and 2.1.4	Problems 2-31, 2-32, 2-74, and 2-124
CL 2-171.	a. $(-2, -1)$ 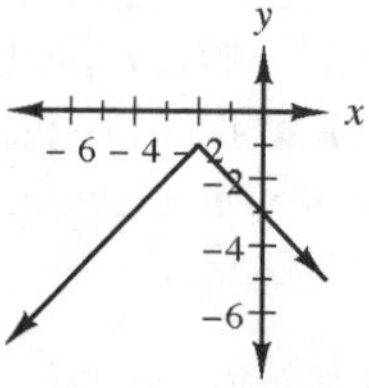 b. $(0, 2)$ $x = 0$; $y = 2$ 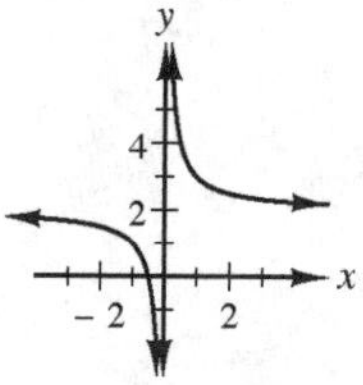 c. $(-5, -2)$ $x = -5$; $y = -2$ 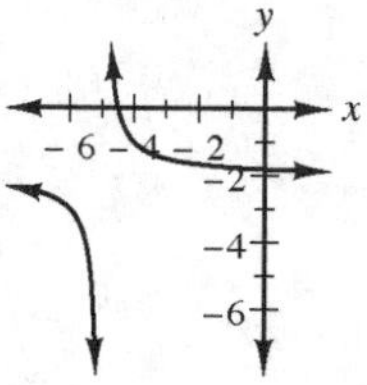 d. $(0, 5)$ 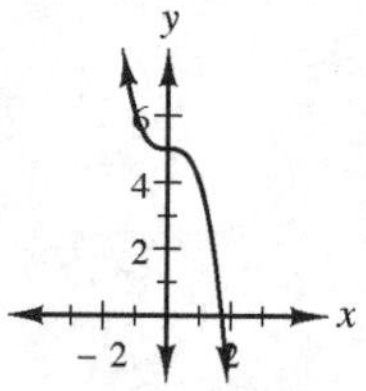	Lessons 2.2.1 and 2.2.2 MN: 2.2.3 LL: 2.2.2 and 2.2.5	Problems 2-74, 2-107, 2-109, 2-118, 2-131, and 2-164

Problem	Solution	Need Help?	More Practice
CL 2-172.	a. 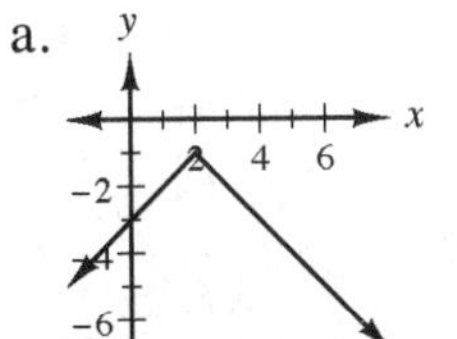 b. 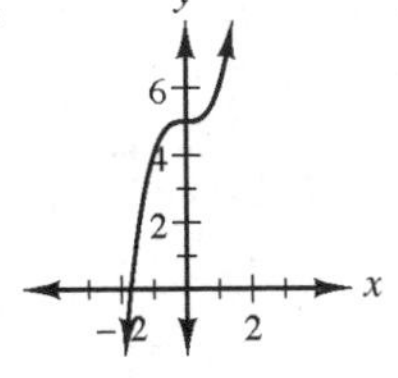 c. 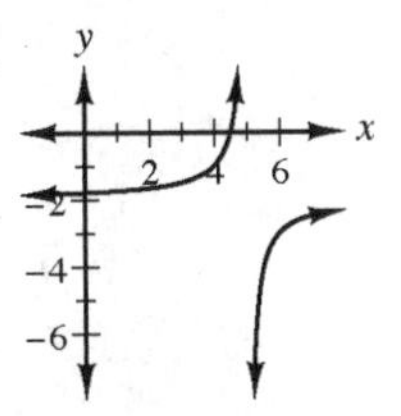 d. 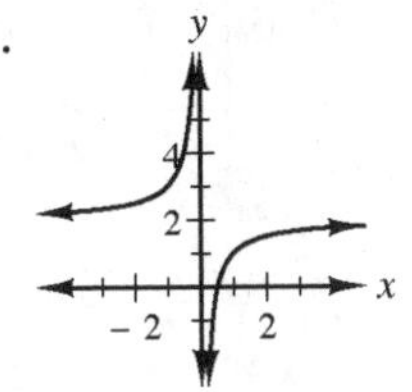	Lesson 2.2.3 LL: 2.2.3	Problems 2-122, 2-126, and 2-156
CL 2-173.	$y=-\frac{5}{49}x(x-28)=-\frac{5}{49}x^2+\frac{20}{7}x$ 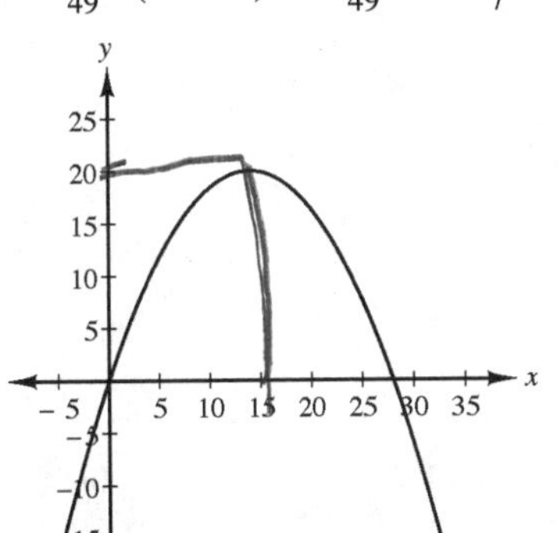	Lesson 2.1.5 LL: 2.1.5	Problems 2-64, 2-66, 2-67, 2-69, and 2-81
CL 2-174.	a. $y=-0.25(x+3)^2-12$ b. $y=2(x+6)^3+1$ c. $y=\frac{1}{x-2}-6$	Lesson 2.2.1 and 2.2.2	Problems 2-25, 2-52, 2-95, 2-96, 2-109, 2-118, and 2-143.
CL 2-175.	a. $y=11\cdot 3^x$ b. $y=40(0.8)^x$	Appendix B Lesson B.2.2	Problems 2-72 and 2-110
CL 2-176.	a. $t(n)=-3n+13$ b. $t(n)=-\frac{1}{2}(4)^n$ or $-2(4)^{n-1}$ Both using $t(1)$ as the first term.	Appendix A Lessons A.2.2 and A.3.2 MN: A.3.2 and B.2.3	Problems 2-8, 2-100, 2-120, and 2-130

Problem	Solution	Need Help?	More Practice
CL 2-177.	a. x-int: $(-6,0),(-2,0)$; y- int: (0, 12); vertex: $(-4,-4)$ $y=(x+4)^2-4$ b. x-int: $(-2,0),(4,0)$; y-int: $(0,-8)$; vertex: $(1,-9)$; $y=(x-1)^2-9$ c. x-int: $(3\pm\sqrt{18},0)$; y-int: $(0,-9)$; vertex: $(3,-18)$; $y=(x-3)^2-18$ d. x-int: $(\frac{-5\pm\sqrt{21}}{2},0)$; y-int: $(0,1)$; vertex: $(-2.5,-5.25)$; $y=(x+2.5)^2-5.25$	Lessons 2.1.2, 2.1.3, and 2.1.4 MN: 2.1.3 and 2.1.4 LL: 2.1.5	Problems 2-17, 2-34, 2-50, 2-73, 2-82, 2-119, and 2-166
CL 2-178.	a. $(2x-1)(x+4)$ b. $2(2x+5)(2x+1)$	Explanations and practice of topics from previous courses are available in the *Core Connections Algebra Parent Guide with Extra Practice,* available free at www.cpm.org.	Problems 2-35, 2-98, and 2-169
CL 2-179.	a. \$17.61 b. \$4.55	Appendix B Lesson B.1.3	Problems 2-29, 2-93, 2-63, and 2-85
CL 2-180.	a. 36 b. $4m^2+20m+25$ c. 2, –4	Section 1.1	Problems 2-75, 2-101, 2-116, and 2-168
CL 2-181.	a. $y=-x-\frac{5}{2}$ b. $y=\pm\sqrt{\frac{x-2}{2}}+1$	Topic from previous course.	Problems 1-37, 1-72, 2-99, and 2-113

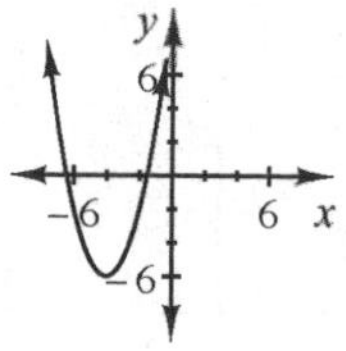

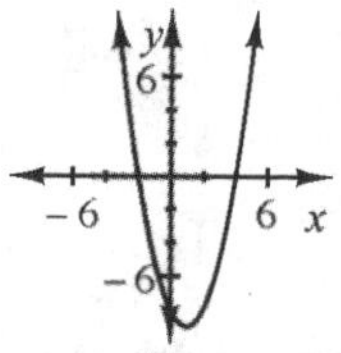

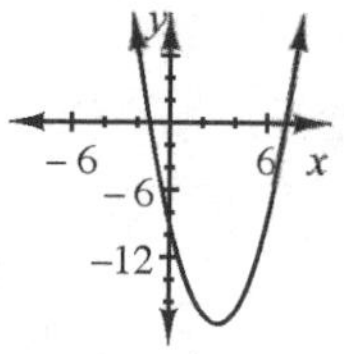

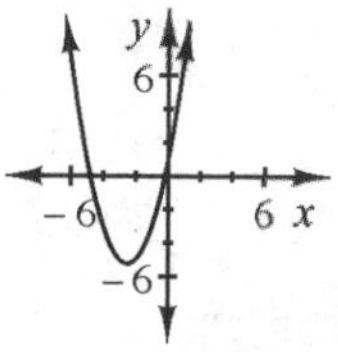

Equivalent Forms
3

Chapter 3 Equivalent Forms

In previous chapters, you looked at ways to organize your algebraic thinking using multiple representations such as graphs, tables, and equations. In this chapter, you will focus on rewriting expressions in order to have more useful equivalent forms. You will remind yourself what it means for two expressions or equations to be equivalent. You will then rewrite equations to solve them more easily.

Another focus of this chapter is learning how to combine algebraic fractions (called "rational expressions") and expressions with exponents. By using the special properties of the number 1 and the meaning of exponents, you will be able rewrite long, complicated expressions into simpler forms. You will then multiply, divide, add, and subtract rational expressions.

Guiding Question

Mathematically proficient students construct viable arguments and critique the reasoning of others.

As you work through this chapter, ask yourself:

How can I show that these forms are equivalent?

Chapter Outline

Section 3.1 In this section, you will rewrite expressions and equations to create simpler versions. You will learn a new way to use substitution to rewrite an expression or equation in simpler form.

Section 3.2 You will study the properties of the number 1 and use them to rewrite and simplify rational expressions. You will multiply, divide, add and subtract rational expressions.

3.1.1 Are they equivalent?

Equivalent Expressions

In this chapter you will look at how to rewrite expressions and equations into equivalent forms that will make them more useful. In this lesson, you will begin by identifying equivalent expressions and then work on developing algebraic strategies to show that they are equivalent.

3-1. Consider the tile pattern at right.

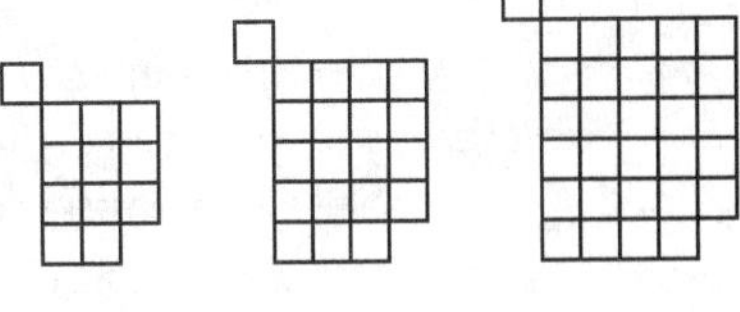

a. Work with your team to describe what the 100th figure would look like. Then find as many different expressions as you can for the area (the number of tiles) in Figure x. Use algebra to justify that all of your expressions are equivalent.

b. What information about the pattern is given by various parts of your different expressions?

c. Write and solve an equation to determine which figure number has 72 tiles. Do you get different results depending upon which expression you choose to use? Explain.

3-2. Jill and Terrell were looking back at their work on problem 1-53 in Lesson 1.2.1. They had come up with two different expressions for the volume of a paper box made from cutting out squares of dimensions x centimeters by x centimeters. Jill's expression was $(15-2x)(20-2x)x$, and Terrell's expression was $4x^3-70x^2+300x$.

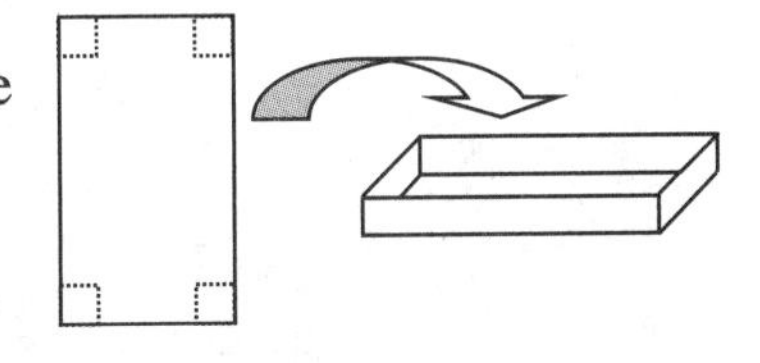

a. Are Jill's and Terrell's expressions equivalent? Justify your answer.

b. If you have not done so already, find an algebraic method to determine whether their expressions are equivalent. Be ready to share your strategy.

c. Gary joined in on their conversation. He had another expression: $(15-2x)(10-x)2x$. Use a strategy from part (b) to decide whether his expression for the volume is equivalent to Jill's or Terrell's. Be prepared to share your ideas with the class.

3-3. For each of the following expressions, find at least three equivalent expressions. Be sure to justify how you know they are equivalent.

a. $(x+3)^2-4$ b. $(2a^2b^3)^3$ c. $m^2n^5 \cdot mn^4$ d. $\frac{(x+1)(2x-1)}{x+2}$

3-4. LEARNING LOG

What does it mean for two expressions to be equivalent? How can you tell if two expressions are equivalent? Answer these questions in your Learning Log. Be sure to include examples to illustrate your ideas. Title this entry "Equivalent Expressions" and label it with today's date.

3-5. For each of the following expressions, find at least three equivalent expressions. Which do you consider to be the simplest?

a. $(2x-3)^2+5$ b. $(\frac{3x^2y}{x^3})^4$

3-6. Match each expression on the left with its equivalent expression on the right. Assume that all variables represent positive values. Be sure to justify how you know each pair is equivalent.

a. $\sqrt{4x^2y^4}$ 1. $2x\sqrt{y}$

b. $\sqrt{8x^2y}$ 2. $2y\sqrt{2x}$

c. $\sqrt{4x^2y}$ 3. $2xy^2$

d. $\sqrt{16xy^2}$ 4. $2x\sqrt{2y}$

e. $\sqrt{8xy^2}$ 5. $4y\sqrt{x}$

3-7. Bonnie and Dylan were both working on simplifying the expression at right. Each of their first steps is shown below. $(\frac{2x^5y^4}{8xy^3})^3$

Bonnie: $\frac{8x^{15}y^{12}}{512x^3y^9}$ Dylan: $(\frac{x^4y}{4})^3$

Each of them is convinced that they have started the problem correctly. Has either of them made an error? If so, explain the error completely. If not, explain how they can both be correct and verify that they will get the same, correct solution. Which student's method do you prefer? Why?

3-8. Describe the graphs of the equations given in parts (a) and (b) below. What are their domains and ranges?

a. $y = 3$ b. $x = -2$ c. Where do the two graphs cross?

3-9. Solve this system for m and b: $342 = 23m + b$
$147 = 10m + b$

3-10. Tanika made this sequence of triangles:

a. If the pattern continues, what do you think the next two triangles in the sequence would be?

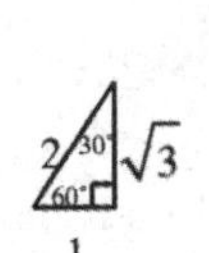

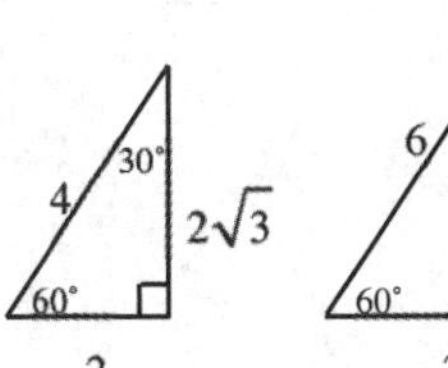

b. Write a sentence to explain how to find the long leg and hypotenuse if you know the short leg (i.e., if the base is n units long).

3-11. Consider the sequence $3, 9, \ldots$

a. Assuming that the sequence is arithmetic with $t(1)$ as the first term, find the next four terms of the sequence and then write an equation for $t(n)$.

b. Assuming that the sequence is geometric with $t(1)$ as the first term, find the next four terms of the sequence and then write an equation for $t(n)$.

c. Create a sequence that begins with 3 that is neither arithmetic nor geometric. For your sequence, write the next four terms and, if you can, write an equation for $t(n)$.

3-12. Simplify each expression without using a calculator.

a. $25^{-1/2}$ b. $(\frac{1}{27})^{-1/3}$ c. $9^{3/2}$ d. $16^{-3/4}$

3.1.2 How can I rewrite it?

Rewriting Expressions and Determining Equivalence

In this lesson, you will continue to think about equivalent expressions. You will use an area model to demonstrate that two expressions are equivalent and to find new ways to write expressions. As you work with your team, use the following questions to help focus your discussion:

How can we be sure they are equivalent?

How would this look in a diagram?

Why is this representation convincing?

3-13. Jonah and Graham are working together. Jonah claims that $(x+y)^2 = x^2 + y^2$. Graham is sure Jonah is wrong, but he cannot figure out how to show it.

a. Help Graham find as many ways as possible to convince Jonah that he is incorrect. How can he rewrite $(x+y)^2$ correctly?

b. Are there any values for x and y for which $(x+y)^2 = x^2 + y^2$? In other words, is $(x+y)^2 = x^2 + y^2$ sometimes true? Justify your answer.

3-14. Do you think that an area model can help rewrite expressions that involve multiplication?

a. The area model at right relates the expressions $(2x-3)(3x+1)$ and $6x^2 - 7x - 3$. With your team, discuss how it can be used to show that these expressions are equivalent. Be prepared to explain your ideas.

	$2x$	-3
$+1$	$2x$	-3
$3x$	$6x^2$	$-9x$

b. Use an area model to write an expression equivalent to $(5k-3)(2k-1)$.

c. Use an area model to write a product that is equivalent to $x^2 - 3x - 4$.

3-15. Rewrite each of the following products as a sum and each sum as a product, drawing an area model when appropriate.

a. $2x^2+5x+2$

b. $(3x-1)(x+2y-4)$

c. $(x-3)(x+3)$

d. $4x^2-49$

e. $(p^2+3p+9)(2p-1)$

f. $(4-x)(x^2+1)+(3x-5)$

3-16. With your team, decide whether the following expressions can be represented with a model and rewrite each expression. Be prepared to share your strategies with the class.

a. $p(p+3)(2p-1)$

b. $x(x+1)+(3x-5)$

3-17. Copy each area model below and fill in the missing parts. Then write the two equivalent expressions represented by each model. Be prepared to share your reasoning with the class.

a.

xy		y^2

(top label: 3; bottom label: x)

b.

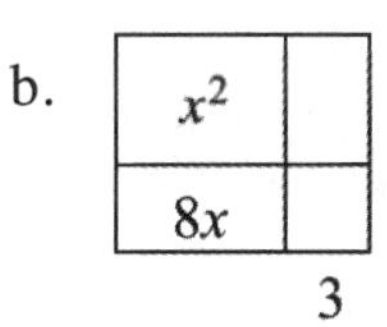

c.

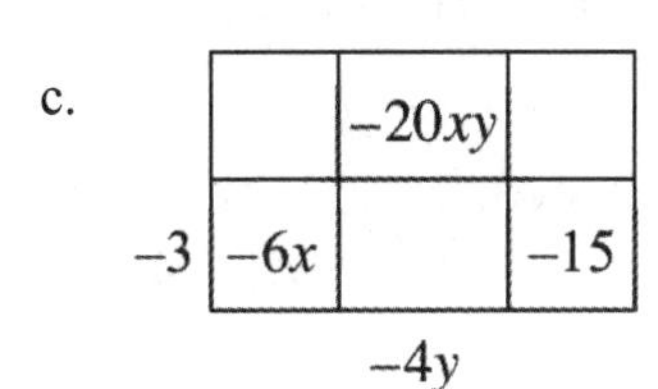

d.

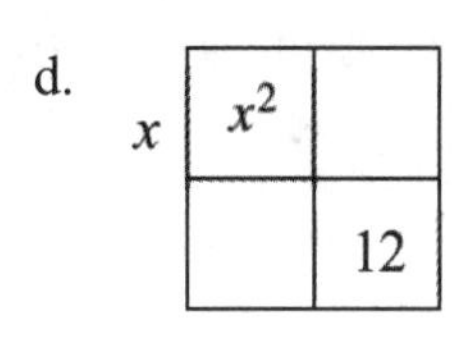

3-18. Shinna noticed a similarity in parts (c) and (d) of problem 3-15.

a. Look back at those two problems and their rewritten form. What might Shinna have noticed? Discuss this with your team and be prepared to share your ideas with the class.

b. Shinna thinks she has found a shortcut that will allow her to rewrite expressions such as those written below without drawing a diagram. What do you think she has figured out? Try your ideas on the expressions shown below.

i. w^2-81

ii. $4m^2-1$

iii. x^2-16y^2

3-19. Shinna has noticed that **differences of squares** can be factored easily.

a. Decide which of the expressions below can be seen as a difference of squares and can therefore be factored using Shinna's shortcut. For each difference of squares, show the squares clearly and then write the product. For example, $16x^2 - 9y^2$ can be rewritten as $(4x)^2 - (3y)^2$ and then as $(4x-3y)(4x+3y)$.

i. $a^2 - 4b^2$

ii. $2x^2 - 16$

iii. $-x^2 + y^4$

iv. $4a^2 + 9b^2$

b. Write two more expressions of your own that are differences of squares and show each in factored form.

3-20. Shinna wants to factor $9x^2y^4 - z^6$. *"Wait!"* she says. *"I think I can see a way to use my shortcut!"*

a. Discuss this with your team. Is Shinna's expression a difference of squares? If so, what are the squares? If not, explain why. Be ready to share your ideas with the class.

b. Shinna decided to rewrite her expression so that its structure was simpler to see. She wrote $9x^2y^4 - z^6$ as $U^2 - V^2$. What was she using *U* to represent? What about *V*?

c. George is confused! *"Shinna," he says, "There was no U or V in your problem! What are you doing?"* Explain to George what is going on.

d. Help Shinna finish factoring the expression $9x^2y^4 - z^6$ by factoring $U^2 - V^2$ and then substituting the original expressions for *U* and *V*.

3-21. How can you use this method of substitution to make use of what you know about other expressions? Work with your team to describe the structure of each of the expressions in parts (a) through (d) below. Use substitution, when appropriate, to make the structure clear. For example, $25x^2 - 100y^4$ is a difference of squares and can be rewritten as $U^2 - V^2$ with $U = 5x$ and $V = 10y^2$.

The following questions might be useful:

What do all of these expressions have in common?

How might we substitute U and V to make rewriting simpler?

a. $a^2 + 2ab + b^2$

b. $x^2 - 6x + 9$

c. $9x^2 + 30xy + 25y^2$

d. $(a+7)^2 - 10(a+7) + 25$

3-22. Now it's your turn!

a. Work with a partner to write two really complicated-looking expressions that can actually be rewritten in a different form using substitution. Be sure to write the solutions for your expressions on a separate paper, so that you will be ready to trade expressions with another pair of students.

b. When you and your partner have been given another pair's expressions, use substitution to rewrite them. Do not let them stump you!

3-23. Decide whether each of the following pairs of expressions are equivalent for all values of x (or a and b). If they are equivalent, show how you can be sure. If they are not, justify your reasoning completely.

a. $(x+3)^2$ and $x^2 + 9$

b. $(x+4)^2$ and $x^2 + 8x + 16$

c. $(x+1)(2x-3)$ and $2x^2 - x - 3$

d. $3(x-4)^2 + 2$ and $3x^2 - 24x + 50$

e. $(x^3)^4$ and x^7

f. ab^2 and a^2b^2

3-24. Look back at the expressions in problem 3-23 that are not equivalent. For each pair of expressions, are there any values of the variable(s) that would make the two expressions equal? Justify your reasoning.

3-25. Jenna wants to solve the equation $2000x - 4000 = 8000$.

a. What easier equation could she solve instead that would give her the same solution? (In other words, what equivalent equation has easier numbers to work with?)

b. Justify that your equation in part (a) is equivalent to $2000x - 4000 = 8000$ by showing that they have the same solution.

c. Now Jenna wants to solve $\frac{3}{50} - \frac{x}{50} = \frac{7}{50}$. Write and solve an equivalent equation with easier numbers that would give her the same answer.

3-26. Find an equation for each sequence below. Then describe its graph.

a.

n	$t(n)$
3	8
5	2
7	–4

b.

n	$t(n)$
1	40
2	32
3	25.6

3-27. For the function $h(x) = -3x^2 - 11x + 4$, find the value of $h(x)$ for each value of x given below.

a. $h(0)$ b. $h(2)$ c. $h(-1)$ d. $h(\frac{1}{2})$

e. For what value(s) of x does $h(x) = 0$?

3-28. Find the x-intercepts for the graph of $y - x^2 = 6x$.

3-29. Multiply each pair of polynomial functions below to find an expression for $f(x) \cdot g(x)$.

a. $f(x) = 2x$, $g(x) = (x + 3)$ b. $f(x) = (x + 3)$, $g(x) = (x - 5)$

c. $f(x) = (2x + 1)$, $g(x) = (x - 3)$ d. $f(x) = (x + 3)$, $g(x) = (x + 3)$

3-30. Describe how the graph of $y + 3 = -2(x + 1)^2$ is different from $y = x^2$.

3-31. Given the parabola $f(x) = x^2 - 2x - 3$, complete parts (a) through (c) below.

a. Find the vertex by averaging the x-intercepts.

b. Find the vertex by completing the square.

c. Find the vertex of $f(x) = x^2 + 5x + 2$ using your method of choice.

d. What are the domain and range for $f(x) = x^2 + 5x + 2$?

3-32. Simplify each of the following expressions, leaving only positive exponents in your answer.

a. $(x^3y^{-2})^{-4}$

b. $-3x^2(6xy - 2x^3y^2z)$

3-33. Determine if each of the following functions are odd, even or neither.

a. $y = 3x^3$

b. $y = x^2 + 16$

c. $y = \frac{x^4}{2}$

3-34. You decide to park your car in a parking garage that charges $3.00 for the first hour and $1.00 for each hour (or any part of an hour) after that.

a. How much will it cost to park your car for 90 minutes?

b. How much will it cost to park your car for 118 minutes? 119 minutes?

c. How much will it cost to park your car for 120 minutes? 121 minutes?

d. Graph the cost in relation to the length of time your car is parked.

e. Is this function continuous?

f. Describe how the graph of this function will change if the parking garage raises their parking rate so that the first hour is now $5.00.

3-35. Give the equation of each circle below in graphing form.

a. A circle with radius of 12 centered at the point $(-2, 13)$.

b. A circle with center $(-1, -4)$ and radius 1.

c. A circle with equation $x^2 + y^2 - 6x + 16y + 57 = 0$. (Hint: Complete the square for both x and y.)

3-36. Giuseppe decides that he really wants some ice cream, so he leaves the house at 3:00 p.m. and walks to the ice cream parlor. He arrives at 3:15 (the ice cream parlor is 6 blocks away). He buys an ice cream cone and sits down to eat it. At 3:45 he heads back home, arriving at 4:05. Find Giuseppe's average walking rate in blocks per hour for each of the following situations.

a. His trip to the ice cream parlor.

b. His trip back home.

c. The entire trip including the time spent eating.

3.1.3 How can I solve it?

Solving by Rewriting

In the past few lessons, you have worked on recognizing and finding equivalent expressions. In this lesson, you will apply these ideas to solve equations. As you work, use the questions below to keep your team's discussion productive and focused.

How can we make it simpler?

Does anyone see another way?

How can we be sure the equations are equivalent?

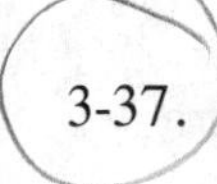

3-37. Graciela was trying to solve the quadratic equation $x^2 + 2.5x - 1.5 = 0$. *"I think I need to use the Quadratic Formula because of the decimals,"* she told Walter. Walter replied, *"I'm sure there's another way! Can't we rewrite this equation so there aren't any decimals?"*

a. What is Walter talking about? Rewrite the equation so that it has no decimals.

b. Rewrite your equation again, this time expressing it as a product.

c. Now solve your new equation. Be sure to check your solution(s) using Graciela's original equation.

3-38. SOLVING BY REWRITING

Rewriting $x^2 + 2.5x - 1.5 = 0$ in problem 3-37 gave you a new, equivalent equation that was much easier to solve. With your team, find an equivalent equation or system that you think might be easier to solve for parts (a) through (f) below. Then solve your new equation or system and check your answer(s) using the original equations.

a. $100x^2 + 100x = 2000$

b. $15x + 10y = -20$
$7x - 2y = 24$

c. $\frac{1}{3}x^2 + \frac{x}{2} - \frac{1}{3} = 0$

d. $\frac{4}{x^2} + \frac{12}{x} + 9 = 0$

e. $\frac{x-3}{x} + \frac{2}{x-1} = \frac{5-x}{x}$

f. $\frac{\sqrt{x^2-15x}}{2y} = 5$
$3\sqrt{x^2 - 15x} - 3y = 27$

3-39. Graciela and Walter were working on solving the system of equations in part (f) of problem 3-38. They tried to rewrite both equations in $y=$ form so that they could set them equal to each other.

$$2y \cdot \frac{\sqrt{x^2-15x}}{2y} = 2y \cdot 5 \quad \Rightarrow \quad \sqrt{x^2 - 15x} = 10y \quad \Rightarrow \quad y = \frac{\sqrt{x^2-15x}}{10}$$

$$\frac{3\sqrt{x^2-15x}-3y}{3} = \frac{27}{3} \quad \Rightarrow \quad \sqrt{x^2 - 15x} - y = 9 \quad \Rightarrow \quad y = \sqrt{x^2 - 15x} - 9$$

Graciela and Walter realized they had a big mess to try to solve. "*Wait,*" Graciela said. "*There's an easier way. Let's use substitution to make this system simpler!*"

a. Discuss this idea with your team. Does it make sense?

b. Walter and Graciela decided to try this new idea, but they were not sure the best choice for what expression to replace with a new variable. They came up with these two options:

$U = x^2 - 15x$ or $U = \sqrt{x^2 - 15x}$

To help Graciela and Walter decide, rewrite the original system from problem 3-38 part (f) twice, each time using a different version of U. Which version of U looks like it will make the system easier to solve?

c. Solve your new system for U and y.

d. Now what? Since your job in solving a system in x and y is to find values for both of those variables, you are not done. Work with your team to find a way to get the value of x from the value you found for U. Be ready to share your strategies with the class.

3-40. Consider each of the following equations and systems. Would substitution make them easier to solve? What expression might you temporarily replace with U? Be ready to share your ideas on substitution with the class. You do not need to actually solve the equation(s).

a. $(m^2+5m-24)^2-(m^2+5m-24)=6$

b. $2x+y^7=6$
$3x-2y^7=-5$

c. $(4x^2+4x-3)^2=(x^2-5x-6)^2$

3-41. MORE EQUIVALENT EQUATIONS

Rewrite each of the following equations in another form by solving for y. (That is, rewrite the equations in $y =$ form.) Check to be sure your new equation is equivalent to the original equation.

a. $5x-2y=8$

b. $xy+3x=2$

3-42. Rewrite the equation from part (b) of problem 3-41 in yet another form by solving for x. Be ready to share your strategies with the class.

3-43. None of the three equations below are equivalent. Show that this is true by rewriting the equations with an equivalent equation.

$2x=2y-6$

$xy+2x=(y+2)(y+3)$

$-x=-y-3$

3-44. Angelica and D'Lee were working on finding roots of two quadratic equations: $y=(x-3)(x-5)$ and $y=2(x-3)(x-5)$. Angelica made an interesting claim: *"Look,"* she said, *"When I solve each of them for* $y=0$*, I get the same solutions. So these equations must be equivalent!"*

D'Lee is not so sure. *"How can they be equivalent if one of the equations has a factor of 2 that the other equation doesn't?"* she asked.

a. Who is correct? Is $y=(x-3)(x-5)$ equivalent to $y=2(x-3)(x-5)$? How can you justify your ideas using tables and graphs?

b. Are the solutions of $0=(x-3)(x-5)$ equivalent to the solutions of $0=2(x-3)(x-5)$? Again, how can you justify your ideas?

METHODS AND MEANINGS

Vocabulary for Expressions

A mathematical **expression** is a combination of numbers, variables, and operation symbols. Addition and subtraction separate expressions into parts called **terms**. For example, $4x^2 - 3x + 6$ is an expression. It has three terms: $4x^2$, $3x$, and 6. The **coefficients** of the terms with variables are 4 and –3. 6 is called a **constant term**.

A single-variable **polynomial** is an expression that involves, at most, the operations of addition, subtraction, and multiplication. Most of the polynomials you will work with can be written as expressions with terms of the following form:

$$(\text{any real number})x^{(\text{whole number})}$$

For example, $4x^2 - 3x^1 + 6x^0$ is a polynomial, as is the simplified form, $4x^2 - 3x + 6$. Also, since $6x^0 = 6$, 6 itself is a polynomial.

The function $f(x) = 7x^5 + 2.5x^3 - \frac{1}{2}x + 7$ is a polynomial function.

A **binomial** is a polynomial with only two terms, for example, $x^3 - 0.5x$ and $2x + 5$.

The following expressions are *not* polynomials: $2^x - 3$, $\frac{1}{x^2-2}$, and $\sqrt{x-2}$.

An expression that can be written as the quotient of two polynomials is a **rational expression**. For example, $\frac{1}{x^2-2}$ is a rational expression.

3-45. Rewrite each equation below. Then solve your new equation. Be sure to check your solution using the original equation.

a. $(n+4) + n(n+2) + n = 0$

b. $\frac{4}{x} = x + 3$

3-46. Decide whether each of the following pairs of expressions or equations are equivalent. If they are, show how you can be sure. If they are not, justify your reasoning completely.

a. $(ab)^2$ and a^2b^2

b. $3x-4y=12$ and $y=\frac{3}{4}x-3$

c. $y=2(x-1)+3$ and $y=2x+1$

d. $(a+b)^2$ and a^2+b^2

e. $\frac{x^6}{x^2}$ and x^3

f. $y=3(x-5)+2$ and $y=2x-8$

3-47. Look back at the expressions in problem 3-46 that are not equivalent. Are there any values of the variables that would make them equal? Justify your reasoning.

3-48. Find the formula for $t(n)$ for the arithmetic sequence in which $t(15)=10$ and $t(63)=106$.

3-49. Jillian's parents bought a house for $450,000, and the value of the house has been increasing steadily by 3% each year.

a. Find the formula $t(n)$ that represents the value of the house each year.

b. If Jillian's parents sell their house 10 years after they bought it, how much profit will they make? (That is, how much more are they selling it for than they bought it for?) Express your answer as both a dollar amount and a percent of the original purchase price.

3-50. Factor $5x^3y+35x^2y+50xy$ completely. Show every step and explain what you did.

3-51. While Jenna was solving the equation $150x+300=600$, she wondered if she could first change the equation to $x+2=4$. What do you think?

a. Solve both equations and verify that they have the same solution.

b. What did Jenna do to the equation $150x+300=600$ to change it to $x+2=4$?

c. Use the same method to rewrite and solve $60t-120=300$.

3-52. Consider the sequence 10, 2, ...

a. Assuming that the sequence is arithmetic with $t(1)$ as the first term, write the next four terms of the sequence and then write an equation for $t(n)$.

b. Assuming that the sequence is geometric with $t(1)$ as the first term, write the next four terms of the sequence and then write an equation for $t(n)$.

c. Create a totally different sequence that begins 10, 2, ... For your sequence, write the next four terms and an equation for $t(n)$.

3-53. Rewrite each radical below as an equivalent expression using fractional exponents.

a. $\sqrt[2]{5}$ b. $\sqrt[3]{9}$ c. $\sqrt[8]{17^x}$ d. $7\sqrt[4]{x^3}$

3-54. Give the equation of each circle below in graphing form.

a. A circle with center (0, 0) and radius 6.

b. A circle with center (2, –3) and radius 6.

c. A circle with equation $x^2 + y^2 - 8x + 10y + 5 = 0$.

3-55. If the cooling system in a light-water nuclear reactor is shut off, the temperature of the fuel rods will increase. The temperature of the fuel rods during the first hour could be modeled by the equation $T = 680(1.0004)^t - 655$, where t is the time in seconds, and T is the temperature of the fuel rods in degrees Fahrenheit. **Average rate of change** can be calculated by finding the slope between two points. Find the average rate at which the temperature changes for the first 30 minutes.

3-56. In the year 2006, the average cost to rent a car was \$39 for the first day and an additional \$23 for each additional day.

a. Graph the relationship between cost and the duration of a car rental in 2006.

b. Describe how the graph would be transformed if the current average cost of a car rental has increased to \$50 for the first day.

3.2.1 Where does the graph go?

Investigating Rational Functions

In your experience with algebra, you have added, subtracted, and multiplied polynomials, but what happens when you divide them? Today you will make some predictions about the graphs that result when two linear functions are combined by adding, subtracting, multiplying, or dividing them. You will further explore division of polynomials in Chapter 8.

3-57. COMBINING LINEAR FUNCTIONS INVESTIGATION

Your team will be assigned a pair of linear functions from the list below.

$f_1(x)=x-2$ $g_1(x)=2x+3$	$f_2(x)=x+3$ $g_2(x)=5x-9$	$f_3(x)=x-4$ $g_3(x)=5x+8$
$f_4(x)=x-1$ $g_4(x)=2x+5$	$f_5(x)=x-3$ $g_5(x)=5x-9$	$f_6(x)=x+4$ $g_6(x)=5x+6$
$f_7(x)=x-3$ $g_7(x)=2x+5$	$f_8(x)=x+3$ $g_8(x)=5x+7$	$f_9(x)=x+2$ $g_9(x)=5x+3$

Your Task: With your team, find out as much as you can about what happens when you combine the two linear functions using each of the operations of addition, subtraction, multiplication, and division. Use the following steps to guide your investigation.

1. Make your own prediction of the shape of each new graph and draw a quick, rough sketch on your paper.
2. Discuss your prediction with your teammates.
3. Use a graphing calculator to check your team's prediction.
4. Summarize your findings.

Be sure to carefully record all of your work and be prepared to share your summary statements about the results for each operation with the class.

Note: When entering operations into the graphing calculator, you may need to insert extra parentheses so the calculator will follow your intended Order of Operations.

Discussion Points

What does the new graph look like?

What happens when we use the expressions in a different order? Why?

What are the domains and ranges of the new graphs?

Further Guidance

3-58. First investigate the graphs for the sum and difference of your two functions. Does the order of subtraction matter? What do you think would happen if you added or subtracted any two linear functions $f(x)$ and $g(x)$. Can you think of any exceptions?

3-59. Now multiply the functions and graph the product $f(x) \cdot g(x)$. How well did your team predict the result? What do you think the resulting graph would look like if you multiplied any two linear functions?

3-60. Divide the two functions, $\frac{f(x)}{g(x)}$, and graph the result. Check the table of values or use the TRACE function on your calculator to find the x-values that are "holes" in your graph. (Your teacher will check if the graph in the standard window of your graphing calculator has extra lines that obscure the picture. If that is the case, the teacher will make some suggestions.)

Further Guidance section ends here.

3-61. CLOSED SETS

Whole numbers (positive integers and zero) are said to be a **closed set** under addition: if you add two whole numbers, you always get a whole number. Whole numbers are not a closed set under subtraction: if you subtract two whole numbers, you do not always get a whole number. For example, $2 - 5 = -3$ and -3 is not a whole number.

a. Investigate with your team whether the set of integers is a closed set under addition and under subtraction. Then investigate whether the integers are a closed set under multiplication and under division. Give examples. If you think the set is closed, explain why. If, not, give counterexamples.

b. Are single-variable polynomials closed under addition, subtraction, and multiplication? In other words, if you add, subtract, or multiply two polynomials that have the same variable, will you always get a polynomial as your answer? If you think the set is closed, explain why. If, not, give counterexamples.

3-62. With your team describe the graphs of $p(x)$ and $q(x)$ and then make an estimate of their sum, difference, product, and quotient functions *before* using a graphing tool.

$$p(x) = x^3 - 3x - 1 \qquad q(x) = x - 1$$

a. $p(x) + q(x)$ b. $p(x) - q(x)$ c. $p(x) \cdot q(x)$ d. $\frac{p(x)}{q(x)}$

e. For parts (a) through (d) above, sketch a careful graph and make a note of the shape, the domain and range, and any other characteristics you notice. Your team should be prepared to share their observations with the class.

3-63. Given that n is the length of the bottom edge of the backward L-shaped figures below, what sequence is generated by the total number of dots in each figure? What is the 46th term, or $t(46)$, of this sequence? The nth term?

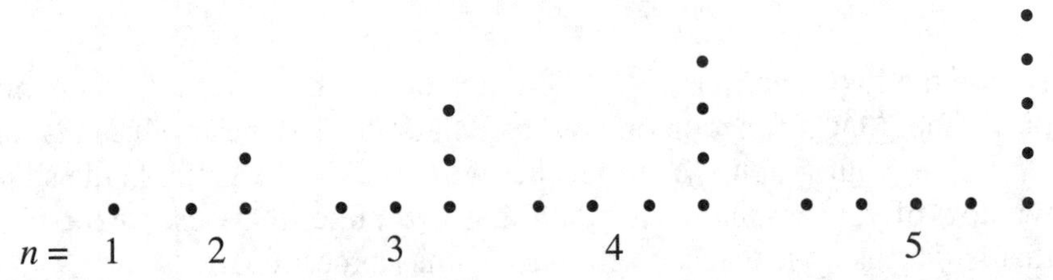

3-64. A piece of metal at 20°C is warmed at a steady rate of 2 degrees per minute. At the same time, another piece of metal at 240°C is cooled at a steady rate of 3 degrees per minute. After how many minutes is the temperature of each piece of metal the same? Explain how you found your answer.

3-65. The price of a movie ticket averages \$10.25 and is increasing by 3% per year. Use that information to complete parts (a) through (c) below.

a. What is the multiplier in this situation?

b. Write a function that represents the cost of a movie ticket n years from now.

c. If tickets continue to increase at the same rate, what will they cost 10 years from now?

3-66. Use the meaning of an exponent to rewrite the expression $(y-2)^3$.

3-67. This problem is a checkpoint for rewriting and simplifying expressions with integral and rational exponents. It will be referred to as Checkpoint 3A.

For parts (a) through (d), rewrite each expression. For parts (e) through (h), simplify each expression.

a. $\sqrt[5]{x}$ b. $\frac{1}{x^3}$ c. $x^{2/3}$ d. $\frac{1}{\sqrt{x}}$

e. $x^{-1}y^{-8}$ f. $(m^2)^{-3/2}$ g. $(x^3y^6)^{1/2}$ h. $(9x^3y^6)^{-2}$

Check your answers by referring to the Checkpoint 3A materials located at the back of your book.

If you needed help solving these problems correctly, then you need more practice. Review the Checkpoint 3A materials and try the practice problems. Also, consider getting help outside of class time. From this point on, you will be expected to do problems like these quickly and easily.

3-68. While David was solving the equation $100x + 300 = 500$, he wondered if he could first change the equation to $x + 3 = 5$. What do you think?

a. Solve both equations and verify that they have the same solution.

b. What could you do to the equation $100x + 300 = 500$ to change it into $x + 3 = 5$?

3-69. Multiply the expressions below using generic rectangles.

a. $(5m - 1)(m + 2)$ b. $(6 - x)(2 + x)$

c. $(5x - y)^2$ d. $3x(2x - 5y + 4)$

3.2.2 How can "1" be useful?

Simplifying Rational Expressions

In this chapter, you will focus on an important number: the number 1. What is special about 1? What can you do with the number 1 that you cannot do with any other number? You will use your understanding of the number 1 to simplify algebraic fractions, which are also known as **rational expressions**.

3-70. What do you know about the number 1? With your team, brainstorm ideas and be ready to report your ideas to the class. Create examples to help show what you mean.

3-71. Mr. Wonder claims that anything divided by itself equals 1 (as long as you do not divide by zero).

a. Mr. Wonder states that $\frac{16x}{16x} = 1$ if x is not zero. What is his hypothesis and his conclusion?

b. Is Mr. Wonder correct? That is, is his statement true? Justify your conclusion.

c. Why can't x be zero?

d. Next he considers $\frac{x-3}{x-3}$. Does this equal 1? What value of x must be excluded in this fraction?

e. Create your own rational expression (algebraic fraction) that equals 1.

f. Mr. Wonder also says that when you multiply any number by 1, the number stays the same. For example, he says that the product below equals $\frac{x}{y}$. Is he correct?

$$\frac{z}{z} \cdot \frac{x}{y} = \frac{x}{y}$$

3-72. Use a calculator to graph the function $f(x) = \frac{16x}{16x}$. Use the trace button to trace along the line and notice what happens at $x = 0$. Is the expression $\frac{16x}{16x}$ equivalent to 1? Explain.

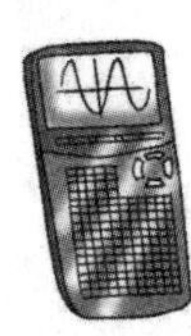

3-73. With your team, compare and contrast the graphs of each of the following functions:

$$f_1(x)=\frac{2x-3}{2x-3} \qquad f_2(x)=\frac{2x-3}{3-2x}$$

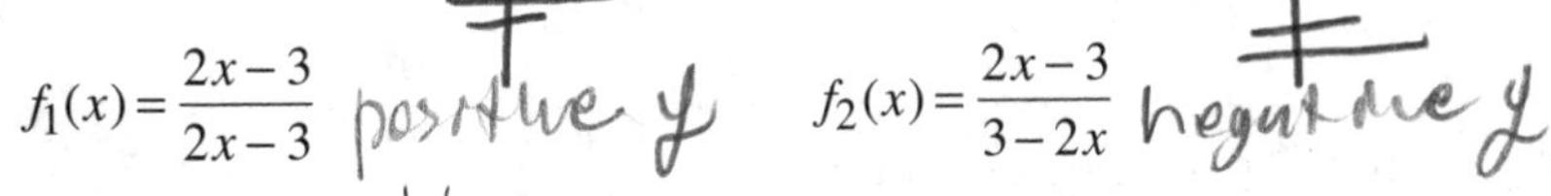

$$f_3(x)=\frac{2x-3}{2x+3} \qquad f_4(x)=\frac{1}{2x-3}$$

a. First visualize and make a quick sketch of what you imagine the graph of each will look like.

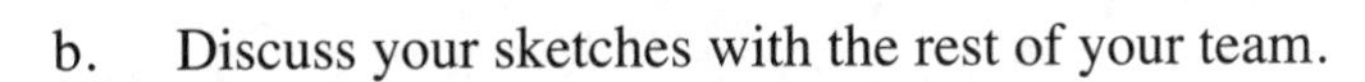

b. Discuss your sketches with the rest of your team.

c. Use calculators to graph each rational function, and adjust your sketches if needed.

d. Use the TRACE function or the table on your graphing calculator to find the location of the "hole" in each of the graphs, and describe their similarities and differences. Include their domains and ranges in the descriptions.

3-74. Use what you know about the number 1 to simplify each expression below, if possible. State any value(s) of the variable that would make the denominator zero.

a. $\frac{x^2}{x^2}$

b. $\frac{x}{x}\cdot\frac{x}{x}\cdot\frac{x}{3}$

c. $\frac{x-2}{x-2}\cdot\frac{x+5}{x-1}$

d. $\frac{9}{x}\cdot\frac{x}{9}$

e. $\frac{h\cdot h\cdot k}{h}$

f. $\frac{(2m-5)(m+6)}{(m+6)(3m+1)}$

g. $\frac{6(n-2)^2}{3(n-2)}$

h. $\frac{3-2x}{(4x-1)(3-2x)}$

3-75. Mr. Wonder now tries to simplify $\frac{4x}{x}$ and $\frac{4+x}{x}$.

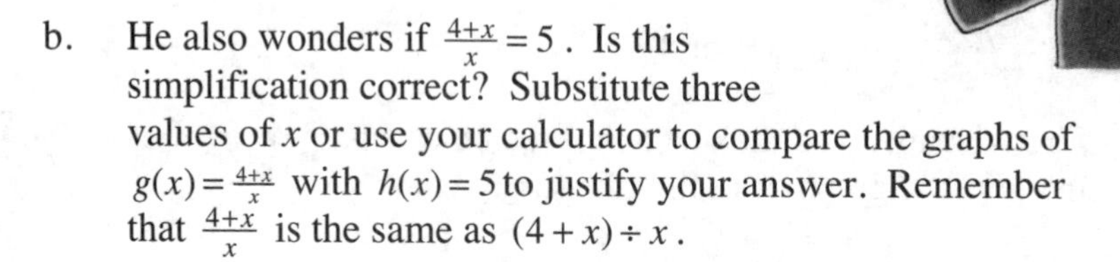

a. Mr. Wonder thinks that since $\frac{x}{x}=1$, then $\frac{4x}{x}=4$. Is he correct? Substitute three values of x to justify your answer.

b. He also wonders if $\frac{4+x}{x}=5$. Is this simplification correct? Substitute three values of x or use your calculator to compare the graphs of $g(x)=\frac{4+x}{x}$ with $h(x)=5$ to justify your answer. Remember that $\frac{4+x}{x}$ is the same as $(4+x)\div x$.

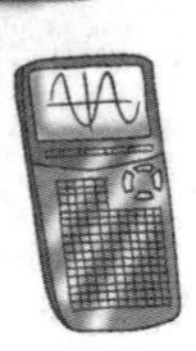

c. Compare the results of parts (a) and (b). When can a rational expression be simplified in this manner?

d. Which of the following expressions below is simplified correctly? Explain how you know.

i. $\frac{x^2+x+3}{x+3}=x^2$ *ii.* $\frac{(x+2)(x+3)}{x+3}=x+2$

3-76. In problem 3-75, you may have noticed that *both* the numerator and denominator of an algebraic fraction must be written as a product before you can use any of the terms to create a **Giant One** (a form of the number 1). Examine the expressions below. Factor the numerator and denominator of each fraction, if necessary. That is, rewrite each one as a product. Then look for "Giant Ones" and simplify. For each expression, assume the denominator is not zero.

a. $\frac{x^2+6x+9}{x^2-9}$ b. $\frac{2x^2-x-10}{3x^2+7x+2}$ c. $\frac{28x^2-x-15}{28x^2-x-15}$ d. $\frac{x^2+4x}{2x+8}$

3-77. LEARNING LOG

In your Learning Log, explain how to simplify rational expressions such as those in problem 3-76. Be sure to include an example. Title this entry "Simplifying Rational Expressions" and include today's date.

3-78. Simplify the expressions below.

a. $\frac{x^2-8x+16}{3x^2-10x-8}$ for $x \neq -\frac{2}{3}$ or 4

b. $\frac{10x+25}{2x^2-x-15}$ for $x \neq -\frac{5}{2}$ or 3

c. $\frac{(k-4)(2k+1)}{5(2k+1)} \div \frac{(k-3)(k-4)}{10(k-3)}$ for $k \neq 3, 4,$ or $-\frac{1}{2}$

3-79. How many solutions does each equation below have?

a. $4x+3=3x+3$

b. $3(x-4)-x=5+2x$

c. $(5x-2)(x+4)=0$

d. $x^2-4x+4=0$

3-80. Now David wants to solve the equation $4000x-8000=16{,}000$.

a. What easier equation could he solve instead that would give him the same solution? (In other words, what equivalent equation has easier numbers to work with?)

b. Justify that your equation in part (a) is equivalent to $4000x-8000=16{,}000$ by showing that they have the same solution.

c. David's last equation to solve is $\frac{x}{100}+\frac{3}{100}=\frac{8}{100}$. Write and solve an equivalent equation with easier numbers that would give him the same answer.

3-81. Solve each of the following inequalities for the given variable. Represent your solutions on a number line.

a. $5+3x<5$

b. $-3x \geq 8-x$

3-82. In Lesson 3.2.3 you will focus on multiplying and dividing rational expressions. Recall what you learned about multiplying and dividing fractions in a previous course as you answer the questions below. To help you, the following examples have been provided.

$$\frac{9}{16} \cdot \frac{4}{6} = \frac{36}{96} = \frac{3}{8}$$

$$\frac{5}{6} \div \frac{20}{12} = \frac{5}{6} \cdot \frac{12}{20} = \frac{60}{120} = \frac{1}{2}$$

a. Without a calculator, multiply $\frac{2}{3} \cdot \frac{9}{14}$ and reduce the result. Then use a calculator to check your answer. Describe your method for multiplying fractions.

b. Without a calculator, divide $\frac{3}{5} \div \frac{12}{25}$ and reduce the result. Then use a calculator to check your answer. Describe your method for dividing fractions.

3-83. Sketch the graph of $y = (x + 2)^3 + 4$.

a. What is the parent graph of this function? How has the graph of this function been transformed from the parent graph?

b. Rewrite the equation $y = (x + 2)^3 + 4$ without parentheses. Remember the Order of Operations.

c. How would the graph in part (a) differ from the graph of the original equation?

3-84. Sketch the graph of the function $f(x) = 3 \cdot 5^x$.

a. What is the domain of $f(x)$?

b. Sketch the graph of the geometric sequence $t(n) = 3 \cdot 5^n$.

c. What is the difference between $f(x)$ and $t(n)$? Explain completely.

3.2.3 How can I rewrite it?

Multiplying and Dividing Rational Expressions

You know how to multiply and divide fractions. But what if the fractions have variables in them? That is, what if they are rational expressions? Is the process the same? Today you will learn how to multiply and divide rational expressions and will continue to practice simplifying rational expressions.

3-85. Review your work from yesterday by simplifying the rational expression below using a "Giant One." What are the excluded values of x? (That is, what values can x <u>not</u> be?)

$$\frac{3x^2+11x-4}{2x^2+11x+12}$$

3-86. With your team, review your responses to homework problem 3-82. Verify that everyone obtained the same answers and be prepared to share with the class how you multiplied and divided the fractions below.

$\frac{2}{3} \cdot \frac{9}{14}$ $\qquad$ $\frac{3}{5} \div \frac{12}{25}$

3-87. Use your understanding of multiplying and dividing fractions to rewrite the expressions below. Then look for "Giant Ones" and simplify. For each rational expression, also state any values of the variables that would make the denominator zero.

a. $\frac{4x+3}{x-5} \cdot \frac{x-5}{x+3}$

b. $\frac{x+2}{9x-1} \div \frac{2x+1}{9x-1}$

c. $\frac{2m+3}{3m-2} \cdot \frac{7+4m}{3+2m}$

d. $\frac{(y-2)^3}{3y} \cdot \frac{y+5}{(y+2)(y-2)}$

e. $\frac{15x^3}{3y} \div \frac{10x^2y}{4y^2}$

f. $\frac{(5x-2)(3x+1)}{(2x-3)^2} \div \frac{(5x-2)(x-4)}{(x-4)(2x-3)}$

3-88. PUTTING IT ALL TOGETHER

Multiply or divide the expressions below. Leave your answers as simplified as possible. For each rational expression, assume the denominator is not zero.

a. $\frac{20}{22} \cdot \frac{14}{35}$

b. $\frac{12}{40} \div \frac{15}{6}$

c. $\frac{5x-15}{3x^2+10x-8} \div \frac{x^2+x-12}{3x^2-8x+4}$

d. $\frac{12x-18}{x^2-2x-15} \cdot \frac{x^2-x-12}{3x^2-9x-12}$

e. $\frac{5x^2+34x-7}{10x} \cdot \frac{5x}{x^2+4x-21}$

f. $\frac{2x^2+x-10}{x^2+2x-8} \div \frac{4x^2+20x+25}{x+4}$

3-89. LEARNING LOG

In your Learning Log, explain how to multiply and divide rational expressions. Be sure to include an example of each. Title this entry "Multiplying and Dividing Rational Expressions" and include today's date.

3-90. Multiply or divide the expressions below. Simplify your results.

a. $\frac{x-7}{9(2x-1)} \div \frac{(x+5)(x-7)}{6x(x+5)}$

b. $\frac{6x^2-x-1}{3x^2+25x+8} \cdot \frac{x^2+4x-32}{2x^2+7x-4}$

3-91. For each rational expression below, state any values of the variables that would make the denominator zero. Then complete each part.

a. Use the fact that $(x+4)^2 = (x+4)(x+4)$ to rewrite $\frac{(x+4)^2}{(x+4)(x-2)}$. Then look for "ones" and simplify.

b. Use the strategy you used in part (a) to simplify the expression $\frac{8(x+2)^3(x-3)^3}{4(x+2)^2(x-3)^5}$.

3-92. Monica's younger sister is just learning how to add fractions, and she is confused. She has to add $\frac{1}{3}+\frac{2}{5}$.

Help Monica explain to her by writing a detailed step-by-step explanation of exactly what she needs to do.

3-93. Solve the systems of equations below using any method.

a. $3x - 3 = y$
$6x - 5y = 12$

b. $3x - 2y = 30$
$2x + 3y = -19$

3-94. Janelle conducted an experiment by mistake when she left her bologna sandwich at school over winter break. When she got back, her sandwich was much larger than it was when she left it. Her science teacher explained that the sandwich had produced large quantities of a rare bacterium, *Bolognicus sandwichae*. Based on a sample taken from the sandwich, Janelle determined that there were approximately 72 million bacteria present. Her science teacher explained that this is not very surprising, since the number of this bacteria triples every 24 hours. Since the sandwich had been made only 15 days ago, Janelle was sure that she could sue the meat company. The food-industry standard for the most bacteria a sandwich-sized portion can have at the time of production is 100. Find out how many of the bacteria were present when the sandwich was made to determine if Janelle has a case.

3-95. Determine if the function shown on the graph at right is odd or even or neither? Explain how you decided.

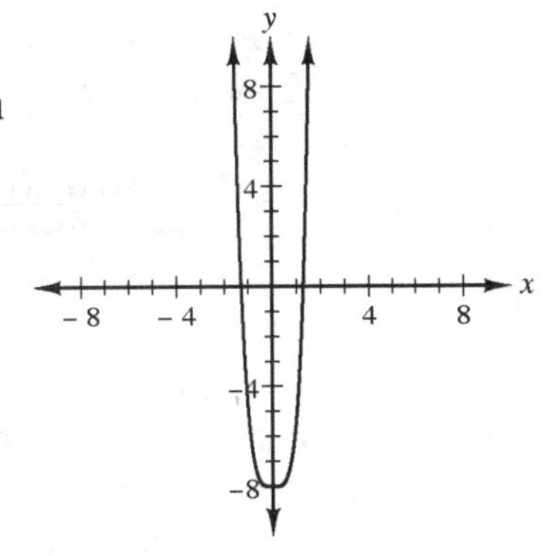

3-96. Solve the equations below. Check your solutions.

a. $\frac{m}{6} = \frac{m+1}{5}$

b. $\frac{3x-5}{2} = \frac{4x+1}{4}$

c. $\frac{8}{k} = \frac{14}{k+3}$

d. $\frac{x}{9} = 10$

3.2.4 How can I rewrite it?

Adding and Subtracting Rational Expressions

So far in this course you have learned quite a bit about rational expressions. You have learned how to simplify complex algebraic fractions by factoring the numerators and denominators. You have also learned how to multiply and divide rational expressions. What else is there? Today you will develop a method to add and subtract algebraic fractions.

3-97. With your team, read your directions for Monica's sister from homework problem 3-92. Verify that everyone obtained the same answer and be prepared to share how you added the fractions with the class.

$$\frac{1}{3}+\frac{2}{5}$$

a. Now Monica's sister wants to know *why*? Why does she have to do all of those steps with the common denominator? What is a fraction anyway, and why does adding them have to be so complicated? Draw some pictures or diagrams or make up some situations that will help her to know what fractions like $\frac{1}{3}$ and $\frac{2}{5}$ mean.

b. Now use your ideas from part (a) to show Monica *why* she needs a common denominator to add the two fractions.

3-98. Extend the procedures your class developed for numerical fractions to add these algebraic fractions.

$$\frac{2x}{x-1}+\frac{3}{x+5}$$

3-99. Now add the fractions below. After you have added them, be sure to check to see if the numerator can be factored. You may be able get a simpler answer.

a. $\frac{x}{3x+1}+\frac{2x^2-2}{(x-5)(3x+1)}$

b. $\frac{9-3x}{(x+3)(x-3)}+\frac{2x}{x+3}$

3-100. Examine the expression below.

$$\frac{2x-1}{3x^2+13x+4}+\frac{x+3}{x^2-3x-28}$$

a. With your team, decide how you can alter the expression so that the fractions have a common denominator. Be ready to share your idea with the class.

b. If you have not already do so, add the fractions. Then simplify the result, if possible.

c. Repeat the process to subtract the expressions below. Simplify the result, if possible.

$$\frac{2}{x+4}-\frac{4x-x^2}{x^2-16}$$

3-101. LEARNING LOG

In your Learning Log, explain how to add and subtract rational expressions. Be sure to include an example. Title this entry "Adding and Subtracting Rational Expressions" and include today's date.

Methods and Meanings

Rewriting Rational Expressions

To simplify a rational expression, both the numerator and denominator must be written in factored form. Then, look for factors that make a "Giant One" (a form of the number 1) and simplify. Study the examples below.

Example 1: $\frac{x^2+5x+4}{x^2+x-12} = \frac{(x+4)(x+1)}{(x+4)(x-3)} = 1 \cdot \frac{x+1}{x-3} = \frac{x+1}{x-3}$ for $x \neq -4$ or 3

Example 2: $\frac{2x-7}{2x^2+3x-35} = \frac{(2x-7)(1)}{(2x-7)(x+5)} = 1 \cdot \frac{1}{x+5} = \frac{1}{x+5}$ for $x \neq -5$ or $\frac{7}{2}$

Just as you can multiply and divide fractions, you can multiply and divide rational expressions.

Example 3: Multiply $\frac{x^2+6x}{(x+6)^2} \cdot \frac{x^2+7x+6}{x^2-1}$ and simplify for $x \neq -6$ or 1.

After factoring, this expression becomes: $\frac{x(x+6)}{(x+6)(x+6)} \cdot \frac{(x+1)(x+6)}{(x+1)(x-1)}$

After multiplying, reorder the factors: $\frac{(x+6)}{(x+6)} \cdot \frac{(x+6)}{(x+6)} \cdot \frac{x}{(x-1)} \cdot \frac{(x+1)}{(x+1)}$

Since $\frac{(x+6)}{(x+6)} = 1$ and $\frac{(x+1)}{(x+1)} = 1$, simplify: $1 \cdot 1 \cdot \frac{x}{(x-1)} \cdot 1 \Rightarrow \frac{x}{(x-1)}$

Example 4: Divide $\frac{x^2-4x-5}{x^2-4x+4} \div \frac{x^2-2x-15}{x^2+4x-12}$ and simplify for $x \neq 2, 5, -3$, or -6.

First, change to a multiplication expression: $\frac{x^2-4x-5}{x^2-4x+4} \cdot \frac{x^2+4x-12}{x^2-2x-15}$

Then factor each expression: $\frac{(x-5)(x+1)}{(x-2)(x-2)} \cdot \frac{(x-2)(x+6)}{(x-5)(x+3)}$

After multiplying, reorder the factors: $\frac{(x-5)}{(x-5)} \cdot \frac{(x-2)}{(x-2)} \cdot \frac{(x+1)}{(x-2)} \cdot \frac{(x+6)}{(x+3)}$

Since $\frac{(x-5)}{(x-5)} = 1$ and $\frac{(x-2)}{(x-2)} = 1$, simplify to get: $\frac{(x+1)(x+6)}{(x-2)(x+3)} \Rightarrow \frac{x^2+7x+6}{x^2+x-6}$

Note: From this point forward in the course, unless specifically asked, you may assume that all values of x that would make a denominator zero are excluded.

3-102. Estacia wants to learn more about excluded values.

a. Explain to Estacia why x cannot be 4 in the expression $\frac{x+2}{x-4}$.

b. Find the excluded values of x in each of the expressions of problem 3-99.

c. Create an expression that has the excluded values of $x \neq -6$ and $x \neq \frac{1}{3}$. Be prepared to share your expression to the class.

3-103. Use the methods developed in class to add or subtract the following rational expressions. Be sure to look for factors before trying to determine a common denominator, and simplify your answers, if possible.

a. $\frac{4x}{x^2-2x-8}+\frac{4}{x-4}$

b. $\frac{16x-12}{4x^2+5x-6}-\frac{3}{x+2}$

3-104. Solve the equations and inequalities below. Check your solutions, if possible.

a. $|5x+8| \geq -4$

b. $x^2+x-20<0$

c. $2x^2-6x=-5$

d. $\frac{5}{9}-\frac{x}{3}=\frac{4}{9}$

3-105. Simplify the rational expressions below as much as possible.

a. $\frac{(x-4)^3(2x-1)}{(2x-1)(x-4)^2}$

b. $\frac{7m^2-22m+3}{3m^2-7m-6}$

c. $\frac{(z+2)^9(4z-1)^7}{(z+2)^{10}(4z-1)^5}$

d. $\frac{(x+2)(x^2-6x+9)}{(x-3)(x^2-4)}$

3-106. Lexington High School has an annual growth rate of 4.7%. Three years ago there were 1500 students at the school.

a. How many students are there now?

b. How many students were there 5 years ago?

c. How many students will there be n years from now?

3-107. Multiply or divide the expressions below. Leave your answers as simplified as possible.

a. $\frac{(3x-1)(x+7)}{4(2x-5)} \cdot \frac{10(2x-5)}{(4x+1)(x+7)}$

b. $\frac{(m-3)(m+11)}{(2m+5)(m-3)} \div \frac{(4m-3)(m+11)}{(4m-3)(2m+5)}$

c. $\frac{2p^2+5p-12}{2p^2-5p+3} \cdot \frac{p^2+8p-9}{3p^2+10p-8}$

d. $\frac{4x-12}{x^2+3x-10} \div \frac{2x^2-13x+21}{2x^2+3x-35}$

3-108. Graph the function $g(x)=\frac{x+2}{x-1}$ on graph paper and name all x- and y-intercepts. What happens at $x=1$?

3-109. If $f(x)=3x-9$ and $g(x)=-x^2$, find:

a. $f(-2)$

b. $g(-2)$

c. x if $f(x)=0$

d. $g(m)$

3.2.5 Pulling it all together

Creating New Functions

In this lesson you will use all four operations of arithmetic to combine rational expressions. As you work with your team on the problems consider the following questions:

What operation are we using here and what steps will we need to take?

Is it possible to factor the numerators or denominators of the expressions?

How can we use the multiplication property of the "Giant One"?

What values of x must be excluded? How will that affect the graph?

Is our answer a rational expression?

3-110. PULLING IT ALL TOGETHER

You now know how to add, subtract, multiply, and divide rational expressions. Pull this all together by simplifying the following expressions.

a. $\frac{2x^2+x}{(2x+1)^2} - \frac{3}{2x+1}$

b. $\frac{x^2-3x-10}{x^2-4x-5} \div \frac{x^2-7x-18}{2x^2-5x-7}$

c. $\frac{15x-20}{x-5} \cdot \frac{x^2-2x-15}{3x^2+5x-12}$

d. $\frac{4}{2x+3} + \frac{x^2-x-2}{2x^2+5x+3}$

e. $\frac{6x-4}{3x^2-17x+10} - \frac{1}{x^2-2x-15}$

f. $\frac{x^2-x-2}{4x^2-7x-2} \div \frac{x^2-2x-3}{3x^2-8x-3}$

3-111. EXPLORING OPERATIONS WITH RATIONAL FUNCTIONS

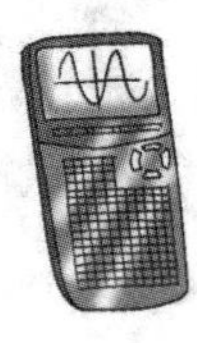

What will the graphs of the sum, difference, product or quotient of two rational functions look like? Graphs of rational functions can be very complicated and difficult to interpret using a graphing calculator, so you will work to get a glimpse of some of the simpler outcomes by using two fairly simple rational functions.

$$f(x)=\frac{1}{x-2} \text{ and } g(x)=\frac{1}{x+1}$$

a. Algebraically find $f(x)\cdot g(x)$ and write this as a single function without any parentheses.

b. Graph the simplified function from part (a), and simultaneously graph the function $f(x)\cdot g(x)$. Are the graphs the same? How can you be sure the graphs are the same, and one graph is not just "hiding" out of the window you chose?

c. The graphs should be the same. If they are not, check your algebra (and your input) to see what happened.

d. Algebraically find $f(x)+g(x)$, $f(x)-g(x)$, and $\frac{f(x)}{g(x)}$, and simplify the function.

e. Graph each of your simplified algebraic functions from part (d) simultaneously with the original operation on two functions. Check that the graphs are the same and correct any mistakes if necessary.

f. Along with exploring the shape of the various function operations, you have discovered a way to check you work when simplifying rational expressions. Check you answer to part (a) of problem 3-110.

3-112. Based on your limited experience with rational expressions so far, do you think that the set of all rational expressions is closed for each of the four operations, addition, subtraction, multiplication, and division? If so, what are some reasons you think so, and if not, why not? Discuss this question with your team and be prepared to defend your conjecture.

METHODS AND MEANINGS

Adding and Subtracting Rational Expressions

In order to add and subtract fractions, the fractions must have a common denominator. One way to do this is to change each fraction so that the denominator is the **least common multiple** of the denominators. For the example at right, the least common multiple of $(x+3)(x+2)$ and $x+2$ is $(x+3)(x+2)$.

$$\frac{4}{(x+2)(x+3)}+\frac{2x}{x+2}$$

The denominator of the first fraction already is the least common multiple. To get a common denominator in the second fraction, multiply the fraction by $\frac{(x+3)}{(x+3)}$, a "Giant One" (a form of the number 1).

$$=\frac{4}{(x+2)(x+3)}+\frac{2x}{x+2}\cdot\frac{(x+3)}{(x+3)}$$

Multiply the numerator and denominator of the second term.

$$=\frac{4}{(x+2)(x+3)}+\frac{2x(x+3)}{(x+2)(x+3)}$$

Distribute the numerator, if necessary.

$$=\frac{4}{(x+2)(x+3)}+\frac{2x^2+6x}{(x+2)(x+3)}$$

Add, factor, and simplify the result.

$$=\frac{2x^2+6x+4}{(x+2)(x+3)}=\frac{2(x+1)(x+2)}{(x+2)(x+3)}=\frac{2(x+1)}{(x+3)}$$

3-113. Add, subtract, multiply, or divide the following rational expressions. Simplify your answers, if possible.

a. $\frac{2x}{3x^2+16x+5}+\frac{10}{3x^2+16x+5}$

b. $\frac{x^2-x-12}{3x^2-11x-4}\cdot\frac{3x^2-20x-7}{x^2-9}$

c. $\frac{2x^2+8x-10}{2x^2+15x+25}\div\frac{4x^2+20x-24}{2x^2+x-10}$

d. $\frac{7}{x+5}-\frac{4-6x}{x^2+10x+25}$

3-114. Examine the graph of $f(x)=|x-3|+1$ at right. Use the graph to find the values listed below.

a. $f(3)$

b. $f(0)$

c. $f(4)$

d. $f(-1)$

3-115. Use the graph of $f(x)=|x-3|+1$ in problem 3-114 to solve the equations and inequalities below. It may be helpful to copy the graph onto graph paper first.

a. $|x-3|+1=1$

b. $|x-3|+1 \leq 4$

c. $|x-3|+1=3$

d. $|x-3|+1>2$

3-116. This problem is a checkpoint for using function notation and identifying domain and range. It will be referred to as Checkpoint 3B.

Given $g(x)=2(x+3)^2$, state the domain and range, calculate $g(-5)$ and $g(a+1)$, and then find the value of x when $g(x)=32$ and when $g(x)=0$.

Check your answers by referring to the Checkpoint 3B materials located at the back of your book.

If you needed help solving these problems correctly, then you need more practice. Review the Checkpoint 3B materials and try the practice problems. Also, consider getting help outside of class time. From this point on, you will be expected to do problems like these quickly and easily.

3-117. Solve the quadratic below *twice*: once by factoring and using the Zero Product Property and once by completing the square. Verify that the solutions match.

$$x^2+14x+33=0$$

3-118. Match each graph below with its domain.

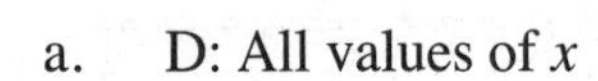

a. D: All values of x

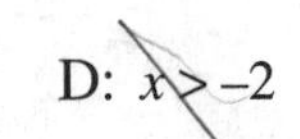

b. D: $x>-2$

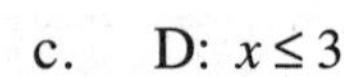

c. D: $x \leq 3$

1)

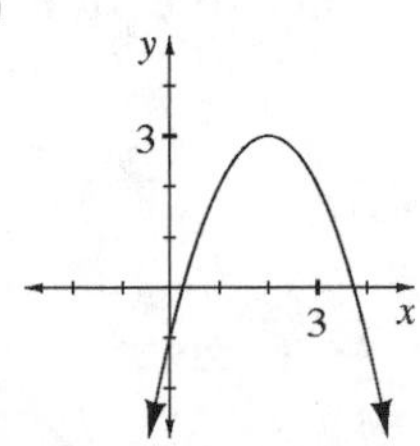

2)

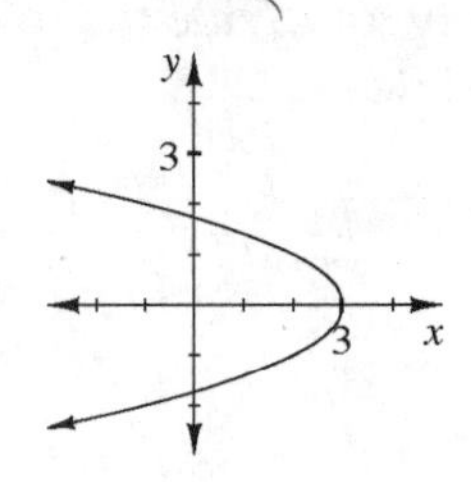

3)

3-119. Graph the two functions below and find all points where they intersect. List all points in the form (x, y).

$$f(x)=x^2-3x-10$$

$$g(x)=-5x-7$$

3-120. Simplify each expression.

a. $\frac{1}{x+2}+\frac{3}{x^2-4}$

b. $\frac{3}{2x+4}-\frac{x}{x^2+4x+4}$

c. $\frac{x^2+5x+6}{x^2-9}\cdot\frac{x-3}{x^2+2x}$

d. $\frac{4}{x-2}\div\frac{8}{2-x}$

3-121. Solve $\sqrt{x+2}=8$ and check your solution.

3-122. Use each pair of points given below to write a system of equations in $y=mx+b$ form to find the equation of a line that passes through the points.

a. (20, 2) and (32, –4)

b. (–3, –17) and (12, –7)

3-123. Phana's garden is 2 meters wide and 5 meters long. She puts a walkway of uniform width around her garden. If the area of the walkway is 30 square meters, what are the outer dimensions of the walkway? Drawing a diagram will help you solve this problem.

3-124. Leadfoot Lilly was driving 80 miles per hour when she passed a parked highway patrol car. By the time she was half a mile past the spot where the patrol car was parked, the officer was driving after her at 100 miles per hour. If these rates remain constant, how long will it take the officer to catch up to Lilly? Write and solve an equation to represent this situation.

3-125. Two congruent overlapping squares are shown at right. If a point inside the figure is chosen at random, what is the probability that it will *not* be in the shaded region?

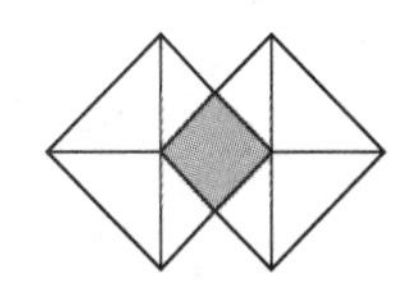

3-126. Factor each expression completely.

a. $25x^2-1$

b. $5x^3-125x$

c. x^2+x-72

d. x^3-3x^2-18x

Chapter 3 Closure What have I learned?

Reflection and Synthesis

The activities below offer you a chance to reflect about what you have learned during this chapter. As you work, look for concepts that you feel very comfortable with, ideas that you would like to learn more about, and topics you need more help with. Look for connections between ideas as well as connections with material you learned previously.

① TEAM BRAINSTORM

What have you studied in this chapter? What ideas were important in what you learned? With your team, brainstorm a list. Be as detailed as you can. To help get you started, a list of Learning Log entries and Math Notes boxes are below.

What topics, ideas, and words that you learned *before* this chapter are connected to the new ideas in this chapter? Again, be as detailed as you can.

How long can you make your list? Challenge yourselves. Be prepared to share your team's ideas with the class.

Learning Log Entries

- Lesson 3.1.1 – Equivalent Expressions
- Lesson 3.2.2 – Simplifying Rational Expressions
  Lesson 3.2.3 – Multiplying and Dividing Rational Expressions
- Lesson 3.2.4 – Adding and Subtracting Rational Expressions

Math Notes

- Lesson 3.1.3 – Vocabulary for Expressions
- Lesson 3.2.4 – Rewriting Rational Expressions
- Lesson 3.2.5 – Adding and Subtracting Rational Expressions

② MAKING CONNECTIONS

Below is a list of the vocabulary used in this chapter. Make sure that you are familiar with all of these words and know what they mean. Refer to the glossary or index for any words that you do not yet understand.

closed set	coefficient	constant term
difference of squares	equivalent	equation
excluded value	exponent	expression
factor	function	Giant One
least common denominator	polynomial	rational expression
rational function	rewrite	simplify
substitution	term	

Make a concept map showing all of the connections you can find among the key words and ideas listed above. To show a connection between two words, draw a line between them and explain the connection. A word can be connected to any other word as long as you can justify the connection.

While you are making your map, your team may think of related words or ideas that are not listed here. Be sure to include these ideas on your concept map.

③ PORTFOLIO: EVIDENCE OF MATHEMATICAL PROFICIENCY

This section gives you an opportunity to show growth in your understanding of key mathematical ideas over time as you complete this course.

Your team has been assigned the task of preparing a set of directions for future algebra students on how to perform operations with rational expressions. Your assignment is to select one rational expressions addition or subtraction problem and one rational expressions multiplication or division problem from the chapter. Show step-by-step how to do the two problems you have selected. Next to each step, include an explanation of why you are making that step. You want to be sure your result is correct, so use a graphing tool to check your answer by comparing the graph of the original problem and with the graph of your answer.

A student who has just enrolled in an Algebra 2 class needs help understanding why $(x+y)^2 = x^2 + 2xy + y^2$. She thinks that $(x+y)^2 = x^2 + y^2$. Justify why $(x+y)^2 = x^2 + 2xy + y^2$ so that she is convinced that your answer is correct.

④ WHAT HAVE I LEARNED?

Most of the problems in this section represent typical problems found in this chapter. They serve as a gauge for you. You can use them to determine which types of problems you can do well and which types of problems require further study and practice. Even if your teacher does not assign this section, it is a good idea to try these problems and find out for yourself what you know and what you still need to work on.

Solve each problem as completely as you can. The table at the end of the closure section has answers to these problems. It also tells you where you can find additional help and practice with problems like these.

CL 3-127. Solve the following systems algebraically. What does each solution reveal about the graph of the equations in the system?

a. $x+2y=17$
$x-y=2$

b. $4x+5y=11$
$2x+6y=16$

c. $4x-3y=-10$
$x=\frac{1}{4}y-1$

d. $2x+y=-2x+5$
$3x+2y=2x+3y$

CL 3-128. Solve each equation after first rewriting it in a simpler equivalent form.

a. $3(2x-1)+12=4x-3$

b. $\frac{3x}{7}+\frac{2}{7}=2$

c. $\frac{3}{4}x^2=\frac{5}{4}x+\frac{1}{2}$

d. $4x(x-2)=(2x+1)(2x-3)$

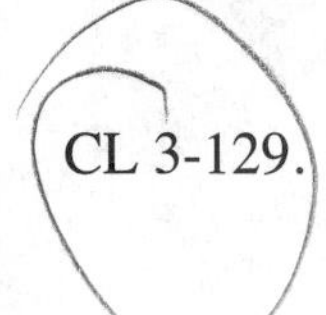

CL 3-129. Which of the following pairs of equations or expressions are equivalent? Justify your reasoning either by using algebra to transform the first equation or expression into the second or by demonstrating with a counterexample.

a. $n(2n+1)(2n-1)$; $4n^2-n$

b. $(2x-1)^2$; $4x^2-1$

c. $10x^2-55x-105$; $5(2x+3)(x-7)$

d. $\left(\frac{4x^{12}}{-2x^8}\right)^3$; $-8x^{12}$

e. $2x-3y=6$; $y=\frac{2}{3}x+6$

f. $\sqrt{108}$; $6\sqrt{3}$

CL 3-130. Perform the indicated operation on each of the following rational expressions. Be sure to state any values of the excluded variable and that your final answer is simplified. If a graphing tool is available, check the graph of the original problem to see if it coincides with the graph of your answer.

a. $\dfrac{x^2-x-6}{x^2-9}\cdot\dfrac{x^2+5x+6}{x^2+4x+4}$

b. $\dfrac{\frac{x^2-1}{x}}{\frac{x^2-2x+1}{2x^2+x}}$

CL 3-131. Evan spent the summer earning money so he could buy the classic car of his dreams. He purchased the car for $2295 from Fast Deal Freddie, the local used car salesman. Freddie told Evan that the car would increase by half its value after five years. Evan knows that this model appreciates 8% annually. Did Freddie try to trick Evan, or was his claim accurate?

CL 3-132. Decide whether each function below is even, odd or neither, and explain your reasoning.

a. $y=x^3+x$

b. $y=x^2+x$

c. $y=x^4+x^2$

CL 3-133. First, identify the parent graphs of the following equations. Then, describe how their graphs would be transformed from the parent graphs.

a. $y=0.25(x-8)^3+2$

b. $(x+3)^2+y^2=25$

c. $y=|x-5|+3$

CL 3-134. Last year, Jennifer paid the following for her electricity based on the number of kWh (kilowatt-hours) that she used each month.

kWh used	0 – 20,000	20,000 +
Cost per kWh (cents)	9.1225	6.5714

a. Make a graph of Jennifer's electrical rates.

b. Describe the domain of each of the pieces of this function. Then write an equation for each part of the domain.

c. This year the electrical company has said it is going to raise its rates by 3%. Describe how this will transform the graph and then write new equations for each part of the domain.

CL 3-135. Describe the domain and range of each function or sequence below.

a. The function $f(x)=(x-2)^2$.

b. The sequence $t(n)=3n-5$.

CL 3-136. Find the x- and y-intercepts of $y=x^2-3x-3$.

CL 3-137. Check your answers using the table at the end of this section. Which problems do you feel confident about? Which problems were hard? Have you worked on problems like these in math classes you have taken before? Use the table to make a list of topics you need help on and a list of topics you need to practice more.

Answers and Support for Closure Activity #4

What Have I Learned?

Note: MN = Math Note, LL = Learning Log

Problem	Solutions	Need Help?	More Practice
CL 3-127.	a. $(7,5)$ b. $(-1,3)$ c. $(-\frac{1}{4},3)$ d. $(1,1)$	Lesson 1.1.3 Checkpoint 2B	Problems 3-9, 3-64, and 3-93
CL 3-128.	a. -6 b. 4 c. $(-\frac{1}{3},2)$ d. $\frac{3}{4}$	Lesson 2.2.3	Problems 3-25, 3-38, 3-43, 3-45, 3-51, 3-68, and 3-80
CL 3-129.	Methods vary. Sample answers below. a. $n(2n+1)(2n-1)=(2n^2+n)(2n-1)$ $=4n^3-2n^2+2n^2-n=4n^3-n$ Not equivalent b. $(2x-1)^2=(2x-1)(2x-1)$ $=4x^2-2x-2x+1=4x^2-4x+1$ Not equivalent c. $10x^2-55x-105=5(2x^2-11x-21)$ $=5(2x+3)(x-7)$ Equivalent d. $(\frac{4x^{12}}{-2x^8})^3=\frac{4^3x^{36}}{(-2)^3x^{24}}=\frac{64x^{(36-24)}}{-8}$ $=-8x^{12}$ Equivalent e. $2x-3y=6$, $-3y=-2x+6$, $y=\frac{2}{3}x-2$ Not equivalent f. $\sqrt{108}=\sqrt{36\cdot3}=\sqrt{6^2\cdot3}=6\sqrt{3}$ Equivalent	Lessons 2.2.1 and 2.2.2	Problems 3-2, 3-3, 3-5, 3-6, 3-15, 3-16, 3-41, and 3-46
CL 3-130.	a. 1 b. $\frac{(x+1)(2x+1)}{(x-1)}=\frac{2x^2+3x+1}{x-1}$	Lessons 3.2.2 and 3.2.3	Problems 3-78, 3-90, 3-91, and 3-113
CL 3-131.	$y=(1.08)^t$ so when $t=5$, $y\approx1.46$ which is about 1.5, so Freddie's claim was fairly accurate.	Lessons A.3.2 and B.2.3	Problems 3-49, 3-65, and 3-94

Problem	Solutions	Need Help?	More Practice
CL 3-132.	a. odd, $f(-x)=-f(x)$ b. neither, $f(-x)$ does not equal $f(x)$ or $-f(x)$ c. even, $f(-x)=f(x)$	Lesson 2.2.3 MN: 2.2.5 LL: 2.2.3	Problems 3-9, 3-29, 3-33, and 3-51
CL 3-133.	a. parent: $y=x^3$; cubic shifted up 2 and right 8 and compressed by a factor of 0.25 b. parent: $x^2+y^2=r^2$; circle with center at $(-3,0)$ and radius of 5 c. parent: $y=\|x\|$; absolute value shifted up 3 and right 5	Lessons 2.2.1, 2.2.2, 2.2.3, and 2.2.4	Problems 3-4, 3-5, 3-35, 3-54, and 3-83
CL 3-134.	a. y; 240000; 160000; 80000; 20000; x b. $0 \le x \le 20{,}000$ and $x > 20{,}000$; $f_1(x)=9.1225x$ and $f_2(x)=6.5714x$ c. The slope of the lines will change. $f_1(x)=9.3962x$ and $f_2(x)=6.7685x$	Lesson 2.2.5	Problems 3-34, 3-56, 3-116, and 3-118
CL 3-135.	a. Domain: all real numbers Range: $y \ge 0$ b. Domain: all positive whole numbers; Range: all numbers of the form $3n-5$	Lesson 1.1.3 Checkpoint 3B MN: 1.1.3	Problems 1-34, 1-62, 1-109, 2-4, 2-108, 3-8, 3-31, and 3-84
CL 3-136.	x-intercepts: $(\frac{3+\sqrt{21}}{2}, 0)$ and $(\frac{3-\sqrt{21}}{2}, 0)$ y-intercept: $(0,-3)$	MN: 1.1.4	Problems 1-48, 1-106, and 3-28

SOLVING AND INTERSECTIONS
4

Chapter 4 Solving and Intersections

This chapter begins with a focus on two ways to solve equations and systems of equations: algebraically and graphically. You will build on your understanding of solving and solutions from previous courses to gain a broader and stronger understanding of the meaning of solutions.

In Section 4.2, you will expand your understanding of solving and solutions to include inequalities. You will solve problems designed to illustrate how inequalities might be used for more complicated applications.

Guiding Question

Mathematically proficient students use appropriate tools strategically.

As you work through this chapter, ask yourself:

Which tools can I use to solve the problems and verify my solutions?

Chapter Outline

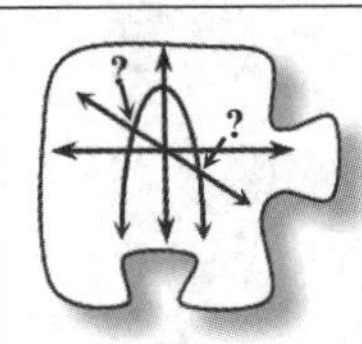

Section 4.1 In this section, you will write and solve equations and systems of equations. You will develop algebraic and graphical methods for solving and you will gain a broader understanding of the meaning of solutions. You will learn multiple ways to understand the meaning of solutions.

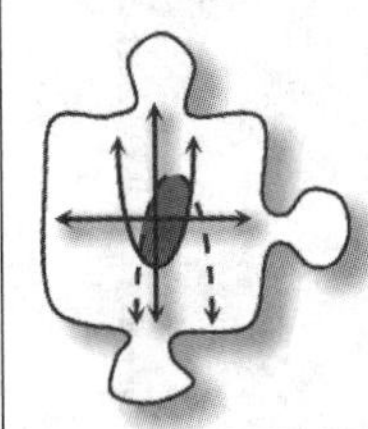

Section 4.2 Here you will extend your understanding of solving and solutions to include inequalities and systems of inequalities.

4.1.1 How can I solve?

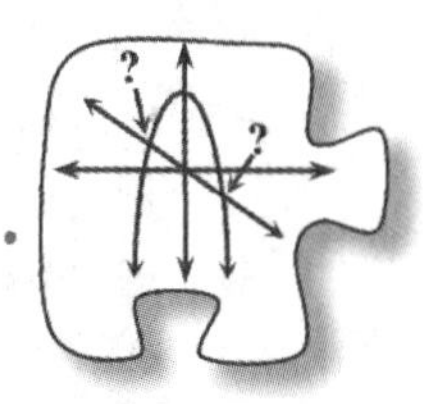

Strategies for Solving Equations

Today you will have the opportunity to solve challenging equations. As you work with your team, the goal of this section is for you to apply your strategies for solving equations to other types of equations. You will be challenged to use multiple approaches and to write clear explanations to show your understanding.

4-1. SOLVING GRAPHICALLY

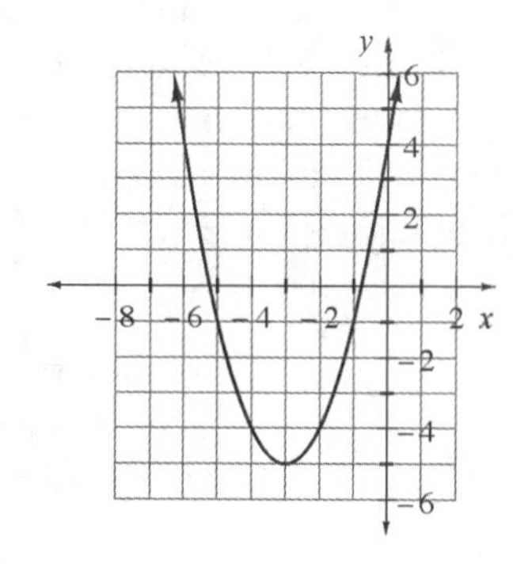

One of the big questions of Chapter 2 was how to the find special points of a function. For example, you now have the skills to look at an equation of a parabola written in graphing form and name its vertex quickly. But what about the locations of other points on the parabola? Consider the graph of $y=(x+3)^2-5$ at right.

a. How many solutions does the equation $y=(x+3)^2-5$ have? How is this shown on the graph?

b. Use the graph to solve the equation $(x+3)^2-5=4$. How did the graph help you solve the equation?

4-2. ALGEBRAIC STRATEGIES

The graph in problem 4-1 was useful to solve an equation like $(x+3)^2-5=4$. But what if you do not have an accurate graph? And what can you do when the solution is not on a grid point or is off your graph?

Your Task: Solve the equation below algebraically (that is, using the equation only and without a graph) in at least three different ways. The "Discussion Points" below are provided to help you get started. Be ready to share your strategies with the class.

$$(x+3)^2-5=4$$

Discussion Points

What algebraic strategies might be useful?

What makes this equation look challenging? How can we make the equation simpler?

How can we be sure that our strategy helps us find *all* possible solutions?

4-3. Three strategies your class or team may have used in problem 4-2 are **Rewriting** (using algebra to write a new equivalent equation that is easier to solve), **Looking Inside** (reasoning about the value of the expression inside the function or parentheses), and **Undoing** (reversing or doing the opposite of an operation; for example, taking the square root to eliminate squaring). These strategies and others will be useful throughout the rest of this course. Examine how each of these strategies can be used to solve the equation below by completing parts (a) through (f).

$$\frac{x-5}{4}+\frac{2}{5}=\frac{9}{10}$$

a. Ernie decided to multiply both sides of the equation by 20 so that his equation becomes $5(x-5)+8=18$. Which strategy did Ernie use? How can you tell?

b. Elle took Ernie's equation and decided to subtract 8 from both sides to get $5(x-5)=10$. Which strategy did Elle use?

c. Eric looked at Elle's equation and said, "*I can tell that (x – 5) must equal 2 because 5 • 2 = 10. Therefore, if x – 5 = 2, then x must be 7.*" What strategy did Eric use?

d. How many solutions does the function $y=\frac{x-5}{4}+\frac{2}{5}$ have? How can you use the graph of $y=\frac{x-5}{4}+\frac{2}{5}$ on your graphing calculator to check your solution to $\frac{x-5}{4}+\frac{2}{5}=\frac{9}{10}$? Where did you look on the graph?

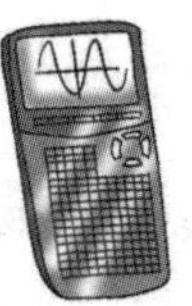

e. How can you use the table for $y=\frac{x-5}{4}+\frac{2}{5}$ on your graphing calculator to check your answer? Where did you look on the table?

f. Use the strategies from parts (a) through (c) in a different way to solve $\frac{x-5}{4}+\frac{2}{5}=\frac{9}{10}$. Did you get the same result?

4-4. Solve each equation below, if possible, using any strategy. Check with your teammates to see what strategies they chose. Be sure to check your solutions.

a. $4|8x-2|=8$

b. $3\sqrt{4x-8}+9=15$

c. $(x-3)^2-2=-5$

d. $(2y-3)(y-2)=-12y+18$

e. $\frac{5}{x}+\frac{1}{3x}=\frac{4x}{3}$

f. $|3-7x|=-6$

g. $\frac{6w-1}{5}-3w=\frac{12w-16}{15}$

h. $(x+2)^2+4(x+2)-5=0$

4-5. Some of the solutions from the previous problem can quickly be checked with a graph or table on the graphing calculator. Check the answers for those problems with your graphing calculator.

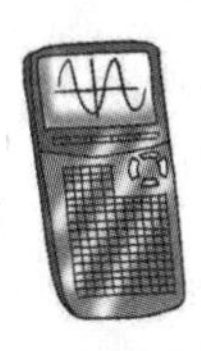

4-6. LEARNING LOG

Create a Learning Log entry about all of the solving strategies you saw today. For each strategy, provide an example and explain which types of equations work best with that strategy. Title this entry "Strategies for Solving Equations" and label it with today's date.

4-7. Solve $(x-2)^2-3=1$ graphically. That is, graph $y=(x-2)^2-3$ and $y=1$ on the same set of axes and find the x-value(s) of any points of intersection. Then use algebraic strategies to solve the equation and verify that your graphical solutions are correct.

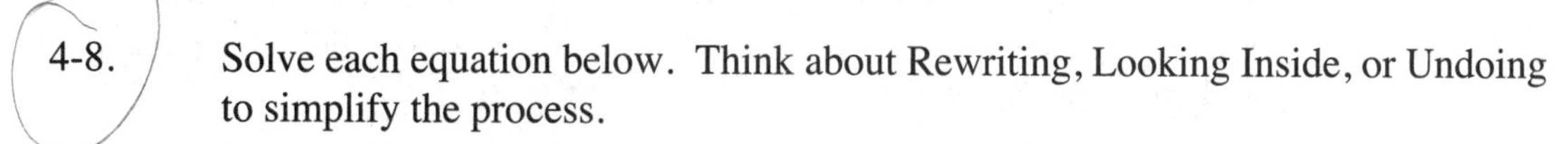

4-8. Solve each equation below. Think about Rewriting, Looking Inside, or Undoing to simplify the process.

a. $2(x-1)^2+7=39$

b. $7(\sqrt{m+1}-3)=21$

c. $\frac{x}{2}+\frac{x}{3}=\frac{5x+2}{6}$

d. $-7+(\frac{4x+2}{2})=8$

4-9. Find the equation of the line that passes through $(0, 2)$ and $(5, 2)$. Then complete parts (a) and (b) below.

a. What is the equation of the x-axis?

b. What is the equation of the y-axis?

4-10. Solve the system of equations shown at right.

$$2x+6y=10$$
$$x=8-3y$$

a. Describe what happened when you tried to solve the system.

b. Draw the graph of the system.

c. How does the graph of the system explain what happened with the equations? Make your answer as clear and thorough as possible.

4-11. Classify the triangle with vertices $A(3,2)$, $B(-2,0)$, and $C(-1,4)$ by finding the length of each side. Be sure to consider all possible triangle types. Include sufficient evidence to support your conclusion.

4-12. Examine the figures at right, and then visualize the figure for $n=4$.

a. How many cubes are in the figure for $n=4$?

b. How many cubes are in the figure for $n=1$?

c. Find the general equation for the number of cubes for any n. Verify your formula with the cases of $n=1$ and $n=5$.

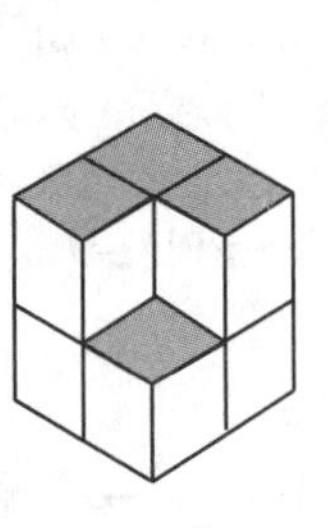

$n=2$

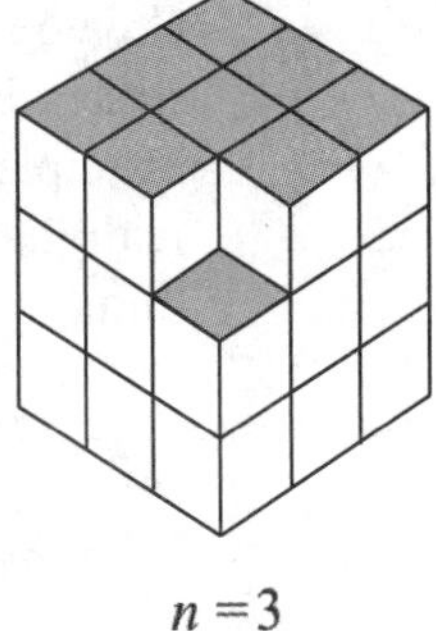

$n=3$

d. Is the sequence arithmetic, geometric, or neither? Explain your reasoning.

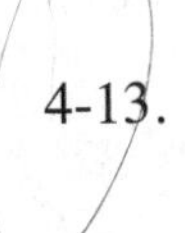

4-13. Simplify each of the expressions below. Express your answers as simply as possible.

a. $\frac{5x^2-11x+2}{x^2+8x+16} \cdot \frac{x^2+10x+24}{10x^2+13x-3}$

b. $\frac{6x+3}{2x-3} \div \frac{3x^2-12x-15}{2x^2-x-3}$

c. $\frac{5m+18}{m+3} + \frac{4m+9}{m+3}$

d. $\frac{3a^2+a-1}{a^2-2a+1} - \frac{2a^2-a+2}{a^2-2a+1}$

4-14. The graph of a line and an exponential can intersect twice, once, or not at all. Describe the possible number of intersections for each of the following pairs of graphs. Your solution to each part should include all of the possibilities and a quickly sketched example of each one.

a. A line and a parabola

b. Two different parabolas

c. A parabola and a circle

d. A parabola and the hyperbola $y=\frac{1}{x}$

4.1.2 How can I use a graph to solve?

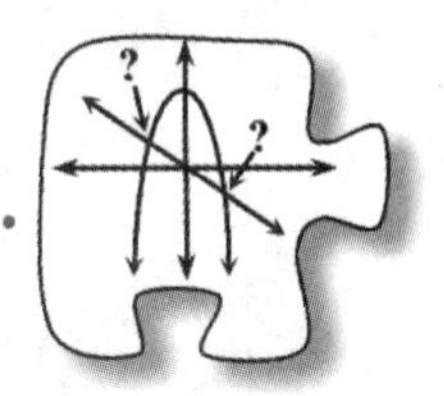

Solving Equations and Systems Graphically

In the previous lesson, you used and named three algebraic methods to solve different kinds of equations. In today's lesson, you will again solve equations, but this time you will use your understanding of graphs, as well as your algebra skills, to solve the equations and to verify your results.

4-15. In problem 4-1, you used a graph to solve an equation. In what other ways can a graph be a useful solution tool? Consider this question as you solve the equation $\sqrt{2x+3}=x$ by completing parts (a) through (d) below.

a. Use algebraic strategies to solve $\sqrt{2x+3}=x$. How many solutions did you find? Which strategies did you use?

b. In thinking about $\sqrt{2x+3}=x$, Miranda wrote down $y=\sqrt{2x+3}$ and $y=x$. How many solutions does $y=\sqrt{2x+3}$ have? How many solutions does $y=x$ have?

c. Miranda said, "*I'll graph both the functions* $y=\sqrt{2x+3}$ *and* $y=x$ *to check the solutions from part (a).*" How will graphing help her find the solution?

d. Miranda looked at the graph on her graphing calculator and said "*I think something is wrong.*" What happened? Graph the system on your graphing calculator and find the intersection(s) of the functions. How many solutions does this equation have?

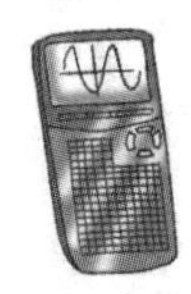

4-16. When a result from an equation-solving process does not make the original equation true, it is called an **extraneous solution**. It is not a solution of the equation, even though it is a result when solving algebraically.

Check your two solutions from part (a) of problem 4-15 algebraically.

4-17. The fact that extraneous solutions can arise after following straightforward solving techniques makes it especially important to check your solutions!

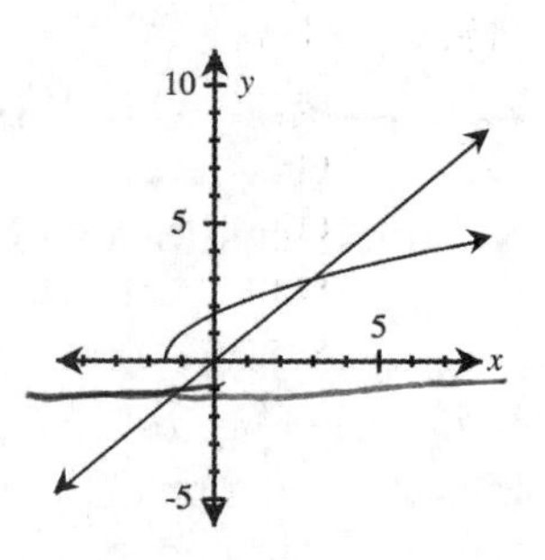

But why did the extraneous solution appear in this problem? Examine the graph of the system of equations $y=\sqrt{2x+3}$ and $y=x$, shown at right. Where would an extraneous solution $x=-1$ appear on the graph? Why do the graphs not intersect at that point? Explain.

4-18. After solving the equation $2x^2+5x-3=x^2+4x+3$, Gustav got called to the office and left his team. When his teammates examined his graphing calculator to try to find out how he found his solution, they only saw the graph of $y=x^2+x-6$. Consider this situation as you answer the questions below.

a. How many solutions do you predict $2x^2+5x-3=x^2+4x+3$ will have?

b. Solve $2x^2+5x-3=x^2+4x+3$ algebraically.

c. Where did Gustav get the equation $y=x^2+x-6$? How many solutions will $y=x^2+x-6$ have?

d. How can you see the solutions to $2x^2+5x-3=x^2+4x+3$ in the graph of $y=x^2+x-6$? Explain why this makes sense.

e. Maiya solved $2x^2+5x-3=x^2+4x+3$ by graphing a system of equations and looking for the points of intersection. What equations do you think she used? Graph these equations on your graphing calculator and explain where the solutions to the equation exist on the graph.

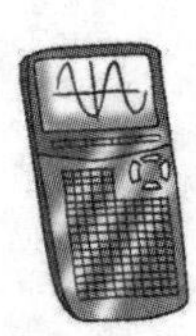

4-19. Karen could not figure out how to solve $20x+1=3^x$ algebraically, so she decided to use her graphing calculator. However, after she finished entering the equations $y=20x+1$ and $y=3^x$, she got the graph shown at right. After studying the graph, Karen suspects there are no solutions to $20x+1=3^x$.

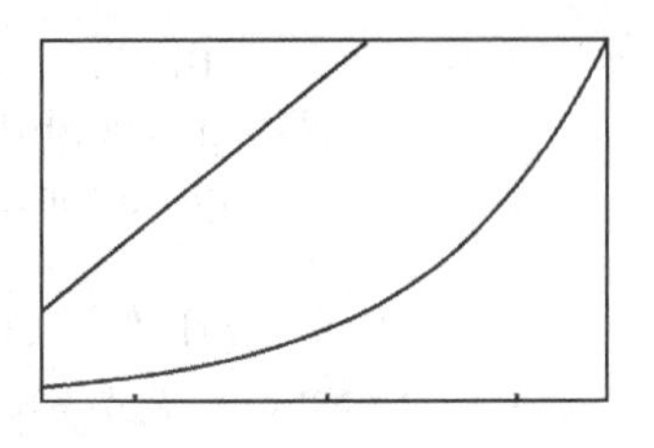

a. What do you think? If there are solutions, find them and prove that they are solutions. If there are no solutions, demonstrate that there cannot be a solution.

b. What should solutions to the equation, $20x+1=3^x$ look like? In other words, will solutions be a single number, or should they be the coordinates of a point? Explain.

c. Elana started to solve first by subtracting 1 from both sides of her equation. So when she graphed her system later, she used the equations $y=20x$ and $y=3^x-1$. Should she get the same solutions? Test your conclusion with your graphing calculator.

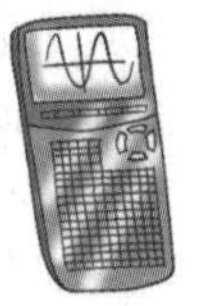

d. Discuss with your team why Karen could not solve the system algebraically. What do you think?

4-20. Jack was working on solving an equation and he graphed the functions $f(x)=\frac{12}{x}$ and $g(x)=-(x-3)^2+4$, as shown at right.

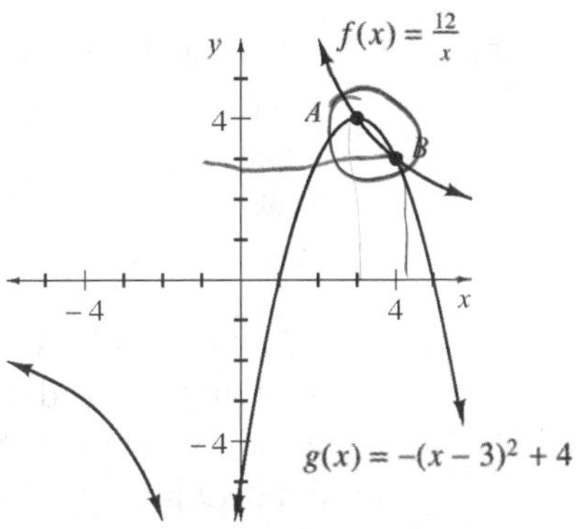

a. What equation was Jack solving?

b. Use points A and B to solve the equation you wrote in part (a).

c. Are there any other solutions to this same equation that are represented by neither point A nor point B? If so, show that these other solutions make your equation true.

4-21. LEARNING LOG

What does the solution to an equation mean? Do you have any new ideas about solutions that you did not have before? Create a Learning Log entry that explains the meaning of a solution in as many ways as possible. Title this entry "The Meaning of a Solution, Part 1" (Parts 2 and 3 will be coming later) and label it with today's date.

4-22. Solve $(x-3)^2 - 2 = x+1$ graphically. Is there more than one way to do this? Explain.

4-23. Graph a system of equations to solve $2|x-4|-3 = \frac{2}{3}x - 3$. Show your solutions clearly on your graph.

4-24. Solve each of the following equations using any method. Be sure to check your solutions.

a. $-3\sqrt{2x-5}+7=-8$

b. $2|3x+4|-10=12$

4-25. Ted needs to find the point of intersection for the lines $y = 18x - 30$ and $y = -22x + 50$. He takes out a piece of graph paper and then realizes that he can solve this problem without graphing. Explain how Ted is going to accomplish this, and then find the point of intersection.

4-26. Consider the arithmetic sequence $2, a-b, a+b, 35, \ldots$. Find a and b.

4-27. Solve the following equations. Be sure to check your answers for any extraneous solutions.

a. $\sqrt{2x-1}-x=-8$

b. $\sqrt{2x-1}-x=0$

4-28. Find the value of x.

a.

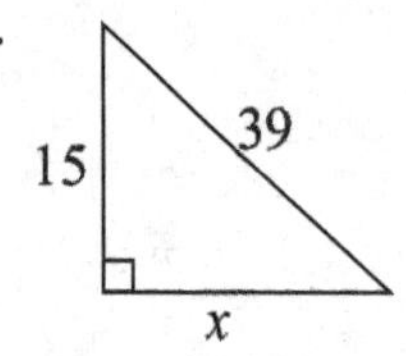

b.

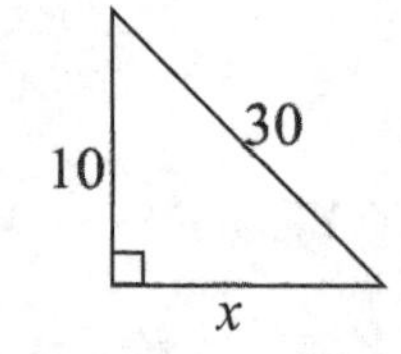

4-29. Solve $3x-1=2^x$ graphically. Could you solve this equation algebraically? Explain.

4-30. Consider the graphs of $f(x)=\frac{1}{2}(x-2)^3+1$ and $g(x)=2x^2-6x-3$ at right.

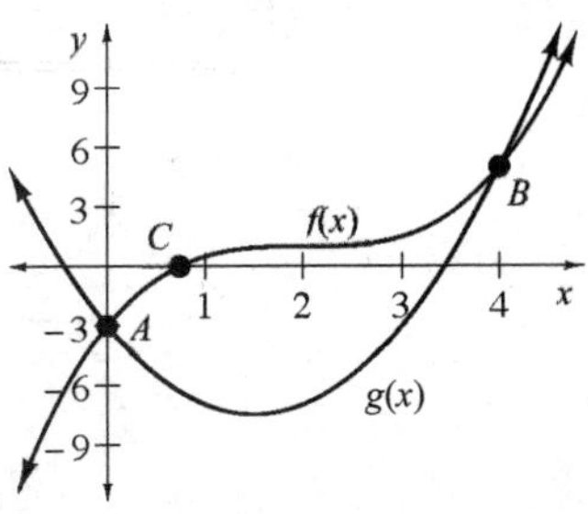

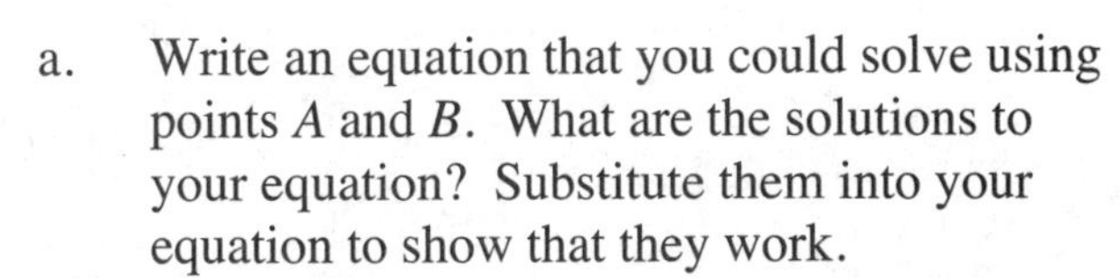

a. Write an equation that you could solve using points A and B. What are the solutions to your equation? Substitute them into your equation to show that they work.

b. Are there any solutions to the equation in part (a) that do not appear on the graph? Explain.

c. Write an equation that you could solve using point C. What does the solution to your equation appear to be? Again, substitute your solution into the equation. How close was your estimate?

d. What are the domains and ranges of $f(x)$ and $g(x)$?

4-31. Solve each of the following equations using any method.

a. $2(x+3)^2-5=-5$

b. $3(x-2)^2+6=9$

c. $|2x-5|-6=15$

d. $3\sqrt{5x-2}+1=7$

4-32. Solve each of the following equations for the indicated variable.

a. $5x-3y=12$ for y

b. $F=\frac{Gm_1m_2}{r^2}$ for m_2

c. $E=\frac{1}{2}mv^2$ for m

d. $(x-4)^2+(y-1)^2=10$ for y

4-33. Paul states that $(a+b)^2$ is equivalent to a^2+b^2. Joyce thinks that something is missing. Help Joyce show Paul that the two expressions are not equivalent. Explain using at least two different approaches: diagrams, algebra, numbers, or words.

4-34. Graph each of the following equations. (Keep the graphs handy, because you will need them for your homework for Lesson 4.1.3.)

a. $y=|x|$

b. $|y|=x$

c. How are the two graphs similar? How are they different?

d. What are the domain and range of each relation?

4-35. Find the value of x.

a.

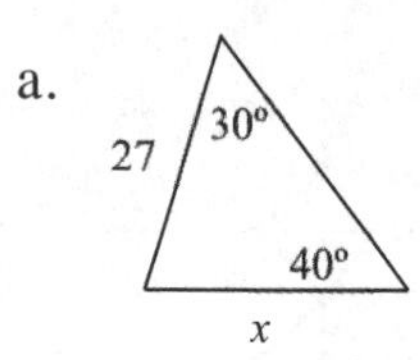

b.

81

27° 39°

x

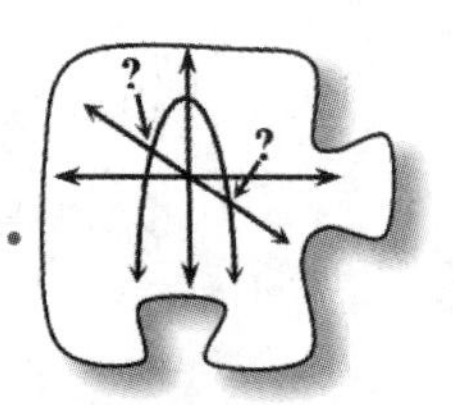

4.1.3 How many solutions are there?

Finding Multiple Solutions to Systems of Equations

You have used many different solving strategies to find solutions of equations with one variable both algebraically and graphically. You have also worked with systems of two equations with two variables. In this lesson, you will use your algebraic and graphing tools to determine the number of solutions that various systems have and to determine the meaning of those solutions.

4-36. Solve each system of equations below without graphing. For each one, explain what the solution (or lack thereof) tells you about the graph of the system.

a. $y = -3x + 5$
$y = -3x - 1$

b. $y = \frac{1}{2}x^2 + 1$
$y = 2x - 1$

c. $y^2 = x$
$y = x - 2$

d. $4x - 2y = 10$
$y = 2x - 5$

4-37. Now consider the system shown at right.

$$x^2 + y^2 = 25$$
$$y = x^2 - 13$$

a. How many solutions do you expect this system to have? Explain how you made your prediction.

b. Solve this system by graphing. How many solutions did you find? Was your prediction in part (a) correct?

c. Find a way to combine these equations to create a new equation so that the only variable is x. Then find another way to combine $x^2 + y^2 = 25$ and $y = x^2 - 13$ to form a different equation that contains only the variable y. Which of these equations would be easier to solve? Why?

d. If you have not already done so, solve one of the combined equations from part (c). If solving becomes too difficult, you may want to switch to the other combined equation.

4-38. In problem 4-37, you analyzed the system shown at right.

$$x^2 + y^2 = 25$$
$$y = x^2 - 13$$

a. What minor adjustments can you make to an equation (or both equations) in this system so that the new system has no solutions? Have each member of your team find a different way to alter the system. Justify that your system has no solution algebraically. Also, be ready to share your strategies for changing the system along with your justification with the class.

b. Work with your team to alter the system three more times so that the new systems have 3, 2, or 1 solution. For each new system that your team creates, solve the system algebraically to study how the algebraic solution helps indicate how many solutions will be possible. Be prepared to explain what different situations occur during solving that result in a different number of solutions.

4-39. LEARNING LOG

Look over your work from today. Name all of the strategies you used to solve systems of equations. Which strategies were most useful for solving linear systems? What about non-linear systems? Write a Learning Log entry describing your ideas about solving systems. Title this entry "Finding Solutions to Systems" and label it with today's date.

4-40. Solve each of the following systems algebraically. What do the solutions tell you about each system? Visualizing the graphs may help with your description.

a. $y = 3x - 5$
$y = -2x - 15$

b. $y - 7 = -2x$
$4x + 2y = 14$

c. $y = 2(x+3)^2 - 5$
$y = 14x + 17$

d. $y = 3(x-2)^2 + 3$
$y = 6x - 12$

4-41. Solve each equation below. Think about rewriting, looking inside, or undoing to simplify the process.

a. $3(y+1)^2 - 5 = 43$

b. $\sqrt{1-4x} = 10$

c. $\frac{6y-1}{y} - 3 = 2$

d. $\sqrt[3]{1-2x} = 3$

4-42. This problem is a checkpoint for writing equations for arithmetic and geometric sequences. It will be referred to as Checkpoint 4A.

a. Write an explicit and recursive rule for $t(n) = 1, 4, 7, 10, \ldots$

b. Write an explicit and recursive rule for $t(n) = 3, \frac{3}{2}, \frac{3}{4}, \frac{3}{8}, \ldots$

In parts (c) and (d), write an explicit rule for the sequence given in the $n \rightarrow t(n)$ tables.

c. An arithmetic sequence

n	$t(n)$
0	
1	17
2	
3	3
4	

d. A geometric sequence

n	$t(n)$
0	
1	
2	7.2
3	8.64
4	

e. If an arithmetic sequence has $t(7) = 1056$ and $t(12) = 116$, what is $t(4)$?

Check your answers by referring to the Checkpoint 4A materials located at the back of your book.

If you needed help solving these problems correctly, then you need more practice. Review the Checkpoint 4A materials and try the practice problems. Also, consider getting help outside of class time. From this point on, you will be expected to do problems like these quickly and easily.

4-43. Wet World has an 18-foot-long water slide. The angle of elevation of the slide (the angle it forms with a horizontal line) is 50°. At the end of the slide, there is a 6-foot drop into a pool. After you climb the ladder to the top of the slide, how many feet above the water level are you? Draw a diagram.

4-44. Find the slope and y-intercept of each line below.

a. $y=-\frac{6}{5}x-7$

b. $3x-2y=10$

c. The line that goes through the points $(5,-2)$ and $(8,4)$.

4-45. Examine the graph of each relation below. For each part below, decide if the relation is a function and then state the domain and range.

a.

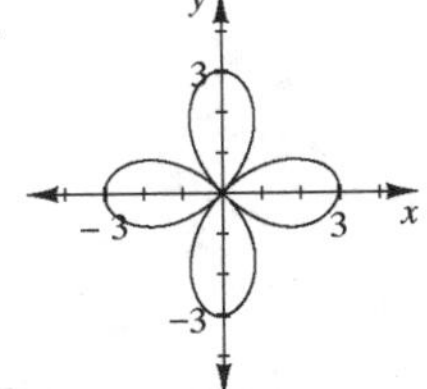

b.

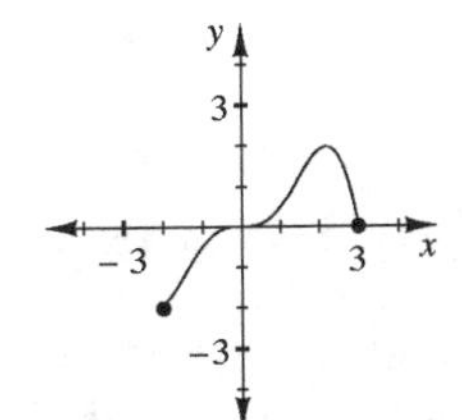

4-46. Solve the system of equations at right.

$$2^{(x+y)}=16$$
$$2^{(2x+y)}=\frac{1}{8}$$

4.1.4 How can I use systems?

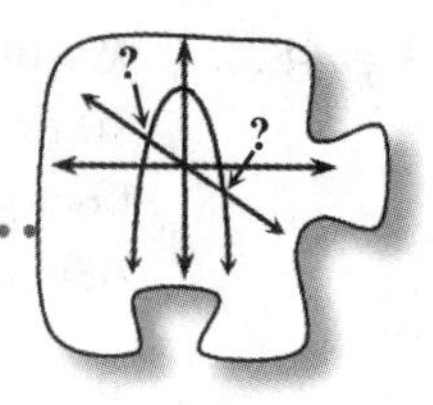

Using Systems of Equations to Solve Problems

You have developed several strategies for solving equations and systems of equations. You have also focused on the meaning of a solution. In this lesson, you will have the opportunity to see how your strategies can be used in everyday contexts. You will expand your understanding of solutions by applying them to these situations. As you work today, use the questions below to help stimulate mathematical conversations:

How can we model this situation with equations?

What does this solution tell us?

How can we solve it?

Are there any other strategies that could be useful?

4-47. HOW TALL IS HAROLD?

Jamal and Dinah were still eating lunch as they came into Algebra 2 class. Someone had left a book on the floor and they both tripped. As they each hit the floor, the food they were carrying went flying across the room directly toward Harold, who was showing off his latest dance moves.

As Jamal and Dinah watched in horror, Jamal's cupcake and Dinah's sandwich splatted right on top of Harold's head! Jamal's cupcake flew on a path that would have landed on the floor 20 feet away from him if it had not hit Harold. Dinah's sandwich flew on a path that would have landed on the floor 24 feet away from her if it had not hit Harold. Jamal's cupcake flew 9 feet high, while Dinah's sandwich reached a height of 6 feet, before hitting Harold.

How tall is Harold? Show your solution in as many ways as you can.

4-48. Write a system of equations to fit the situation below. Then solve the system using as many strategies as you can. How many solutions are possible?

Your math class wants to collect money for a field trip, so it decides to sell two kinds of bags of candy. The Chocolate Lover's Bag costs $4.25 for five chocolate truffles and two caramel turtle candies. The Combusting Caramel Bag costs $3.50 for eight caramel turtle candies and two chocolate truffles. How much does each chocolate truffle and caramel turtle candy cost?

4-49. Lucky you! You are a new college graduate and you have already been offered two jobs. Each job involves exactly the same tasks, but the salary plans differ, as shown below.

- Job A offers a starting salary of $52,000 per year with an annual increase of $3,000.
- Job B starts at $36,000 per year with a raise of 11% each year.

a. Under what conditions would Job A be the better choice? When would Job B be the better choice? Use graphs, tables, and equations to help you justify your answer.

b. How could you change this problem slightly so that Job B is always the better choice? How could you change it so that Job A is always better? If it is not possible for Job A or Job B always to be a better choice, explain why not.

4-50. LEARNING LOG

Earlier you completed a Learning Log entry about the meaning of the solution of an equation. Now think about, "What does the solution to a *system of equations* mean?" Can you find more than one way to answer that question? Create a Learning Log entry that expands on your thinking about the meaning of solutions. Title this entry "The Meaning of a Solution, Part 2" and label it with today's date.

4-51. Gloria is weighing combinations of geometric solids. She found that 4 cylinders and 5 prisms weigh 32 ounces and that 1 cylinder and 8 prisms weigh 35 ounces. Write and solve a system of equations to determine the weight of each cylinder and prism.

4-52. Is $x = -1$ a solution to the inequality $2x^2 + 5x - 3 \le x^2 + 4x + 3$? What about $x = 5$? Show how you know. Then find three more solutions.

4-53. Solve each equation below algebraically. Think about Rewriting, Looking Inside, or Undoing to simplify the process.

a. $5 - 3(\frac{1}{2}x + 2) = -7$

b. $5(\sqrt{x-2} + 1) = 15$

c. $12 - (\frac{2x}{3} + x) = 2$

d. $-3(2x+1)^3 = -192$

4-54. Given the parabola $y = x^2 - 8x + 10$, complete parts (a) through (c) below.

a. Find the vertex by averaging the x-intercepts.

b. Find the vertex by completing the square.

c. Find the vertex of $y = x^2 - 3x$ using your method of choice.

4-55. Refer back to the graphs you made for problem 4-34. (It was a homework problem from Lesson 4.1.2.) Use those graphs to help you graph each of the following inequalities.

a. $y \le |x|$

b. $|y| \ge x$

4-56. **Multiple Choice:** Which of the points below is a solution to $y < |x - 3|$?

a. (2, 1) b. (−4, 5) c. (−2, 8) d. (0, 3)

4-57. For the equation $y = -(x+1)^3 + 2$:

a. Draw a graph.

b. Use your graph to estimate the solution to $-3 = -(x+1)^3 + 2$.

4.2.1 How can I solve inequalities?

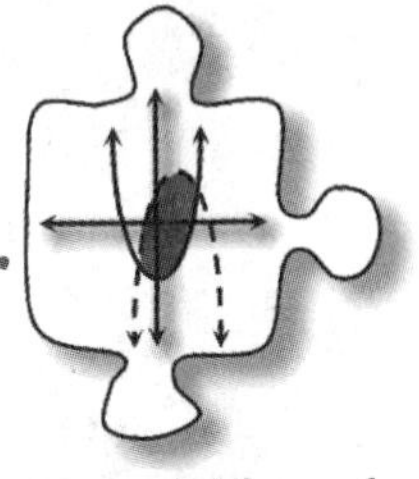

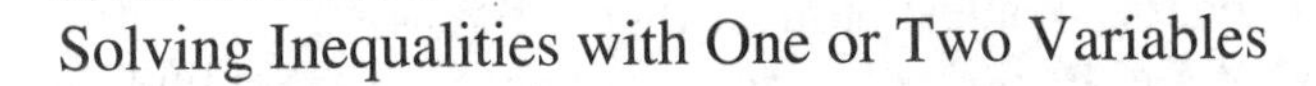

Solving Inequalities with One or Two Variables

In this chapter, you developed many strategies for solving equations with one variable and systems of equations with two variables. But what if you want to solve an inequality or system of inequalities instead? Today you will explore how to use familiar strategies to find solutions for an inequality. As you work, the questions below can help focus team discussions:

What strategy should we use?

How do we know if this solution is correct?

How can we be sure we have found all of the solutions?

4-58. In the previous section, you learned how to use the graph of a system to solve an equation. How can the graphs of $y = 2x^2 + 5x - 3$ and $y = x^2 + 4x + 3$ (shown at right) help you solve an *inequality*? Consider this as you answer the questions below.

a. How are the solutions of $2x^2 + 5x - 3 = x^2 + 4x + 3$ represented on this graph? What are the solutions?

b. Obtain a Lesson 4.2.1A Resource Page from your teacher. On the resource page, label each graph with its equation and highlight each function with a different color. How did you decide which graph matches which function?

c. On the graph, identify the x-values for which $2x^2 + 5x - 3 \le x^2 + 4x + 3$. How did you locate the solutions? How many solutions are there? Find a way to describe all of the solutions.

d. How can these solutions be represented on a number line? Locate the number line labeled with $2x^2 + 5x - 3 \le x^2 + 4x + 3$ below the graph on your resource page. Use a colored marker to highlight the solutions to the inequality on the number line.

e. What about the inequality $2x^2 + 5x - 3 > x^2 + 4x + 3$? What are the solutions to this inequality? Represent your solutions algebraically and on a number line.

4-59. Consider the inequality $4|x+1|-2>6$.

a. How many boundary points are there? Remember that, in this case, a **boundary point** would be the smallest number that will make the inequality *not* true. What are the boundary points? Should they be marked with filled or unfilled circles? Make the appropriate markings on a number line.

b. Which portion(s) of the number line contain the solutions for this inequality? How many regions do you need to test? Represent the solutions algebraically and on a number line.

4-60. Burt and Ernie were solving the inequality $2x^2+5x-3<x^2+4x+3$. They were looking at the graph in problem 4-58 when Burt had an idea. *"Can't we change this into one parabola and solve our inequality that way?"* he said.

Ernie asked, *"What do you mean?"*

"Can't we find the solutions by looking at the graph of $f(x)=x^2+x-6$?" Burt replied.

a. Where did Burt get the equation $y=x^2+x-6$?

b. Try Burt's idea. Graph the parabola and show how it can be used to solve the original inequality.

c. *"Just a minute!"* mumbled Ernie, *"I think I have a short cut. Instead of graphing the parabola, can't we just rewrite the original inequality as $x^2+x-6<0$ and then solve the equation $x^2+x-6=0$? This would give us the boundary points and then we could test numbers to find the regions that contain the solutions."* Check Ernie's short cut. Does it give the same solution?

d. Use any method to solve the inequality $x^2-3x-10\geq 0$.

4-61. Next, Burt and Ernie were working on solving the inequality $4|x+1|-2>6$ from problem 4-59. This time, Ernie had an idea. *"Why don't we find the solutions to this by graphing a system of equations like we did in problem 4-58?"*

a. What system of equations should they graph?

b. Graph the system and explain how you can use it to find the solutions to $4|x+1|-2>6$.

4-62. In problem 4-58 you looked at solutions to an inequality with one variable (x). Now consider the system of inequalities with two variables (x and y) below.

$$y \geq 2x^2 + 5x - 3$$
$$y < x^2 + 4x + 3$$

a. Which points make both inequalities true? For example, does the point $(-3, 0)$ make both inequalities true? What about $(-1, 1)$? $(1, 5)$? Refer back to your Lesson 4.2.1A Resource Page to help you think about these questions.

b. What is the difference between a solution to the *system* of inequalities above and a solution to the inequality found in problem 4-58?

c. How are the graphs of the equations $y = 2x^2 + 5x - 3$ and $y = x^2 + 4x + 3$ related to the graph of the system of inequalities?

d. With your team, find a way to represent all of the solutions to the system of inequalities on the Lesson 4.2.1A Resource Page graph.

4-63. For each of the following graphs, find an equation, inequality, or system that could have the solution shown. Note that the equations for the line and the parabola are given.

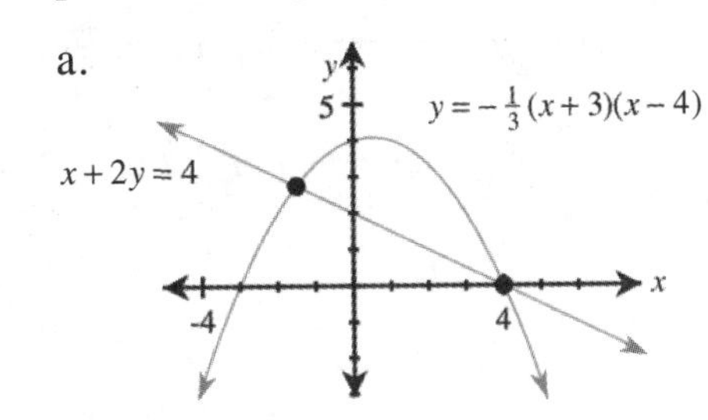

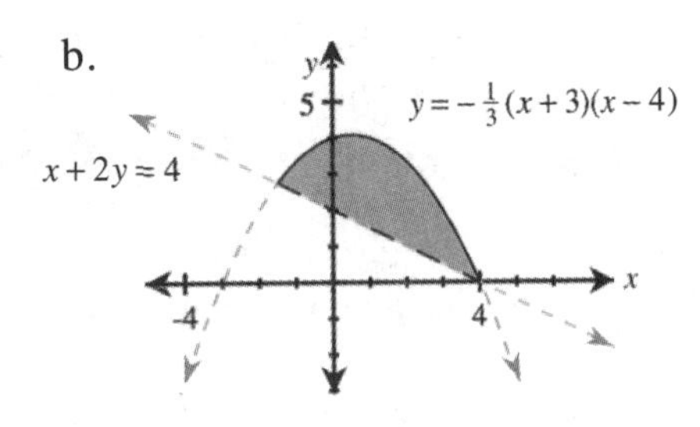

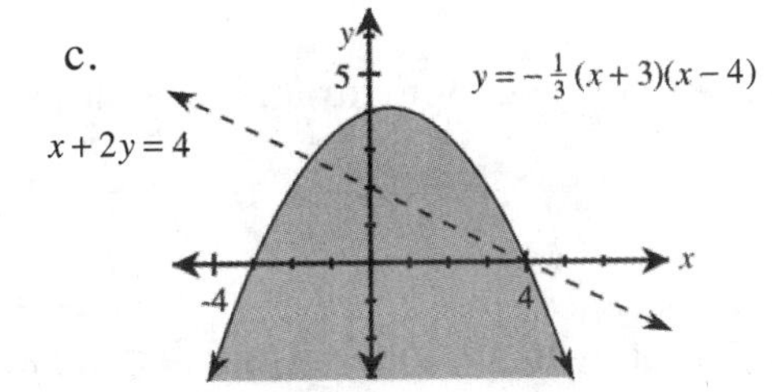

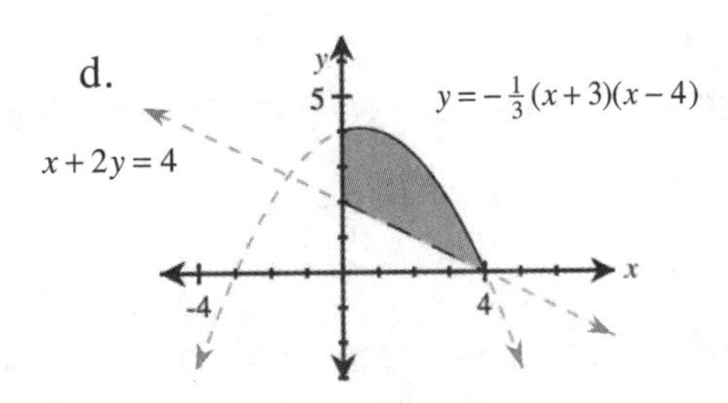

4-64. LEARNING LOG

Now you will reflect for a third time about the meaning of solutions. What does the solution to an *inequality* or a *system of inequalities* mean? Does it matter if the inequality has one variable or two? Create a Learning Log entry that expands on your thinking about the meaning of a solution. Title this entry "The Meaning of a Solution, Part 3" and label it with today's date.

4-65. Find boundary points for each of the following inequalities. Draw the boundaries on a number line and shade the solution regions.

a. $3x+2 \geq x-6$

b. $2x^2-5x<12$

4-66. Solve the following inequalities and draw a number line graph to represent each solution.

a. $|2x+3|<5$

b. $|2x+3| \geq 5$

c. $|2x-3|<5$

d. $|2x-3| \geq 5$

e. $|3-2x|<5$

f. $|3-2x| \geq 5$

g. Describe any relationships you see among these six problems.

4-67. Solve each equation for y so that it could be entered into a graphing calculator.

a. $5-(y-3)=3x$

b. $4(x+y)=-2$

4-68. Solve each equation below. Remember to check for extraneous solutions.

a. $(y-3)^2=2y-10$

b. $|y-3|=2y-10$

4-69. Add, subtract, multiply, or divide the following rational expressions. Then simplify your expression, if possible.

a. $\frac{x-4}{2x^2+9x-5}+\frac{x+3}{x^2+5x}$

b. $\frac{4x^2-11x+6}{2x^2-x-6}-\frac{x+2}{2x+3}$

c. $\frac{(x+4)(2x-1)(x-7)}{(x+8)(2x-1)(3x-4)} \div \frac{(4x-3)(x-7)}{(x+8)(3x-4)}$

d. $\frac{2m^2+7m-15}{m^2-16} \cdot \frac{m^2-6m+8}{2m^2-7m+6}$

4-70. Using the technique of completing the square, solve $x^2 + 12x + 15 = 75$ for x.

4-71. Factor each expression in parts (a) and (b). Then, in parts (c) and (d), factor and simplify each expression.

a. $bx + ax$
b. $x + ax$
c. $\frac{ax+a}{x^2+2x+1}$
d. $\frac{x^2-b^2}{ax+ab}$

4-72. Graph the four inequalities below on the same set of axes.

i. $2y \geq x - 3$
ii. $x - 2y \geq -7$
iii. $y \leq -2x + 6$
iv. $-9 \leq 2x + y$

a. What type of polygon is formed by the solution of this set of inequalities? Write a convincing argument to justify your answer.

b. Find the vertices of the polygon. If your graph is very accurately drawn you will be able to determine the points from the graph. If it is not, you will need to solve the systems (pairs) of equations that represent the corners of your graphs.

4-73. Solve the following absolute value inequalities.

a. $|x - 4| < 9$
b. $\left|\frac{1}{2}x - 45\right| \geq 80$
c. $|2x - 5| \leq 2$

4-74. Your family plans to buy a new air conditioner. They can buy the Super Cool X1400 for $800, or they can buy the Efficient Energy X2000 for $1200. Both models will cool your home equally well, but the Efficient Energy model is less expensive to operate. The Super Cool X1400 will cost $60 per month to operate, while the Efficient Energy X2000 costs only $40 per month to operate.

a. Write an equation to represent the cost of buying and operating the Super Cool X1400 where C = cost and m = months.

b. Write an equation to represent the cost of buying and operating the Efficient Energy X2000.

c. How many months would your family have to use the Efficient Energy model to compensate for the additional cost of the original purchase?

d. Figuring your family will only use the air conditioner for 4 months each year, how many years will you have to wait to start saving money overall?

4-75. MARVELOUS MARK'S FUNCTION MACHINES

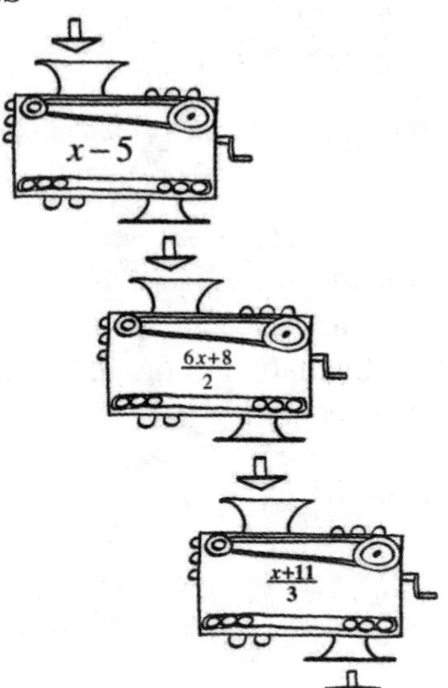

Mark has set up a series of three function machines that he claims will surprise you.

a. Try a few numbers. Are you surprised by your results?

b. Carrie claims that she was not surprised by her results. She also says that she can show why the sequence of machines does what it does by simply dropping in a variable and writing out step-by-step what happens inside each machine. Try it. (Use something like c or m.) Be sure to show all of the steps.

4-76. Multiply or divide the rational expressions below. Write each answer in simplified form.

a. $\frac{(x-3)^2}{2x-1} \cdot \frac{2x-1}{(3x-14)(x+6)} \cdot \frac{x+6}{x-3}$

b. $\frac{4x^2+5x-6}{3x^2+5x-2} \div \frac{4x^2+x-3}{6x^2-5x+1}$

4-77. Find all of the points at which the parabolas below intersect. Write your solution(s) in (x, y) form.

$$y = x^2 - x + 12$$
$$y = 2x^2 + 3x + 7$$

4-78. Find the equation (in $y = mx + b$ form) of each line described below.

a. A line with slope $\frac{1}{2}$ passing through the point $(6, 1)$.

b. The line $y = 2x + b$ passing through the point $(1, 4)$.

4.2.2 How can I organize the possibilities?

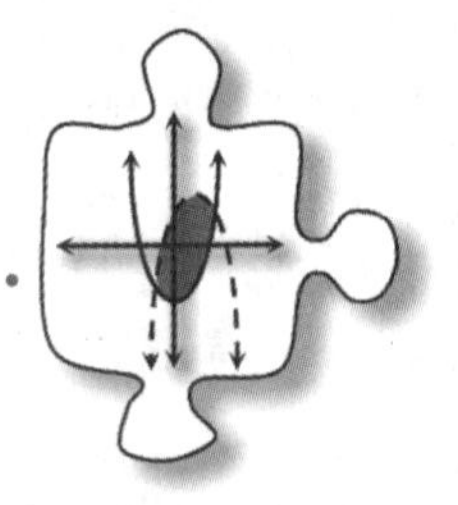

Using Systems to Solve a Problem

Businesses and industries often use equations and inequalities to model their services and production. Creating a system of equations and inequalities allows them to mathematically optimize their operation and maximize profits. Today you will investigate this technique.

4-79. THE TOY FACTORY

Otto Toyom builds toy cars and trucks. To make each car, he needs 4 wheels, 2 seats, and 1 gas tank. To make each truck, he needs 6 wheels, 1 seat, and 3 gas tanks. His storeroom has 36 wheels, 14 seats, and 15 gas tanks. He is trying to decide how many cars and trucks to build so he can make the largest possible amount of money when he sells them. Help Otto figure out what his options are. What are all of the choices he could make about how many cars and how many trucks he will build? Make a list of all possible combinations. Then plot the number of possible cars and trucks in the first quadrant of a graph.

4-80. Otto wants to make as much profit as possible. Use your list from problem 4-79 to find which combination of cars and trucks will make the most profit based on the information below.

a. Which of Otto's options gives him the greatest profit if he makes \$1 on each car and \$1 on each truck he sells? How do you know?

b. The market has changed, and Otto can now make \$2 for each truck but only \$1 for each car. What is his best choice for the number of cars and the number of trucks to make in this situation? How can you be sure? Explain.

4-81. To convince Otto that your recommendation was a good one, you probably had to show many calculations in problem 4-80. Now, you will take another look at Otto's business using algebra and graphing tools.

a. Write three inequalities to represent the relationship between the number of cars (x), the number of trucks (y), and the number of:

i. wheels   *ii.* seats   *iii.* gas tanks

b. Graph this system of inequalities on the same set of axes you used for problem 4-79. Shade the solution region lightly. Why is it okay to assume that $x \geq 0$ and $y \geq 0$?

c. What are the vertices of the polygon that outlines your region? Explain how you could find the exact coordinates of those points if you could not read them easily from the graph.

d. Are there any points in the solution region that represent choices that seem more likely to give Otto the maximum profit? Where are they? Why do you think they show the best choices?

e. Write an equation to represent Otto's total profit (P) if he makes \$1 on each car and \$2 on each truck. What if Otto ended up with a profit of only \$8? Show how to use the graph of the profit equation when $P = 8$ to figure out how many cars and trucks he made.

f. Which points do you need to test in the profit equation to get the maximum profit? Is it necessary to try all of the points? Why or why not?

g. What if Otto got greedy and wanted to make a profit of \$14? How could you use a profit line to show Otto that this would be impossible based on his current pricing?

4-82. Find Otto's highest possible profit if he gets \$3 per car and \$2 per truck. Find the profit expression and find the best combinations of cars and trucks to maximize the profit.

MATH NOTES

METHODS AND MEANINGS

Inequalities with Absolute Value

If k is any positive number, an inequality of the form $|f(x)| > k$ is equivalent to the statement $f(x) > k$ OR $f(x) < -k$.

For example, $|2x-17| > 9$ is equivalent to $2x-17 > 9$ or $2x-17 < -9$. Solving yields $x > 13$ or $x < 4$.

$|f(x)| < k$ is equivalent to the statement $-k < f(x) < k$. Another way to write this is $f(x) > -k$ AND $f(x) < k$. For example, $|x+4| < 9$ is equivalent to $-9 < x+4 < 9$. Solving yields $-13 < x < 5$, that is, $x > -13$ and $x < 5$.

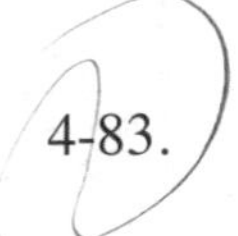

4-83. Solve the system of equations at right. What sub-problems did you need to solve?

$$x + 2y = 4$$
$$2x - y = -7$$
$$x + y + z = -4$$

4-84. Solve each of the following inequalities. Express the solutions algebraically and on a number line.

a. $3x - 5 \leq 7$

b. $x^2 + 6 > 42$

4-85. Three red rods are 2 cm longer than two blue rods. Three blue rods are 2 cm longer than four red rods. How long is each rod?

4-86. Simone has been absent and does not know the difference between the graph of $y \leq 2x - 2$ and the graph of $y < 2x - 2$. Explain thoroughly so that she completely understands what points are excluded from the second graph and why.

4-87. This problem is a checkpoint for solving for one variable in an equation with two or more variables. It will be referred to as Checkpoint 4B.

Rewrite the following equations so that you could enter them into a graphing calculator. In other words, solve for y.

a. $x-3(y+2)=6$

b. $\frac{6x-1}{y}-3=2$

c. $\sqrt{y-4}=x+1$

d. $\sqrt{y+4}=x+2$

Check your answers by referring to the Checkpoint 4B materials located at the back of your book.

If you needed help solving these problems correctly, then you need more practice. Review the Checkpoint 4B materials and try the practice problems. Also, consider getting help outside of class time. From this point on, you will be expected to do problems like these quickly and easily.

4-88. Think about the axis system in the two-dimensional coordinate plane. What is the equation of the x-axis? What is the equation of the y-axis?

4-89. Sammy has a 10-foot wooden ladder, which he needs to climb to reach the roof of his house. The roof is 12 feet above the ground. The base of the ladder must be at least 1.5 feet from the base of the house. How far is it from the top step of the ladder to the edge of the roof? Draw a sketch.

4.2.3 How can I find the best combination?

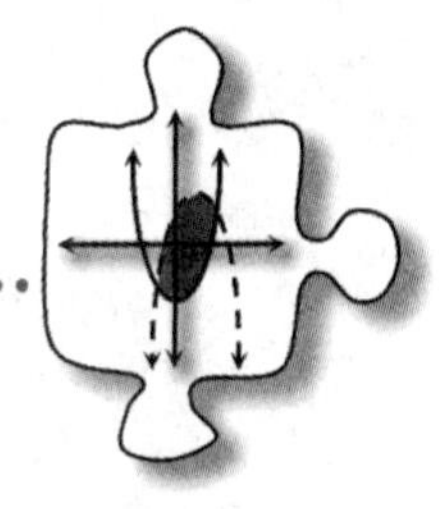

Application of Systems of Linear Inequalities

The process of using linear systems to find the optimal solution to a problem with multiple constraints is called **linear programming**. You used this process while solving "The Toy Factory." Now you will work on a problem using this technique, only this time you can use a system of inequalities and will not need to list all of the possible outcomes.

4-90. SANDY DANDY DUNE BUGGIES

Jacklyn Toyom, CEO of the Sandy Dandy Dune Buggy Company and Otto's sister, has discovered that your team has found a way to optimize the profit for the Toy Factory. She would like to hire your team to help her company. Here is her letter:

> *Dear Study Team,*
>
> *I was so impressed to hear about how you helped Otto maximize his profits at his Toy Factory! I think your team could help my company as well.*
>
> *Here at the Sandy Dandy Dune Buggy Company we make two popular models of off-road vehicles: the Crawler and the Rover. Each week, we receive enough parts to build at most 15 Crawlers and 12 Rovers. The only exceptions to the supply of parts are the colored night lamps and high-definition speakers, which have to be specially manufactured for our off-road vehicles. Each of the Crawlers requires 5 of the lamps and 2 of the speakers. The Rover requires 3 lamps and 6 speakers. Our supplier is a small company that can only manufacture 81 of the lamps and 78 of the speakers for us each week.*
>
> *Since we are also a small company, we have only 12 employees. By contract, the maximum number of hours each employee can work is 37.5 hours per week. It takes our employees 20 hours to assemble one Crawler and 30 hours to assemble one Rover.*
>
> *Each Crawler sold brings in a profit of $500. The Rover, that is less expensive to manufacture than the Crawler, is very popular and sells for a profit of $1000 each.*
>
> *I need a detailed proposal of how to maximize our profit that I can submit to our Board of Trustees. I look forward to a profitable business relationship!*
>
> *Sincerely,*
> *Ms. Jacklyn Toyom*
> *CEO, Sandy Dandy Dune Buggy Company*

Problem continues on next page →

4-90. *Problem continued from previous page.*

Your Task: Find the best combination of Crawlers and Rovers to produce each week to maximize the company's profit. Create a detailed proposal to submit to Ms. Toyom that includes:

- The number of Crawlers and Rovers to manufacture each week.
- The maximum profit the company can expect to make.
- Calculations and graphs to justify your recommendation.

Constraints to keep in mind are the number of:

(1) speakers available
(2) lamps available
(3) total employee hours each week

Discussion Points

How does this problem compare to "The Toy Factory" from the previous lesson?

What is the maximum number of hours for all of the employees that can be worked in one week?

How can we justify that we have found the most profitable combination of each vehicle to manufacture?

Further Guidance

4-91. After emailing a few questions to Ms. Toyom, your team received the following email:

From: "Ms. Toyom" <toyom@welovemath.com>
To: <studyteam@thinkingisgood.net>
Subject: Clarifications to your Questions

Dear Study Team,

Thank you for your questions. I am happy to clarify them. Our Board of Trustees requires the following information in your proposal:

1. A list of all of the constraints (to make sure you took them into consideration).
2. An inequality for each of the constraints.
3. A full-page graph showing all inequalities and the resulting solution region (use a different color for each inequality).
4. Calculations for each of the vertices on your solution region. List these points at their vertex.
5. Profit calculations, with maximum profit included on your graph.

Please make sure to include a cover letter summarizing your proposal. Also include a brief explanation for each of the items listed above.

Sincerely, Ms. Toyom

Further Guidance section ends here.

METHODS AND MEANINGS

MATH NOTES

Graphing Inequalities with Two Variables

To graph an inequality with two variables, first graph the boundary line or curve. If the inequality does not include equality (that is, if it is $>$ or $<$ rather than $\geq$ or $\leq$), then the graph of the boundary is dashed to indicate that it is not included in the solution. Otherwise, the boundary is a solid line or curve.

Once the boundary is graphed, choose a point that does not lie on the boundary to test in the inequality. If that point makes the inequality true, then the entire region in which that point lies is a solution. If that point makes the inequality false, then the entire region in which the point lies is not a solution. Examine the two examples below.

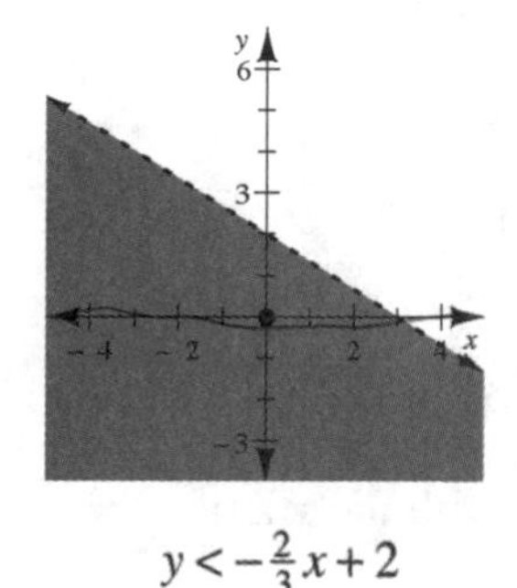

$y < -\frac{2}{3}x + 2$

Test $(0, 0)$:

$0 \overset{?}{<} -\frac{2}{3}(0) + 2$

$0 \overset{?}{<} 2$

True, so shade below the line.

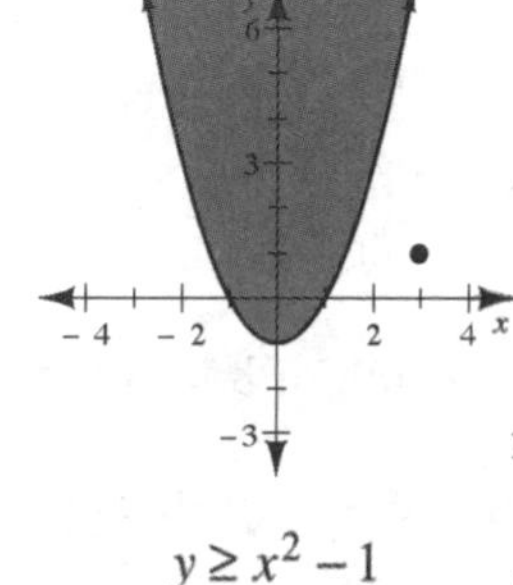

$y \geq x^2 - 1$

Test $(3, 1)$:

$1 \overset{?}{\geq} 3^2 - 1$

$1 \overset{?}{\geq} 8$

False, so shade the region that does not contain the test point, that is, shade above the parabola.

Review & Preview

4-92. Solve the system of equations at right algebraically and explain what the solution tells you about the graphs of the two equations.

$$3x + 2 = y$$
$$-9x + 3y = 11$$

4-93. Draw the graph of the system of inequalities at right.

$$y \geq |x| - 3$$
$$y \leq -|x| + 5$$

a. What polygon does the intersection form? Justify your answer.

b. What are its vertices?

c. Find the area of the intersection.

4-94. Solve each of the following inequalities. Express the solutions algebraically and on a number line.

a. $3(x+2) > 4x-7$

b. $3x^2-4x+2 \le x^2+x+6$

4-95. Solve the equations below.

a. $\sqrt{x+15} = 5+\sqrt{x}$

b. $(y-6)^2+10 = 3y$

4-96. Solve the system of equations at right.

$$x+3y=16$$
$$x-2y=31$$

a. Now rewrite the system and replace x with x^2.

b. What effect will this have on the solution to the system? Solve the new system.

4-97. A line intersects the graph of $y=x^2$ twice. One point has an x-coordinate of -4, and the other point has an x-coordinate of 2.

a. Draw a sketch of both graphs, and find the equation of the line.

b. Find the measure of the angle that the line makes with the x-axis.

4.2.4 What can I learn from a graph?

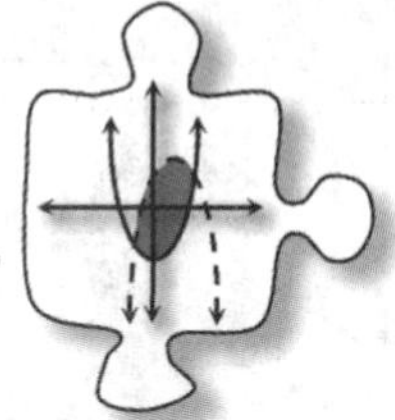

Using Graphs to Find Solutions

You have seen that you can find solutions to problems, equations, inequalities and systems using graphs. In this lesson, you will apply this knowledge to a math competition challenge.

4-98. MATH TEAM CHALLENGE

At the annual two-day Math Challenge, teams from various high schools get together for a sometimes not-too-friendly math competition. Your school's biggest rival, Silicon Mountain High School, has won the competition the last five years and is already bragging that they will take first place again. However, your team has worked exceptionally hard this year to understand the Algebra 2 curriculum and its challenging concepts. Everyone on your team feels confident that they can beat Silicon Mountain High.

At the end of the first day of competition, scores for each school are posted, and WOW! Your team and Silicon Mountain's team are tied for first place! Before the teams leave for the day, they are handed a copy of the final problem in the competition (shown below). At first your team is excited, but when your team reads the "Final Challenge," you all realize that everyone has a lot of work to do before tomorrow's event.

> ***Final Challenge***
>
> The three math judges will ask your team five questions that can be answered by looking at the graph of the functions at right. Your score for each answer will depend on its accuracy and completeness.

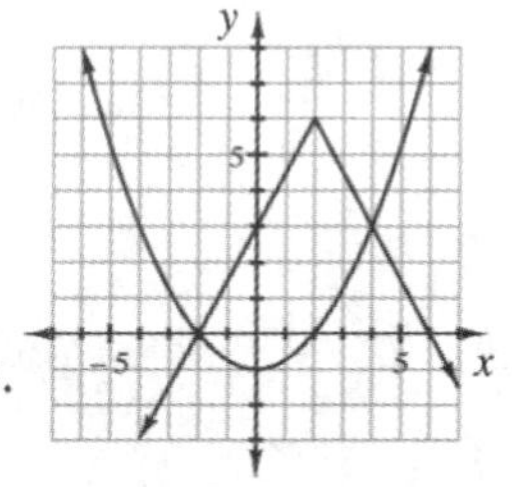

Your Task: Obtain a Lesson 4.2.4 Resource Page from your teacher, which contains a copy of the graph in the "Final Challenge." With your team, discuss the graph and make a list of questions that the judges might ask about it. For each question, form a complete response so that your team is prepared for the "Final Challenge."

Discussion Points

What can a graph tell us about equations? About inequalities?

Can we use the graph to get information about equations and inequalities in one variable and in two variables?

Methods and Meanings

MATH NOTES

Solutions to One- and Two-Variable Equations

When an equation has one variable, solutions are single numbers. When an equation contains two variables, solutions are ordered pairs.

For example, the solutions for the system of equations shown at right are the ordered pairs (4, 44) and (–1, –11) because these are the (x, y) pairs that make both equations true. They are also the points at which the graphs of the two equations intersect.

$$y = x^2 + 8x - 4$$
$$y = 2x^2 + 5x - 8$$

The solutions for the one-variable equation $2x^2 + 5x - 8 = x^2 + 8x - 4$ are the numbers 4 and –1, because they are the two x-values that make the equation true.

4-99. Consider the graph at right as you answer the following questions.

a. Find the equation of the parabola.

b. Find the equation of the line.

c. Use your graph to solve $x + 5 = \frac{1}{2}(x+3)^2 - 2$.

d. Use your graph to solve the system.

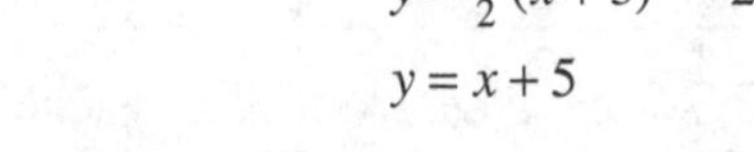

$$y = \frac{1}{2}(x+3)^2 - 2$$
$$y = x + 5$$

e. Use your graph to solve the inequality $x + 5 < \frac{1}{2}(x+3)^2 - 2$.

f. Use your graph to solve $\frac{1}{2}(x+3)^2 - 2 = 0$.

g. Use your graph to solve $x + 5 = 4$.

h. How could you change the equation of the parabola so that the parabola and the line do not intersect? Is there more than one way?

4-100. Write the three inequalities that form the triangle shown at right.

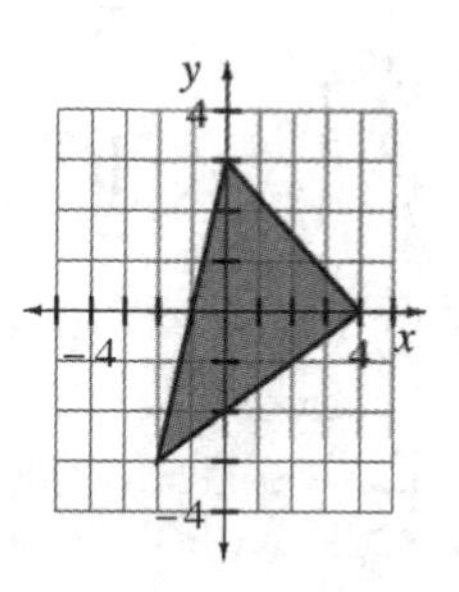

4-101. Solve each of the following inequalities. Represent the solutions algebraically and on a number line.

a. $2|3x-5| \geq 4$

b. $\frac{1}{3}(3x-6)^3+4<13$

4-102. On separate pairs of axes, sketch the graph of each equation or inequality below.

a. $y+5=(x-2)^2$

b. $y \leq (x+3)^3$

c. $y=4+\frac{1}{x-3}$

4-103. Find the measure of $\angle$CPM in the diagram at right.

List any sub-problems that were necessary to solve this problem.

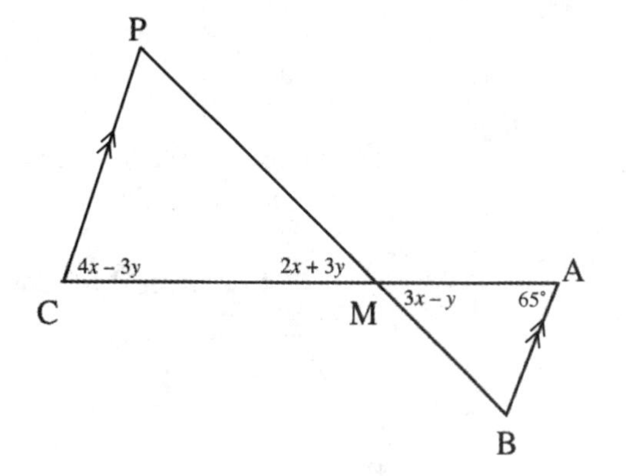

4-104. Graph the solutions to each of the following inequalities on a different set of axes. Label each graph with the inequality as given and with its *y*= form. Choose a test point and show that it gives the same result in both forms of your inequality.

a. $3x-3<y$

b. $3>y$

c. $3x-2y \leq 6$

d. $x^2-y \leq 9$

4-105. Solve for *w* in each equation below.

a. $w^2+4w=0$

b. $5w^2-2w=0$

c. $w^2=6w$

Chapter 4 Closure What have I learned?

Reflection and Synthesis

The activities below offer you a chance to reflect about what you have learned during this chapter. As you work, look for concepts that you feel very comfortable with, ideas that you would like to learn more about, and topics you need more help with. Look for connections between ideas as well as connections with material you learned previously.

① TEAM BRAINSTORM

What have you studied in this chapter? What ideas were important in what you learned? With your team, brainstorm a list. Be as detailed as you can. To help get you started, a list of Learning Log entries and Math Notes boxes are below.

What topics, ideas, and words that you learned *before* this chapter are connected to the new ideas in this chapter? Again, be as detailed as you can.

How long can you make your list? Challenge yourselves. Be prepared to share your team's ideas with the class.

Learning Log Entries

- Lesson 4.1.1 – Strategies for Solving Equations
- Lesson 4.1.2 – The Meaning of a Solution, Part 1
- Lesson 4.1.3 – Finding Solutions to Systems
- Lesson 4.1.4 – The Meaning of a Solution, Part 2
- Lesson 4.2.1 – The Meaning of a Solution, Part 3

Math Notes

- Lesson 4.2.2 – Inequalities with Absolute Value
- Lesson 4.2.3 – Graphing Inequalities with Two Variables
- Lesson 4.2.4 – Solutions to One- and Two-Variable Equations

② MAKING CONNECTIONS

Below is a list of the vocabulary used in this chapter. Make sure that you are familiar with all of these words and know what they mean. Refer to the glossary or index for any words that you do not yet understand.

solution	boundary curve	boundary line
boundary point	extraneous solution	intercept
intersection	linear programming	Looking Inside
maximize	one-variable equation	one-variable inequality
Rewriting	solution region	system of equations
system of inequalities	two-variable equation	two-variable inequality
Undoing		

Make a concept map showing all of the connections you can find among the key words and ideas listed above. To show a connection between two words, draw a line between them and explain the connection. A word can be connected to any other word as long as you can justify the connection. For each key word or idea, provide an example or sketch that shows the idea.

While you are making your map, your team may think of related words or ideas that are not listed here. Be sure to include these ideas on your concept map.

③ PORTFOLIO: EVIDENCE OF MATHEMATICAL PROFICIENCY

This section gives you an opportunity to show growth in your understanding of key mathematical ideas over time as you complete this course.

Explain everything that you know about $f(x) = 2^x - 3$.

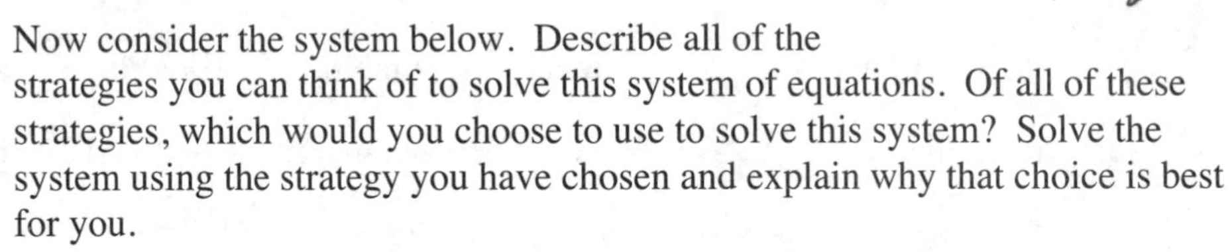

Now consider the system below. Describe all of the strategies you can think of to solve this system of equations. Of all of these strategies, which would you choose to use to solve this system? Solve the system using the strategy you have chosen and explain why that choice is best for you.

$$y = 2x - 1 \qquad\qquad y = -\tfrac{1}{3}x + 6$$

Find a problem from this chapter that can be solved using more than one strategy. Why did you choose to solve it the way you did? Now solve the problem again, this time using a different strategy.

Alternatively, your teacher may ask you to showcase your use of inequalities with your work from "Sandy Dandy Dune Buggies," problem 4-90.

Your teacher may give you the Chapter 4 Closure Resource Page: Solutions Graphic Organizer page to work on. A "Graphic Organizer" is a tool you can use to organize your thoughts and communicate your ideas clearly.

④ WHAT HAVE I LEARNED?

Most of the problems in this section represent typical problems found in this chapter. They serve as a gauge for you. You can use them to determine which types of problems you can do well and which types of problems require further study and practice. Even if your teacher does not assign this section, it is a good idea to try these problems and find out for yourself what you know and what you still need to work on.

Solve each problem as completely as you can. The table at the end of the closure section has answers to these problems. It also tells you where you can find additional help and practice with problems like these.

CL 4-106. Use one of the strategies of Looking Inside, Rewriting, or Undoing to solve each equation.

a. $2(y-1)^2+8=80$

b. $\sqrt{1-2x}=10$

c. $\frac{6y-1}{y}-2=3$

d. $|2x+1|=5$

CL 4-107. Solve each system of equations without graphing. For each case, explain what the solution tells you about the graph of the system.

a. $y=\frac{1}{3}x^2+1$
$y=2x-2$

b. $y=\sqrt{x-3}$
$y=x-5$

c. $6x-2y=-4$
$y=3x+2$

CL 4-108. Estelle and Carlos will be hosting a party and will buy 6 pies for their guests. Two lemon meringue pies cost \$3 less than 4 blueberry pies. Three lemon meringue pies cost \$9 more than 3 blueberry pies. How much does each type of pie cost?

CL 4-109. Graph the following inequality or systems of inequalities.

a. $y \le 4x+16$
$y > -\frac{4}{3}x-4$

b. $y < x^2-2x-3$
$y \le \frac{3}{4}x+2$

c. $y \ge |x+2|-3$

d. $y \le \frac{1}{2}x+3$
$y \ge (x+1)^2-2$

CL 4-110. Solve each inequality and graph the solution on a number line.

a. $x^2-2x-15<0$

b. $|3x-2| \ge 10$

CL 4-111. Find the equation of each of the lines described below.

a. The line that passes through $(6, 1)$ and $(-10, -7)$.

b. The line that is perpendicular to $y=\frac{2}{3}x+1$ and passes through $(0, 5)$.

CL 4-112. Solve each equation for y.

a. $2y^2 + 3y = 7$

b. $3(2x - y) + 12 = 4x - 3$

c. $y(2y+1) + 3(2y+1) = 0$

d. $-4y - 1 = 4y(y - 2)$

CL 4-113. Add, subtract, multiply, or divide the expressions below. Be sure to simplify your answer.

a. $\frac{4x^2-13x+3}{5x^2+23x-10} \cdot \frac{5x-2}{x^2+6x-27} \cdot \frac{x^2+5x-36}{4x-1}$

b. $\frac{x^2-9}{x^2+6x+9} \div \frac{x^2-x-6}{x^2+4}$

c. $6 + \frac{3}{x+1}$

d. $\frac{5}{x} - \frac{10}{x^2+2x}$

CL 4-114. Consider the system of equations at right.

$$x^2 + y^2 = 25$$
$$y = x^2 + 3$$

a. Solve the system graphically.

b. Now solve the system algebraically.

CL 4-115. Check your answers using the table at the end of this section. Which problems do you feel confident about? Which problems were hard? Have you worked on problems like these in math classes you have taken before? Use the table to make a list of topics you need help on and a list of topics you need to practice more.

Answers and Support for Closure Activity #4

What Have I Learned?

Note: MN = Math Note, LL = Learning Log

Problem	Solutions	Need Help?	More Practice
CL 4-106.	a. $y=7$ or $y=-5$ b. $x=-\frac{99}{2}$ c. $y=1$ d. $x=2$ or $x=-3$	Lesson 4.1.1	Problems 4-3, 4-4, 4-8, 4-24, 4-31, 4-41, and 4-53
CL 4-107.	a. (3, 4); a line tangent to parabola b. (7, 2); a line intersecting the positive portion of a parabola, the second algebraic solution, $x=4$, is extraneous c. infinite solution; lines are coinciding	Lessons 4.1.2 and 4.1.3 Checkpoint 2B MN: 2.1.1, 2.1.3, and 4.2.4	Problems 4-10, 4-36, 4-40, 4-92, and 4-96
CL 4-108.	$2L=4B-3$ $3L=3B+9$ Lemon meringue pies cost $7.50 each and blueberry pies cost $4.50 each.	Lessons 4.1.3 and 4.1.4 Checkpoint 2B MN: 2.1.1 and 2.1.3	Problems 4-49, 4-51, and 4-85
CL 4-109.	a. 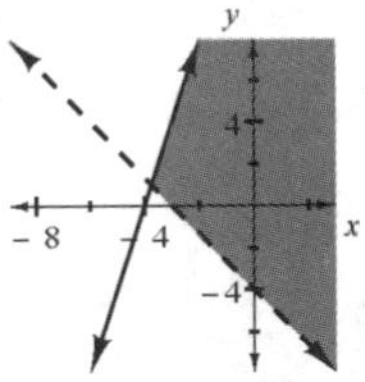 b. 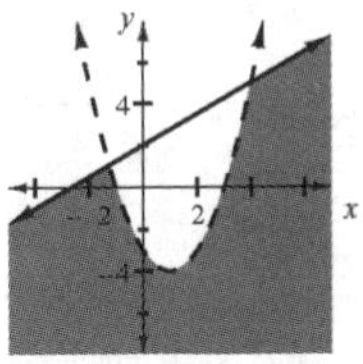 c. 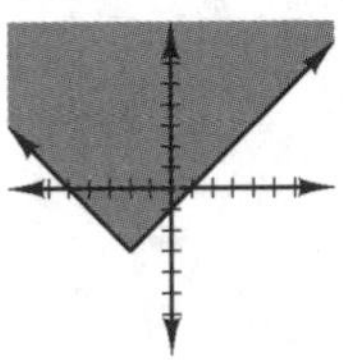 d. 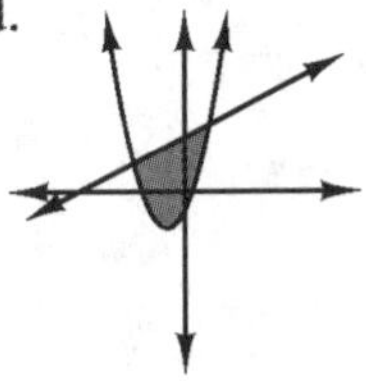	Lesson 4.2.1 MN: 4.2.3	Problems 4-62, 4-63, 4-72, 4-93, 4-100, and 4-104
CL 4-110.	a. $-3<x<5$ b. $x\le-\frac{8}{3}$ or $x\ge4$ 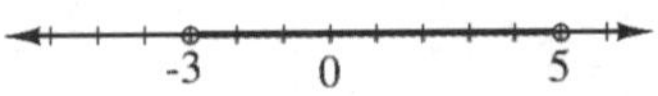 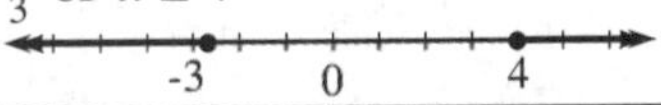	Lesson 4.2.1 MN: 4.2.2	Problems 4-59, 4-65, 4-66, 4-73, 4-94, and 4-101

Problem	Solutions	Need Help?	More Practice
CL 4-111.	a. $y=\frac{1}{2}x-2$ b. $y=-\frac{3}{2}x+5$	Checkpoint 2A	Problems 2-9, 2-10, 2-89, 2-105, and 4-9
CL 4-112.	a. $y=\frac{-3\pm\sqrt{65}}{4}$ b. $y=\frac{2}{3}x+5$ c. $y=-\frac{1}{2},-3$ d. $y=\frac{1}{2}$	Checkpoint 4B MN: 1.1.2 and 1.1.4	Problems 4-32, 4-67, and 4-87
CL 4-113.	a. $\frac{x-4}{x+5}$ b. $\frac{x^2+4}{(x+3)(x+2)}$ c. $\frac{6x+9}{x+1}$ d. $\frac{5}{x+2}$	Lessons 3.2.2, 3.2.3, and 3.2.4	Problems 4-13, 4-69, and 4-76
CL 4-114.	a. See graph at right. Approximately $(1.35, 4.82)$ and $(-1.35, 4.82)$ 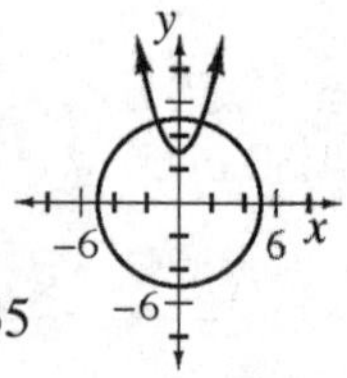 b. $x=\pm\sqrt{\frac{-1+\sqrt{113}}{2}-3}\approx\pm1.35$ $y=\frac{-1+\sqrt{113}}{2}\approx 4.82$	Lessons 4.1.2 and 4.2.4 MN: 4.2.4 LL: 4.1.2 and 4.1.4	Problems 4-7, 4-22, 4-23, 4-30, and 4-57

INVERSES AND LOGARITHMS

Chapter 5 Inverses and Logarithms

In Chapter 4, one of the strategies that you used to solve complicated equations was Undoing. In this chapter you investigate some new functions that "undo" each other. You will learn about inverse relationships and investigate the relationships between functions and their inverses. You will also learn about compositions of functions.

In Section 5.2, you will find the inverses of many parent graphs and add them to the tools you have for working with parent graphs. You will find inverses for exponential functions, which are called logarithmic functions. You will then investigate this family of functions and transform its graphs.

Guiding Question

Mathematically proficient students look for and make use of structure.

As you work through this chapter, ask yourself:

How can I use the reflective nature of inverse graphs to find the equations for inverses?

Chapter Outline

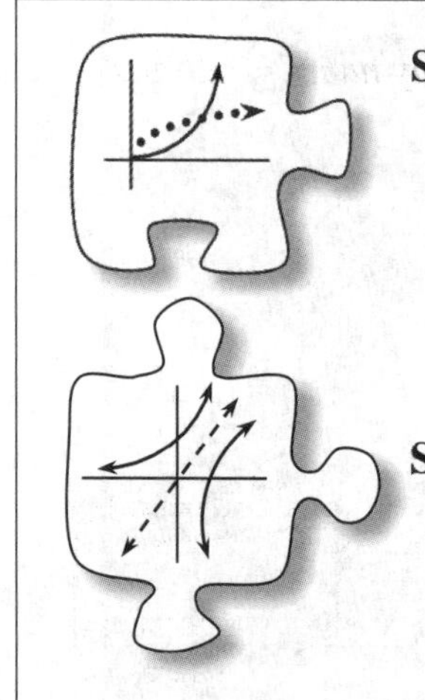

Section 5.1 You will examine relationships, called inverses, that "undo" the actions of functions. You will also learn how to create composite functions by "stacking" function machines, and you will investigate what happens when you compose functions and their inverses.

Section 5.2 You will be introduced to an important new family of functions, called logarithms, which are the inverses of exponential functions. You will investigate this family and learn to transform its graphs.

5.1.1 How can I "undo" a function?

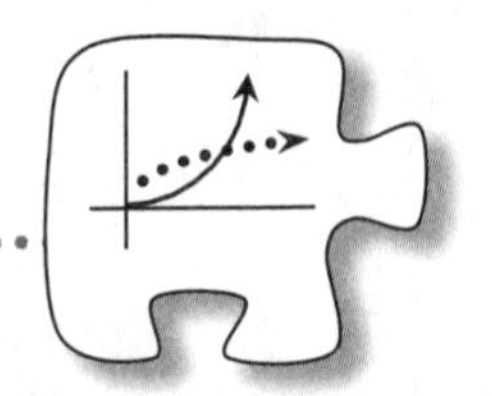

"Undo" Equations

Have you ever heard the expression, "She knows it forward and backward," to describe someone who understands an idea deeply? Often, being able to reverse a process is a way to show how thoroughly you understand it. Today you will reverse mathematical processes, including functions. As you work today, keep these questions in mind:

How can I "undo" it?

How can I justify each step?

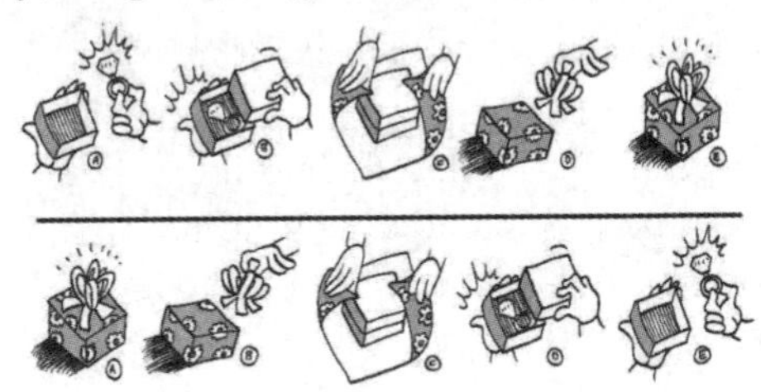

5-1. GUESS MY NUMBER

Today you will play the "Guess My Number" game. Your teacher will think of a number and tell you some information about that number. You will try to determine your teacher's number. (You can use your calculator or paper if it helps.) When you think you know the number, sit silently and do not tell anyone! Be sure to give others a chance to figure it out!

For example your teacher might say: *"When I add 4 to my number and then multiply the sum by 10, I get –70. What is my number?"*

Your task will be to find the number and explain your reasoning.

5-2. A picture of Anita's function machine is shown at right. When she put 3 into the machine, 7 came out. When she put in 4, 9 came out, and when she put in –3, –5 came out.

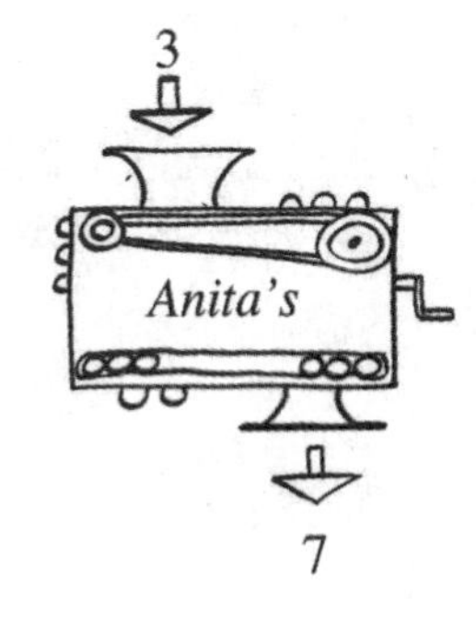

a. Make a table to organize the inputs and outputs from Anita's function machine. Explain in words what this machine is doing to the input to generate an output.

Problem continues on next page →

5-2. *Problem continued from previous page.*

b. Anita's function machine suddenly started working backwards: it began pulling outputs back up into the machine, reversing the machine's process, and returning the original input. If 7 is pulled back into this machine, what value do you think will come out of the top? Anita sets up her new backwards function machine and enters the other outputs. What would you expect to come out the top if 9 is entered? If –5 is entered? Explain.

c. Record the inputs and outputs of the backwards function machine in a table. Record the numbers going in as x, and the numbers coming out as y. Explain in words what Anita's backwards function machine is doing.

d. Write equations for Anita's original function machine and for her backwards machine. How are the two equations related?

5-3. The function machine at right follows the equation $h(x) = 5x + 2$.

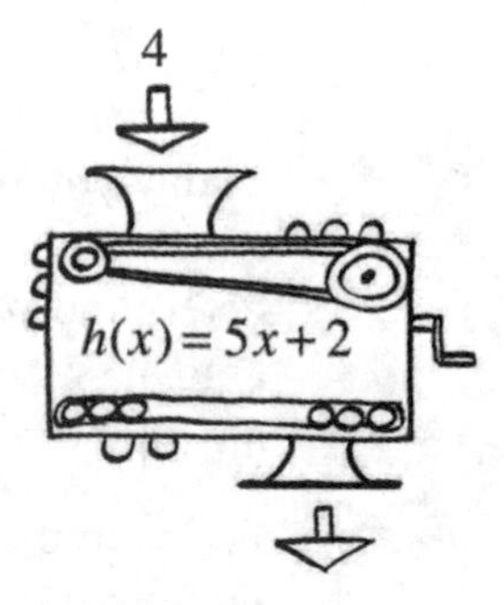

a. If the crank is turned backwards, what number should be pulled up into the machine in order to have a 4 come out of the top?

b. Keiko wants to build a new machine that will undo what $h(x)$ does to an input. What must Keiko's machine do to 17 to undo it and return a value of 3?

c. An "undo" function is called an **inverse** and has the notation $h^{-1}(x)$. Note that the –1 is not a negative exponent. It is the mathematical symbol that indicates the inverse function of $h(x)$. Write an equation for $h^{-1}(x)$, the "undo" function machine.

d. Choose a value for x. Then find a strategy to show that your equation, $h^{-1}(x)$, undoes the effects of the function machine $h(x)$.

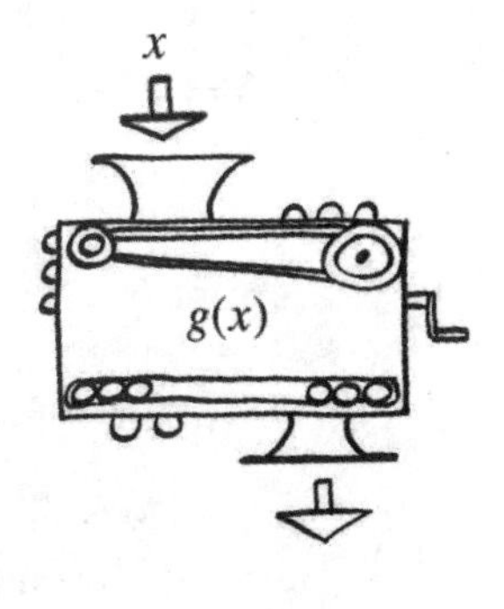

5-4. Keiko was working with a new function, $g(x)$. He wrote down the following steps for $g(x)$:

- Add 5.
- Divide by 2.
- Cube it. (Find the third power.)
- Multiply by 6.

a. What is the equation for $g(x)$? What is the output when 3 is put in?

b. Help Keiko write down the steps (in words) of the inverse machine, $g^{-1}(x)$, and then write its equation.

c. Verify that your equation in part (b) correctly "undoes" the output of $g(x)$ in part (a).

5-5. Find the inverse equations for each of the functions below. Use function notation. Justify that each inverse equation works for its function.

a. $f(x)=3x-6$

b. $g(x)=x^3-5$

c. $p(x)=2(x+3)^3$

d. $t(x)=\frac{10(x-4)}{3}$

5-6. Each team member should choose one function and its inverse from the previous problem. Then they should create a graph and a table for each pair. Be sure to graph the function and its inverse equation on the same set of axes.

When each person in your team has finished, put everyone's work into the middle of the workspace. Describe what relationships you see between the representations of a function and its inverse equation.

5-7. LEARNING LOG

What strategies did your team use to find inverse equations? How can you be sure that the inverse equations you found are correct? Discuss this idea and then write a Learning Log entry about the strategies you have for finding inverse equations and checking that they work. Title this entry "Finding and Checking Inverse Equations" and label it with today's date.

5-8. Graph $y = \frac{1}{2}x - 3$ and its inverse function on the same set of axes.

a. What is the equation of the inverse function?

b. Does this graph, including both lines, have a line of symmetry? If so, what is the equation of the line of symmetry?

5-9. Antonio's function machine is shown at right.

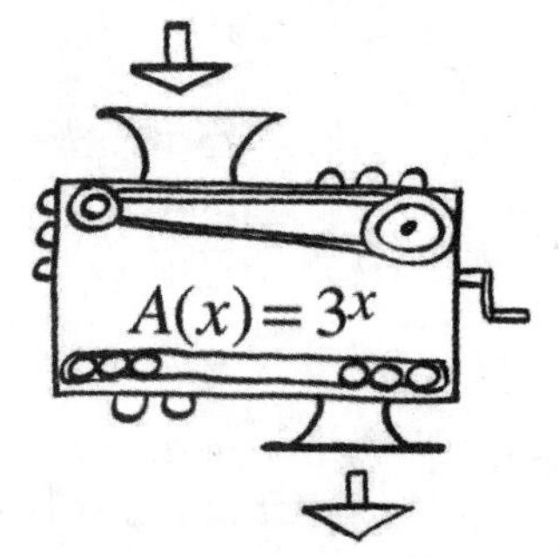

a. What is $A(2)$?

b. If 81 came out, what was dropped in?

c. If 8 came out, what was dropped in? Be accurate to two decimal places.

5-10. Nossis has been working on his geometry homework and he is almost finished. His last task is to find a solution of $\sin(x) = 0.75$. Nossis cannot figure out what x could be! Explain how he can find a value for x and show that it works.

5-11. If $10^x = 10^y$, what is true about x and y? Justify your answer.

5-12. Solve each of the following equations for x.

a. $\frac{x}{3} = \frac{4}{5}$ b. $\frac{x}{x+1} = \frac{5}{7}$ c. $\frac{6}{15} = 2 - \frac{x}{5}$ d. $\frac{2}{3} + \frac{x}{5} = 6$

5-13. Sketch the solution of this system of inequalities.

$$y \geq x^2 - 5$$
$$y \leq -(x-1)^2 + 7$$

5-14. Jamilla collected data comparing the weight and cost of pieces of sterling silver jewelry. Her data is listed as (weight in ounces, cost in dollars): $(5, 44.00)$, $(8.5, 78.50)$, $(12, 112.00)$, $(10, 93.00)$, $(7, 63.50)$, $(9, 83.20)$.

a. Plot the data on a set of axes.

b. Use a ruler to draw a line that best approximates the data.

c. Determine the equation of the line of best fit drawn in (b).

d. Use your equation to predict the cost of a 50-ounce silver bracelet.

5-15. The angle of elevation of the sun (the angle the rays of sunlight make with the flat ground) at 10:00 a.m. is $29°$. At that point, a tree's shadow is 32 feet long. How tall is the tree?

5.1.2 How can I find an inverse?

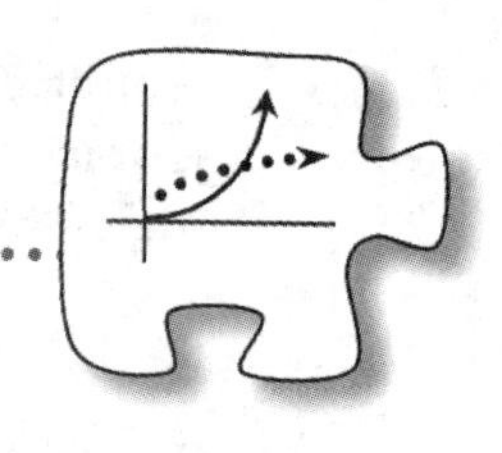

Using a Graph to Find an Inverse

What factors would you consider if you were thinking about buying a car? The first things that come to mind might be color or cost, but increasingly people are considering fuel efficiency (the number of miles a car can drive on a gallon of gas). You can think of the average number of miles per gallon that a car gets as a function that has *gallons* as the input and *miles traveled* as the output. A graph of this function would allow you to use what you know about the number of gallons in your tank to predict how far you could travel.

What would happen if you wanted to look at this situation differently? Imagine you regularly travel a route where there are many miles between gas stations. In this scenario, you would start with the information of the number of miles to the next filling station, and want to determine how many gallons of gas you would need to get there. In this case, you would start with the number of miles and work backwards to find gallons. Your new function would reverse the process.

5-16. In Lesson 5.1.1 you started with functions and worked backwards to find their inverse equations. Now you will focus on functions and their inverses represented as graphs. Use what you discovered yesterday as a basis for answering the questions below.

$y = 0.5x + 3$

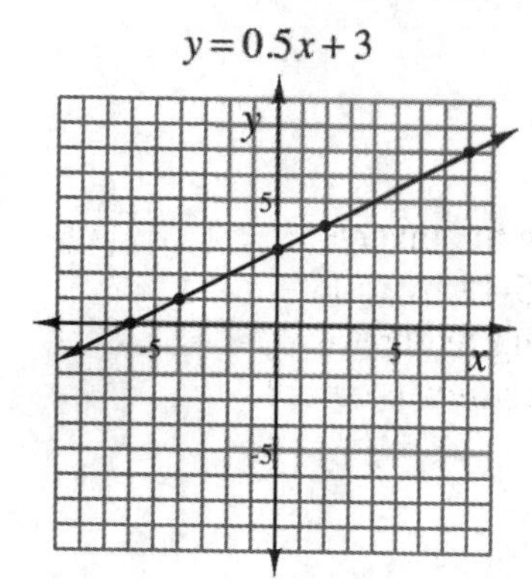

$y = 3(x+2)^2 - 6$

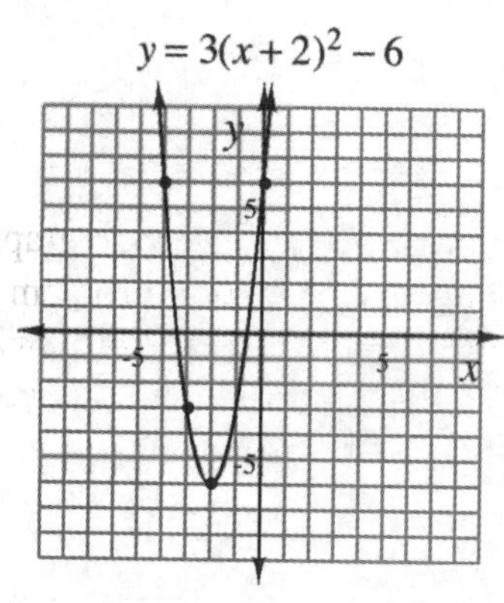

$y = \frac{1}{6}x^3 - \frac{13}{6}x + 2$

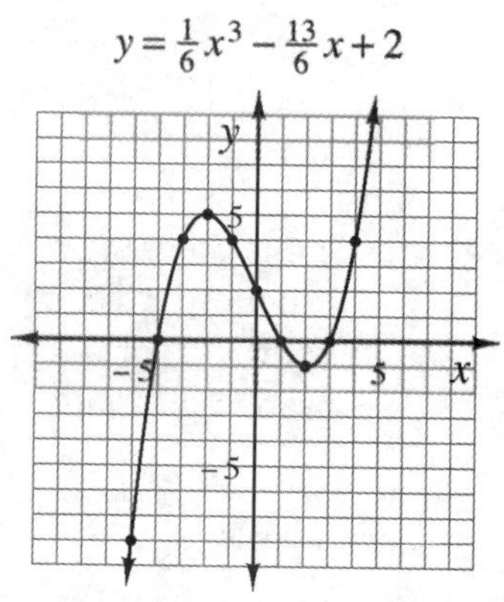

a. Obtain a Lesson 5.1.2 Resource Page from your teacher and make a careful graph of each inverse equation on the same set of axes as its corresponding function. Look for a way to make the graph without finding the inverse equation first. Be prepared to share your strategy with the class.

b. Make statements about the relationship between the coordinates of a function and the coordinates of its inverse. Use $x \rightarrow y$ tables of the function and its inverse to show what you mean.

5-17. When you look at the graph of a function and its inverse, you can see a symmetrical relationship between the two graphs demonstrated by a line of symmetry.

a. Draw the line of symmetry for each pair of graphs in problem 5-16.

b. Find the equation of the line of symmetry for each graph.

c. Why do you think this line makes sense as the line of symmetry between the graphs of a function and its inverse relation?

5-18. The line of symmetry you identified in problem 5-17 can be used to help graph the inverse of a function without creating an $x \rightarrow y$ table.

a. Graph $y = (\frac{x}{2})^2$ carefully on a full sheet of graph paper. Scale the x- and y-axes the same way on your graph.

b. On the same set of axes, graph the line of symmetry $y = x$.

c. Trace over the curve $y = (\frac{x}{2})^2$ with a pencil or crayon until the curve is heavy and dark. Then fold your paper along the line $y = x$, with the graphs on the inside of the fold. Rub the graph to make a "carbon copy" of the parabola.

d. When you open the paper you should see the graph of the inverse. Fill in any pieces of the new graph that did not copy completely. Justify that the graphs you see are inverses of each other.

5-19. Your graphing calculator can also help you to graph the inverse of a function. Check your inverse graph from problem 5-18 by following your teacher's instructions to use the inverse-drawing feature of your graphing calculator. Was the inverse graph that you drew correct?

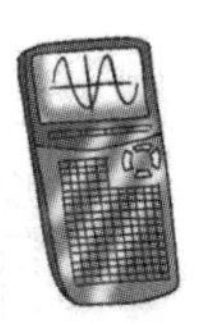

5-20. Find the equation of the inverse of $y = (\frac{x}{2})^2$. Is there another way you could write it? If so, show how the two equations are the same. Justify that your inverse equation undoes the original function and use a graphing calculator to check the graphs.

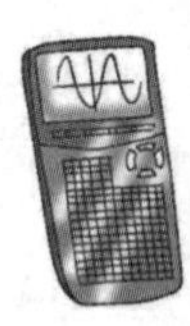

5-21. Consider your equation for the inverse of $y=(\frac{x}{2})^2$.

a. Is the inverse a function? How can you tell?

b. Use color to trace over the portion of your graph of $y=(\frac{x}{2})^2$ for which $x \geq 0$. Then use another color to trace the inverse of *only this part* of $y=(\frac{x}{2})^2$. Is the inverse of this part of $y=(\frac{x}{2})^2$ a function?

c. Find an equation for the inverse of the restricted graph of $y=(\frac{x}{2})^2$. How is this equation different from the one you found in problem 5-20?

5-22. Consider the function $f(x)=(x-3)^2$.

a. How could you restrict the domain of $f(x)$ so that its inverse will be a function?

b. Graph $f(x)$ with its restricted domain and then graph its inverse on the same set of axes.

c. Find the equation of the inverse of $f(x)$ with its restricted domain.

5-23. Is there a way to look at any graph to determine if its inverse will be a function? Explain. Find examples of other functions whose inverses are not functions.

5-24. Use graphs to find the inverses for the following functions. Label the graph of each function and its inverse with its equation.

a. $y=5(x-2)$

b. $y=1+\frac{2}{x}$

5-25. Look at the graph at right of a function and its inverse. If $p(x)$ is a function and $q(x)$ is its inverse, can you tell which is which? Why or why not?

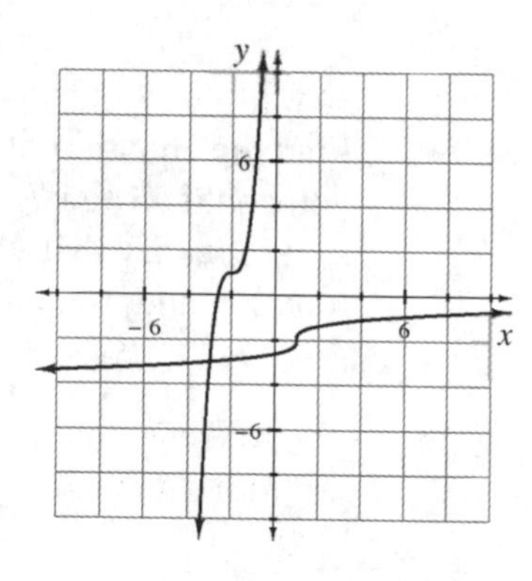

METHODS AND MEANINGS

Notation for Inverses

When given a function $f(x)$, the notation for the inverse of the function is $f^{-1}(x)$. Note that the –1 is not a negative exponent. It is the mathematical symbol that indicates the "undo" or **inverse** function of $f(x)$.

For example, if $f(x)=x^3-1$ then $f^{-1}(x)=\sqrt[3]{x+1}$.

This same inverse notation is used to identify the inverse of trigonometric functions. For example the inverse of $\sin(x)$ is written $\sin^{-1}(x)$.

5-26. Make a graph of $f(x)=\frac{1}{2}(x-1)^3$ and then graph its inverse on the same set of axes.

5-27. Write the inverse equation for each of the following equations.

a. $y=3x-8$ b. $y=\frac{1}{2}x+6$ c. $y=\frac{x+6}{2}$

5-28. Solve the equation $3=8^x$ for x, accurate to the nearest hundredth (two decimal places).

5-29. Multiply each expression below.

a. $(x+2)(x-7)$ b. $(3m+7)(2m-1)$

c. $(x-3)^2$ d. $(2y+3)(2y-3)$

5-30. Write the equation of a circle with a center at $(-3, 5)$ that is tangent to the y-axis (in other words, it touches the y-axis at only one point). Sketching a picture will help.

5-31. Perform the indicated operation to simplify each of the following expressions. In some cases, factoring may help you simplify.

a. $\frac{(x+2)(x-3)}{(x+1)(x-4)} \cdot \frac{(x+1)}{x(x+2)}$

b. $\frac{x^2+5x+6}{x^2-4} \cdot \frac{4}{x+3}$

c. $\frac{2x}{x+4} + \frac{8}{x+4}$

d. $\frac{x}{x+1} - \frac{1}{x+1}$

5-32. Barnaby's grandfather is always complaining that back when he was a teenager, he used to be able to buy his girlfriend dinner for only $1.50.

a. If that same dinner that Barnaby's grandfather purchased for $1.50 sixty years ago now costs $25.25, and the price has increased exponentially, write an equation that will give you the costs at different times.

b. How much would you expect the same dinner to cost in 60 years?

5-33. The function $f(x)$ is represented in the graph at right. Draw a graph of its inverse function. Be sure to state the domain and range for both $f(x)$ and $f^{-1}(x)$.

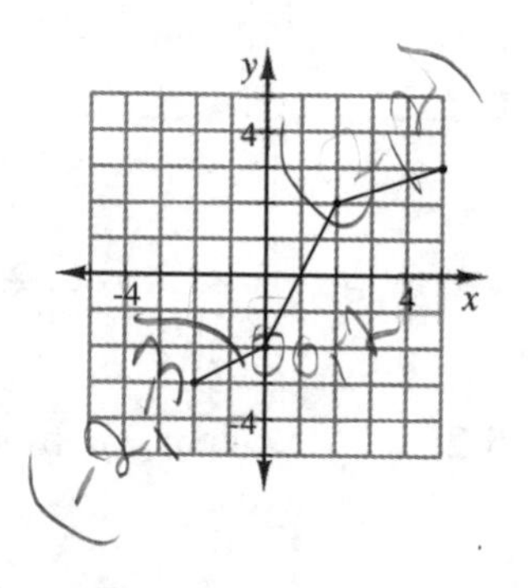

5-34. Lacey and Richens each have their own personal function machines. Lacey's machine, $L(x)$, squares the input and then subtracts one. Richens' function machine, $R(x)$, adds 2 to the input and then multiplies the result by three.

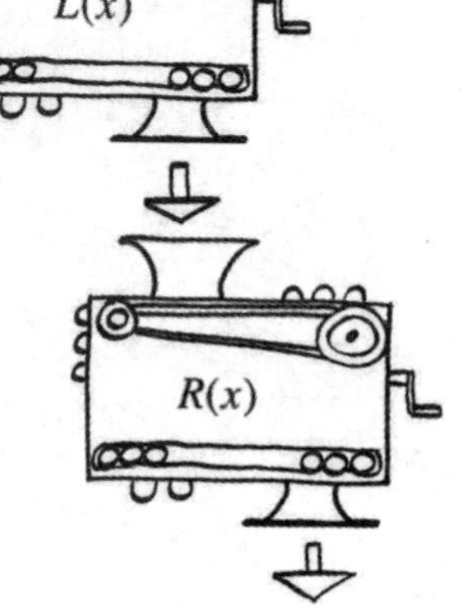

a. Write the equations that represent $L(x)$ and $R(x)$.

b. Lacey and Richens decide to connect their two machines, so that Lacey's output becomes Richens' input. If 3 is the initial input, what is the eventual output?

c. What if the order of the machines was changed? Would it change the output? Justify your answer.

5-35. Solve the system of equations at right.

$$x - 2y = 7$$
$$6y - 3x = 33$$

a. What happened? What does this mean?

b. What does the solution tell you about the graphs?

5-36. Dana's mother gave her \$175 on her sixteenth birthday. "*But you must put it in the bank and leave it there until your eighteenth birthday,*" she told Dana. Dana already had \$237.54 in her account, which pays 3.25% annual interest, compounded quarterly. If she adds her birthday money to the account, how much money will she have on her eighteenth birthday if she makes *no* withdrawals before then? Justify your answer.

5-37. Multiply each expression below.

a. $(x+4)(x-14)$

b. $(2m+5)(2m-1)$

c. $(x-9)(x+9)$

d. $(3y+2)^2$

5-38. Calculate the x-intercepts for the graph of each function below.

a. $y=(x-2)(x+1)$

b. $y=2x^2+16x+30$

5-39. If $2^{x+4}=2^{3x-1}$, what is the value of x?

5.1.3 What can I do with inverses?

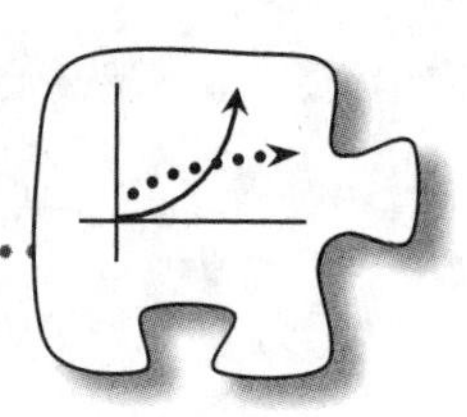

Finding Inverses and Justifying Algebraically

In this chapter you first learned how to find an inverse by undoing a function, and then you learned how to find an inverse graphically. You and your team may also have developed other strategies. In this lesson you will determine how to find an inverse by putting these ideas together and rewriting the equation. You will also learn a new way to combine functions that you can use to decide whether they have an inverse relationship.

5-40. Consider the table at right.

x	y
1	–5
3	7
5	19
7	31

a. Write an equation for the relationship represented in the table.

b. Make a table for the inverse.

c. How are these two tables related to each other?

d. Use the relationship between the tables to find a shortcut for changing the equation of the original function into its inverse.

e. Now solve this new equation for y.

f. Justify that the equations are inverses of each other.

5-41. Find the inverse function of the following functions using your new algebraic method, clearly showing all your steps.

a. $y = 2(x-1)^3$

b. $y = \sqrt{x-2} + 3$

c. $y = 3\left(\frac{x-9}{2}\right) + 20$

d. $y = \frac{4}{3}(x-1)^3 + 6$

5-42. Adriena's strategy for checking that the functions $f(x)$ and $g(x)$ are inverses is to think of them as stacked function machines. She starts by choosing an input to drop into $f(x)$. Then she drops the output from $f(x)$ into $g(x)$. If she gets her original number, she is pretty sure that the two equations are inverses.

a. Is Adriena's strategy sufficient? Is there anything else she should test to be sure?

b. With your team, select a pair of inverse equations from problem 5-41, name them $f(x)$ and $g(x)$, then use Adriena's ideas to test them.

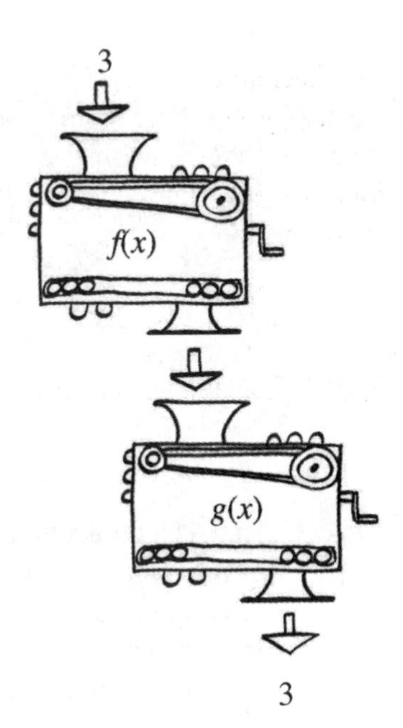

c. Adriena wants to find a shortcut to show her work. She knows that if she chooses her input for $f(x)$ to be 3, she can write the output as $f(3)$. Next, $f(3)$ becomes the input for $g(x)$, and her output is 3. Since $f(3)$ is the new input for $g(x)$, she thinks that she can write this process as $g(f(3)) = 3$. Does her idea make sense? Why or why not?

d. Her friend, Cemetra thinks she could also write $f(g(3))$. Is Cemetra correct? Why or why not.

e. Will this strategy for testing inverses work with any input? Choose a variable to use as an input to test with your team's functions, $f(x)$ and $g(x)$.

5-43. Statler, Adriena's teammate, is always looking for shortcuts. He thinks he has a way to adapt Adriena's strategy, but wants to check with his team before he tries it. *"If I use her strategy but instead of using a number, I skip a step and put the expression $f(x)$ directly into $g(x)$ to create $g(f(x))$, will I still be able to show that the equations are inverses?"*

a. What do you think about Statler's changes? What can you expect to get out?

b. Try Statler's idea on your team's equations, $f(x)$ and $g(x)$.

c. Describe your results.

d. Does Statler's strategy show that the two equations are inverses? How?

5-44. Trejo says that if you know the x-intercepts, y-intercepts, domain, and range of an equation then you automatically know the x-intercepts, y-intercepts, domain, and range for the inverse. Hilary disagrees. She says you know the intercepts but that is all you know for sure. Who is correct? Justify your answer.

5-45. Adriena was finding inverses of some equations. Use Statler's strategy from problem 5-43 to check Adriena's work below and test if each pair of equations are inverses of each other. If they are not, explain what went wrong and show how to get the inverse correctly.

a. $f(x)=\frac{3}{5}x-15$
$g(x)=\frac{5}{3}x+25$

b. $f(x)=\frac{2(x+6)}{3}+10$
$g(x)=\frac{3}{2}x-21$

c. $e(x)=\frac{(x-10)^2}{4}$
$d(x)=4\sqrt{x}+10$

5-46. Rebecca thinks that she has found a quick way to graph an inverse of a function. She figures that if you can interchange x and y to find the inverse, she can interchange the x- and y-axes by flipping the paper over so that when she looks through the back the x-axis is vertical and the y-axis is horizontal as shown in the pair of graphs at right. Copy the graph below onto your paper and try her technique. Does it work? If so, do you like this method? Why or why not?

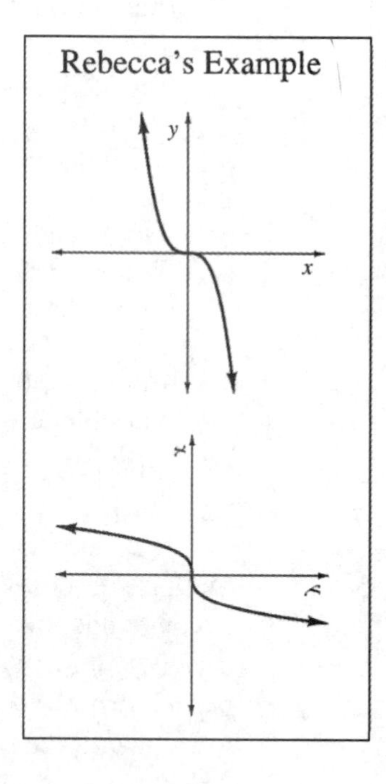

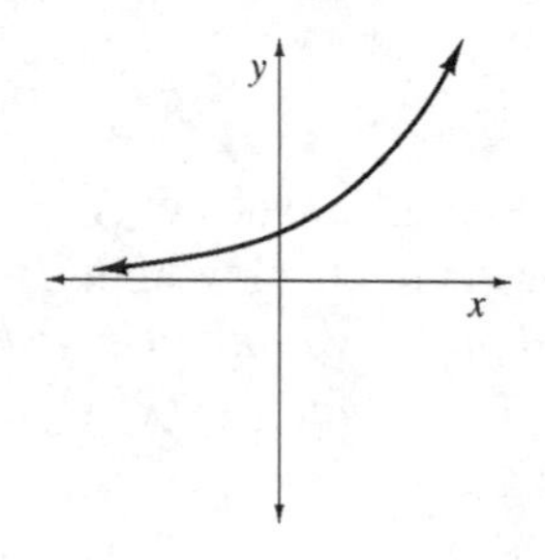

5-47. Make a personal poster that shows what you have learned about inverses so far. Choose an equation and its inverse then justify that your equations are inverses of each other using several representations.

MATH NOTES

METHODS AND MEANINGS

Composition of Functions

When you stack one function machine on top of another so that the output of the first machine becomes the input of the second, you create a new function, which is a **composition** of the two functions. If the first function is $g(x)$ and the second is $f(x)$, the composition of f and g can be written $f(g(x))$. (Note that the notations $f \circ g$ or $f \circ g(x)$ are used in some texts to denote the same composition.)

Note that the order of the composition matters. In general, the compositions $g(f(x))$ and $f(g(x))$ will be different functions.

5-48. Two function machines, $f(x) = 5x - 3$ and $g(x) = (x - 1)^2$, are shown at right.

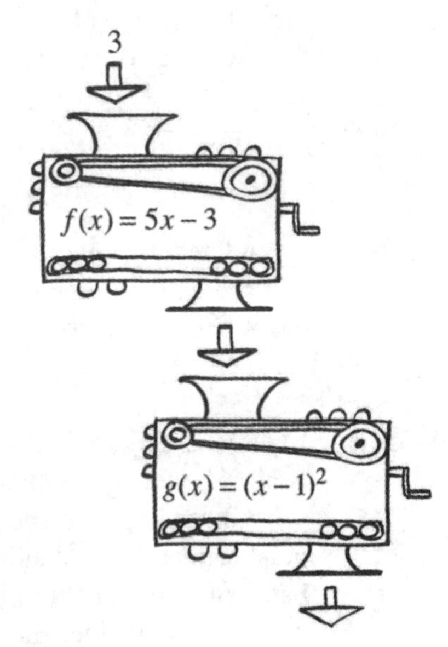

a. Suppose $f(3)$, (*not* $x = 3$), is dropped into the $g(x)$ machine. This is written as $g(f(3))$. What is this output?

b. Using the same function machines, what is $f(g(3))$? Be careful! The result is different from the last one because the *order* in which you use the machines has been switched! With $f(g(3))$, first you find $g(3)$, then you substitute that answer into the machine named $f(x)$.

5-49. This problem is a checkpoint for multiplying polynomials. It will be referred to as Checkpoint 5A.

Multiply and simplify each expression below.

a. $(x+1)(2x^2-3)$

b. $(x+1)(x^2-2x+3)$

c. $2(x+3)^2$

d. $(x+1)(2x-3)^2$

Check your answers by referring to the Checkpoint 5A materials located at the back of your book.

If you needed help solving these problems correctly, then you need more practice. Review the Checkpoint 5A materials and try the practice problems. Also, consider getting help outside of class time. From this point on, you will be expected to do problems like these quickly and easily.

5-50. Solve each of the following equations.

a. $\frac{3x}{5}=\frac{x-2}{4}$

b. $\frac{4x-1}{x}=3x$

c. $\frac{2x}{5}-\frac{1}{3}=\frac{137}{3}$

d. $\frac{4x-1}{x+1}=x-1$

5-51. Find the inverse of each of the following functions by first switching x and y and then solving for y.

a. $y=x^2+3$

b. $y=\left(\frac{1}{4}x+6\right)^3$

c. $y=\sqrt{5x-6}$

5-52. Complete the square (for x) to write the equation that follows in graphing form and sketch the graph of $x^2+y^2-4x-16=0$. What is the parent graph and how has it been transformed?

5-53. Ever eat a maggot? Guess again! The FDA publishes a list, the Food Defect Action Levels list, which indicates limits for "natural or unavoidable" substances in processed food (*Time*, October 1990). So in 100 grams of mushrooms, for instance, the government allows 20 maggots! The average batch of rich and chunky spaghetti sauce has 350 grams of mushrooms. How many maggots does the government allow in a batch?

5-54. Perform each operation below and simplify your results.

a. $\frac{x^2+4x+3}{x^2+3x}\cdot\frac{3x}{x+1}$

b. $\frac{y^2}{y+4}-\frac{16}{y+4}$

c. $\frac{x^2+x}{x^2-4x-5}\div\frac{3x^2}{x-5}$

d. $\frac{x^2-6x}{x^2-4x+4}+\frac{4x}{x^2-4x+4}$

5.2.1 How can I undo an exponential function?

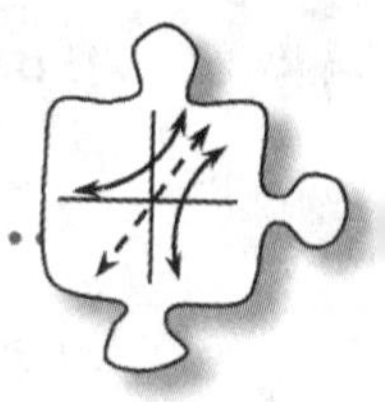

Finding the Inverse of an Exponential Function

When you first began investigating exponential functions, you looked at how their different representations were interconnected, as in the web at right. So far in this chapter, you have considered how functions and their inverses are related in different representations including equations, $x \rightarrow y$ tables, and graphs. What would the inverse equation for each of the parent functions you worked with in Chapter 2 look like in each representation?

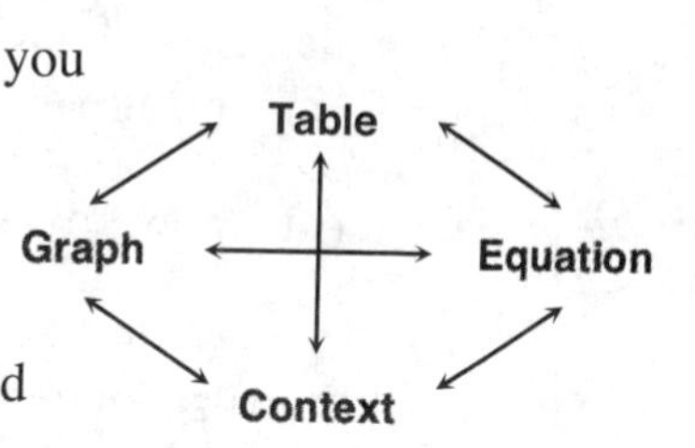

As you work with your team today, ask each other these questions:

What does the parent function look like in this representation?
How can that help us see the inverse relation?

Would another representation be more helpful?

How can we describe the relationship in words?

5-55. So far, you have worked with eight different parent graphs:

i. $y = x^2$ *ii.* $y = x^3$ *iii.* $y = x$ *iv.* $y = |x|$

v. $y = \sqrt{x}$ *vi.* $y = \frac{1}{x}$ *vii.* $y = b^x$ *viii.* $x^2 + y^2 = 1$

a. For each parent, find its inverse, if possible. If you can, write the equation of the inverse in $y =$ form. Include a sketch of each parent graph and its inverse. Remember that you can use the DrawInv function on your graphing calculator to help test your ideas.

b. Are any parent functions their own inverses? Explain how you know.

c. Do any parent functions have inverses that are not functions? If so, which ones?

5-56. THE INVERSE EXPONENTIAL FUNCTION

There are two parent functions, $y=|x|$ and $y=b^x$, that have inverses that you do not yet know how to write in y = form. You will come back to $y=|x|$ later. Since exponential functions are so useful for modeling situations in the world, the inverse of an exponential function is also important. Use $y=3^x$ as an example. Even though you may not know how to write the inverse of $y=3^x$ in y = form, you already know a lot about it.

a. You know how to make an $x \rightarrow y$ table for the inverse of $y=3^x$. Make the table.

b. You also know what the graph of the inverse looks like. Sketch the graph.

c. You also have one way to write the equation based on your algebraic shortcut that you used in part (d) of problem 5-40. Write an equation for the inverse, even though it may not be in y = form.

d. If the input for the inverse function is 81, what is the output? If you could write an equation for this function in y = form, or as a function $g(x)=$, and you put in any number for x, how would you describe the outcome?

5-57. AN ANCIENT PUZZLE

Parts (a) through (f) below are similar to a puzzle that is more than 2100 years old. Mathematicians first created the puzzle in ancient India in the 2nd century BC. More recently, about 700 years ago, Muslim mathematicians created the first tables allowing them to find answers to this type of puzzle quickly. Tables similar to them appeared in school math books until recently.

Here are some clues to help you figure out how the puzzle works:

$\log_2 8 = 3$ $\qquad$ $\log_3 27 = 3$

$\log_5 25 = 2$ $\qquad$ $\log_{10} 10{,}000 = 4$

Use the clues to find the missing pieces of the puzzles below:

a. $\log_2 16 = ?$ $\qquad$ b. $\log_2 32 = ?$ $\qquad$ c. $\log_? 100 = 2$

d. $\log_5 ? = 3$ $\qquad$ e. $\log_? 81 = 4$ $\qquad$ f. $\log_{100} 10 = ?$

5-58. How is the Ancient Puzzle related to the problem of the inverse function for $y=3^x$ in problem 5-56? Show how you can use the idea in the Ancient Puzzle to write an equation in y = form or as $g(x)=$ for the inverse function in problem 5-56.

5-59. THE INVERSE OF ABSOLUTE VALUE

a. Find the inverse equation and graph of $y = 2|x+1|$.

b. Although you know how to find the table, graph, and equation for the inverse of absolute value, this is another function whose inverse equation cannot easily be written in $y =$ form. In fact, there is no standard notation for the inverse of the absolute value function. With your team, invent a symbol to represent the inverse, and give examples to show how your symbol works. Be sure to explain how your symbol handles that fact that the inverse of $y = |x|$ is not a function or explain why it is difficult to come up with a reasonable notation.

5-60. In problem 5-56, you looked at the inverse of $y = 3^x$. Finish investigating this function.

5-61. Consider the function $f(x) = \frac{2}{7-x}$.

a. What is $f(7)$?

b. What is the domain of $f(x)$?

c. If $g(x) = 2x+5$, what is $g(3)$?

d. Now use the output of $g(3)$ as the input for f to calculate $f(g(3))$.

5-62. Amanda wants to showcase her favorite function: $f(x) = 1 + \sqrt{x+5}$. She has built a function machine that performs these operations on the input values. Her brother Eric is always trying to mess up Amanda's stuff, so he created the inverse of $f(x)$, called it $e(x)$, and programmed it into a machine.

a. What is Eric's equation for his function $e(x)$?

b. What happens if the two machines are pushed together? What is $e(f(-4))$? Explain why this happens.

c. If $f(x)$ and $e(x)$ are graphed on the same set of axes, what would be true about the two graphs?

d. Draw the two graphs on the same set of axes. Be sure to show clearly the restricted domain and range of Amanda's function.

5-63. Sketch the graph of $y+3=2^x$.

a. What are the domain and range of this function?

b. Does this function have a line of symmetry? If so, what is it?

c. What are the x- and y-intercepts?

d. Change the equation so that the graph of the new equation has no x-intercepts.

5-64. Solve for x in the following problems.

a.

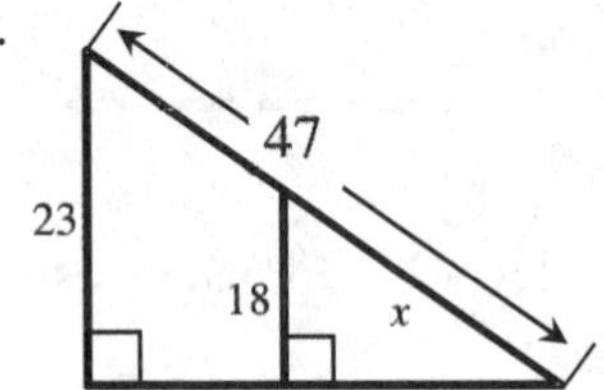

b.

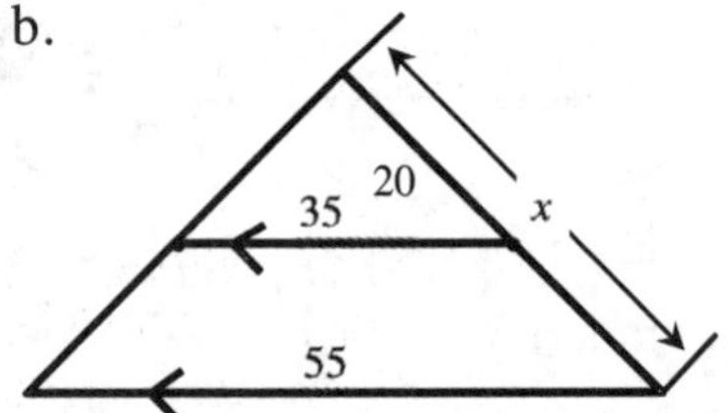

5-65. A woman plans to invest x dollars. Her investment counselor advises her that a safe plan is to invest 30% of that money in bonds and 70% in low risk stocks. The bonds currently have a simple interest rate of 7% and the stock has a dividend rate (like simple interest) of 9%.

a. Write an expression for the annual income that will come from the bond investment.

b. Write an expression for the annual income that will come from the stock investment.

c. Write an equation and solve it to find out how much the client needs to invest to have an annual income of $5,000.

5-66. Factor each expression completely.

a. x^2-49 b. $6x^2+48x$ c. x^2-x-72 d. $2x^3-8x$

5-67. Sketch the solution to this system of inequalities.

$$y \geq (x+5)^2-6$$
$$y \leq -(x+4)^2-1$$

5.2.2 What is a logarithm?

Defining the Inverse of an Exponential Function

You have learned how to "undo" many different functions. However, the exponential function has posed some difficulty. In this lesson, you will learn more about the inverse exponential function. In particular, you will learn how to write an inverse exponential function in $y =$ form.

5-68. SILENT BOARD GAME

Your teacher will put an $x \rightarrow y$ table on the board or overhead that the whole class will work together to complete. The table will be like the one below. See which values you can fill in.

x	8	32	$\frac{1}{2}$	1	16	4	3	64	2	0	0.25	−1	$\sqrt{2}$	0.2	$\frac{1}{8}$
$g(x)$	3	5	−1	0	4	2	≈1.6	6	1	N/A	−2	N/A	1/2	−2.3	−3

a. Describe an equation that relates x and $g(x)$.

b. Look back at the Ancient Puzzle in problem 5-57. If you have not already done so, use the idea of the Ancient Puzzle to write an equation for $g(x)$.

c. Why was it difficult to think of an output for the input of 0 or −1?

d. Find an output for $x = 25$ to the nearest hundredth.

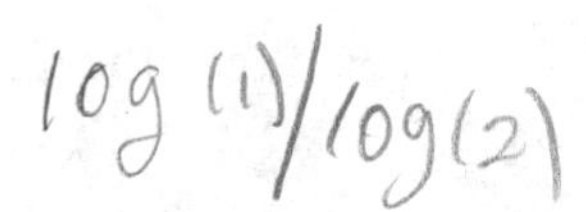

5-69. ANOTHER LOGARITHM TABLE

Lynn was supposed to fill in this table for $g(x)=\log_5 x$. She thought she could use the log button on her calculator, but when she tried to enter 5, 25, and 125, she did not get the outputs the table below displays. She was fuming over how long it was going to take to guess and check each one when her sister suggested that she did not have to do that for all of them. She could fill in a few more and then use what she knew about exponents to figure out some of the others.

x	$\frac{1}{25}$	$\frac{1}{5}$	$\frac{1}{2}$	1	2	3	4	5	6	7	8	10	25	100	125	625
$g(x)$	-2	–1	~-.43	0	.43	.68	.86	1	1.11	1.21	1.3	1.43	2	2.86	3	4

a. Discuss with your team which outputs can be filled in without a calculator. Fill those in and explain how you found these entries.

b. With your team, use your calculator to estimate the remaining values of $g(x)$ to the nearest hundredth. Once you have entered several, use your knowledge of exponent rules to see if you can find any shortcuts.

c. What do you notice about the results for $g(x)$ as x increases?

d. Use your table to draw the graph of $y=\log_5 x$. How does your graph compare to the graph of $y=5^x$?

5-70. Find each of the values below, and then justify your answers by writing the equivalent exponential form.

a. $\log_2(32)=?$ 5 $\quad 2^5=32$

b. $\log_2(\frac{1}{2})=?$ –1 $\quad 2^{-1}=1/2$

c. $\log_2(4)=?$ 2 $\quad 2^2=4$

d. $\log_2(0)=?$ N/A

e. $\log_2(?)=3$ $\quad 2^x=3$, $1.58\approx x$

f. $\log_2(?)=\frac{1}{2}$ $\quad 2^x=1/2$ $\sqrt{2}$ ~~$2^{-1}=1/2$~~

g. $\log_2(\frac{1}{16})=?$ $\quad 2^4=16$, $2^{-4}=1/16$

h. $\log_2(?)=0$ N/A

5-71. While the idea behind the Ancient Puzzle is more than 2100 years old, the symbol **log** is more recent. It was created by John Napier, a Scottish mathematician in the 1600's. "log" is short for **logarithm**, and represents the function that is the **inverse of an exponential function**. You can use this idea to find the inverse equations of each of the following functions. Find the inverses and write your answers in $y =$ form.

a. $y=\log_9(x)$ $\quad 9^y=x$

b. $y=10^x$ $\quad x=10^y$

c. $y=\log_6(x+1)$ $\quad 6^y=x+1$

d. $y=5^{2x}$ $\quad x=5^{2y}$

5-72. Practice your logarithm fluency by calculating each of the following, *without changing the expressions to exponential form*. Be ready to explain your thinking.

a. $\log_7 49 =$ __ b. $\log_3 81 =$ __ c. $\log_5 5^7 =$ __

d. $\log_{10} 10^{1.2} =$ __ e. $\log_2 2^{w+3} =$ __

METHODS AND MEANINGS

MATH NOTES

Logarithms and Their Notation

A **logarithm** (called a "log" for short) is an exponent. An expression in logarithmic form, such as $\log_2(32)$, is read, *"the log, base 2, of 32."* To evaluate log expressions, think of the exponent: $\log_2(32) = 5$, because the exponent needed for base 2 to become 32 is 5.

An equation in logarithmic form is equivalent to another equation in exponential form, as shown at right. This conversion helps show why (based on an $x \to y$ interchange) $y = \log_b(x)$ and $y = b^x$ are inverse functions.

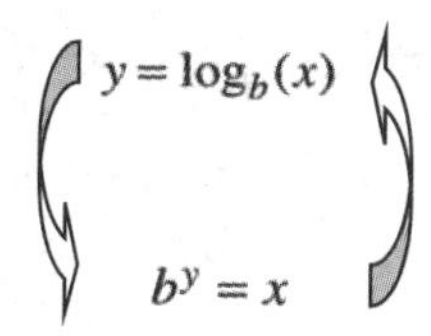

5-73. Let $y = \log_2(x)$. Rewrite the equation so that it begins with $x =$. Think about how you defined $y = \log_2(x)$ if you get stuck. Put a large box around both equations. Do the two equations look the same? Do the two equations mean the same thing? Are they equivalent? How do you know? This is very important. Think about it, and write a clear explanation.

exp form
$a^y = x$

log form
$\log_a x = y$
base
exponent

ex $\log_2 8 = 3$ $2^3 = 8$

5-74. Every exponential equation has an equivalent logarithmic form and every logarithmic equation has an equivalent exponential form. For example:

exponent ↓

$4^3 = 64$ is equivalent to $3 = \log_4 64$

↑ base   ↑ exponent ↑ base

Copy the table shown below and fill in the missing form in each row.

	Exponential Form	Logarithmic Form
a.	$y = 5^x$	
b.		$y = \log_7(x)$
c.	$8^x = y$	
d.	$A^K = C$	
e.		$K = \log_A(C)$
f.		$\log_{1/2}(K) = N$

5-75. Suppose you want to buy sugar. Packages of different sizes cost different amounts, but the relationship is not always proportional. That is, a bag twice as big does not usually cost twice as much. The chart shows the prices for various sizes of bags of sugar.

½ lb bag	\$0.95
1 lb bag	\$1.38
2 lb bag	\$1.92
5 lb bag	\$4.70
10 lb bag	\$9.04
20 lb bag	\$17.52

a. Find the rates in cost per pound. (Stores refer to this as unit pricing.)

b. Does the unit price increase or decrease with the size of the bag?

c. Does the unit rate change more drastically for smaller sizes or for larger sizes?

5-76. Although the Quadratic Formula always works as a strategy to solve quadratic equations, for many problems it is not the most efficient method. Sometimes it is faster to factor or complete the square or even just "out-think" the problem. For each equation below, choose the method you think is most efficient to solve the equation and explain your reason. Then solve the problems that can be factored.

a. $x^2 + 7x - 8 = 0$

b. $(x+2)^2 = 49$

c. $5x^2 - x - 7 = 0$

d. $x^2 + 4x = -1$

5-77. If $10^{3x} = 10^{(x-8)}$, solve for x. Show that your solution works by checking your answer.

5-78. Find the value of x in each diagram below.

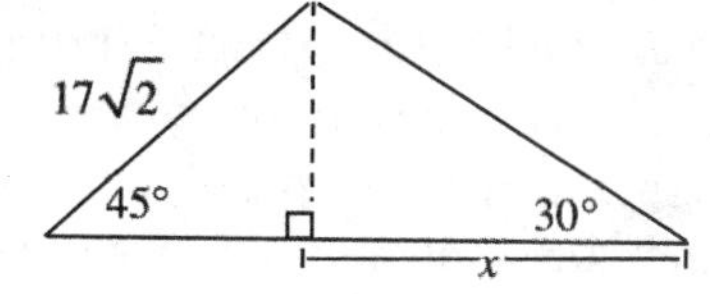

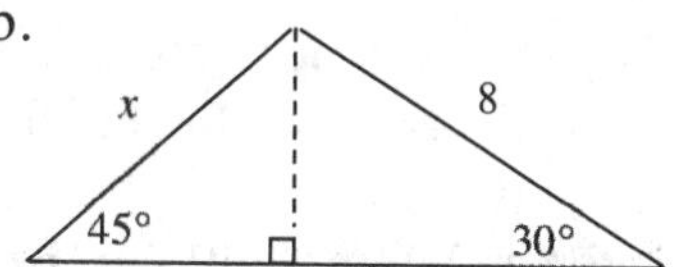

5-79. Consider the function defined by inputs that are the length of the radii of a circle, and the outputs are the areas of those circles. Write the equation for this function and investigate it completely.

5-80. Consider the equation $y = (x+6)^2 - 7$.

a. Explain completely how to get a good sketch of the graph of $y = (x+6)^2 - 7$.

b. Explain how to change the graph from part (a) to represent the graph of $y = (x+6)^2 + 2$.

c. Given your original graph, how can you get the graph of $y = \left|(x+6)^2 - 7\right|$?

d. Restrict the domain of the original parabola to $x \geq -6$ and graph its inverse function.

e. What would be the equation for the inverse function if you restricted the domain to $x \geq -6$?

5.2.3 What can I learn about logs?

Investigating the Family of Logarithmic Functions

In the last two lessons you have learned what a log is and how to convert an equation in log form to exponential form (and back again). In this lesson, you will explore logs as a family of functions.

5-81. INVESTIGATING THE FAMILY OF LOGARITHMIC FUNCTIONS

You have learned that a logarithm is the inverse of an exponential function. Since exponential functions can have different bases, so can logarithms. Investigate the family of logarithmic functions $y = \log_b(x)$. The questions below will help you investigate.

Your Task: Generate data with your team and use it to write summary statements about this family of functions. For each summary statement you find, prepare a poster that shows and explains the summary statement and be prepared to present it to the class. Remember that summary statements should always include thorough justification.

Discussion Points

How can we collect data for this family? How much data is enough?

What have we learned about logs and inverses that can help us work with this family? How can "DrawInv" help?

What patterns can we find in our data? Why do they happen?

What are all the possible inputs for our function? Are there some x-values that do not make sense? Why or why not? How do these results appear in different mathematical representations?

What are some characteristics that all logarithmic functions have in common?

What happens as the value of b changes? What values of b make sense?

Further Guidance

5-82. As a team, begin your investigation of $y = \log_b x$ by choosing a positive value for b and work together to generate a table and a graph. Then, have each member of your team choose a different value for b. Since there is no key for a log of base b on your calculator, you will need to find another method to generate data for a table. Several strategies are suggested below.

- While it may still be hard to make a table for your equation, your knowledge of inverses will help you. Write the inverse of your equation and make an $x \rightarrow y$ table for it. Use this table to help you make a table for your original function.
- Use the calculator to guess and check possible outcomes.
- Rewrite your log equation as an equivalent exponential equation and reverse your thinking.

Further Guidance section ends here.

5-83. LEARNING LOG

Write a Learning Log entry about the family of functions $y = \log_b x$. Include the summary statements your team came up with and any others that you think should be added from the class discussion. As you write, think about which statements are very clear to you and which need further clarification. Title this entry "The Family of Logarithmic Functions" and label it with today's date.

5-84. Write the equation of an increasing exponential function that has a horizontal asymptote at $y = 15$.

5-85. If $x = 7^y$, how would you write this equation in $y =$ form? Explain.

5-86. Solve for n: $n^3 = 49$.

5-87. A circle has the equation $x^2 + (y+2)^2 = r^2$. If the circle is shifted 2 units to the left, 5 units up, and the radius is doubled, what will its new equation be?

5-88. On Wednesdays at Tara's Taquería four tacos are the same price as three burritos. Last Wednesday the Lunch Bunch ordered five tacos and six burritos, and their total bill was $8.58 (with no tax or drinks included). Nobody in the Lunch Bunch can remember the cost of one of Tara's tacos. Help them figure it out.

5-89. Graph the two functions at right on the same set of axes.

$y = 3(2^x)$

$y = 3(2^x) + 10$

a. How do the two graphs compare?

b. Suppose the first equation is $y = km^x$ and the graph is shifted up b units. What is the new equation?

5-90. Solve each equation or inequality.

a. $|x-1| = 9$

b. $2|x+1| + 3 = 9$

c. $|x-1| < 3$

d. $|x+5| \geq 8$

5-91. Factor each expression below.

a. $x^2 + 8x$

b. $x^2y^2 - 81z^2$

c. $2x^2 + 14x - 16$

d. $3x^2 - 11x - 4$

5-92. For each of the following rational expressions, add or subtract, then simplify.

a. $\frac{2-x}{x+4} + \frac{3x+6}{x+4}$

b. $\frac{3}{(x+2)(x+3)} + \frac{x}{(x+2)(x+3)}$

c. $\frac{3}{x-1} - \frac{2}{x-2}$

d. $\frac{8}{x} - \frac{4}{x+2}$

5.2.4 How can I transform log functions?

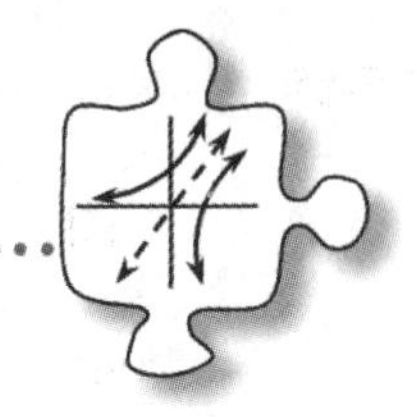

Transformations of Logarithmic Functions

In Lesson 5.2.3, you investigated logarithmic functions with different bases. To do this, you had to convert a log equation into its corresponding exponential form. In this lesson, you will figure out what a calculator can and cannot do with logs. This will help you write a general equation for a log function. As you work with your team, use the following questions to help focus your discussions.

What is a log?

How are logarithms and exponential equations related to each other?

How can we find an equivalent exponential equation for an equation that is in log form?

How can we transform the graphs of log functions?

5-93. SOLVE THE LOG MYSTERY!

Have you noticed the LOG key on your calculator? Clearly it is a logarithm, but what is its base? It would have been nice if the designers of your graphing calculator had allowed the LOG key to work with any base, but they did not!

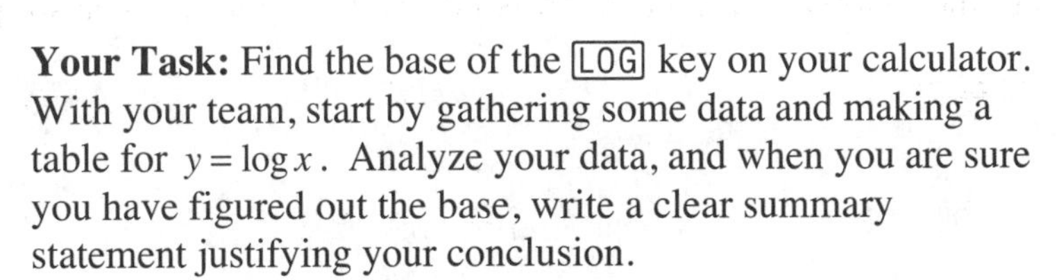

Your Task: Find the base of the LOG key on your calculator. With your team, start by gathering some data and making a table for $y = \log x$. Analyze your data, and when you are sure you have figured out the base, write a clear summary statement justifying your conclusion.

Discussion Points

What input values give whole number outputs?
What do those values tell us?

How can we rewrite $y = \log_{?} x$?

5-94. Now that you know the base of $f(x) = \log x$, you are ready to use your transformation skills to write a general equation.

a. Copy and complete the following table for $f(x) = \log x$.

x								1	2	3	4	5	6
y	–6	–5	–4	–3	–2	–1	0						

b. Using a full sheet of graph paper, make an accurate graph of $f(x) = \log(x)$. Remember that, just like the graphs of exponential functions, the graphs of log functions have asymptotes, so make sure any asymptotes on your graph are clearly shown.

c. Find all of the possible types of transformations of the graph of $f(x) = \log x$. For each transformation you find, show the graph and its equation. Then, find the general form for this family of logarithm graphs. Be prepared to explain your reasoning to the class.

5-95. You have learned a lot about logs in a short time. Use what you have learned so far to answer the questions below.

a. Why does your calculator say that $\log(6) \approx 0.778$?

b. Justify why $\log(6)$ must have a value less than 1 but greater than 0.

c. Create a Learning Log entry that includes your answers to the focus questions from today's lesson, reprinted below. Show examples and use color or arrows to help explain your ideas. Title this entry "Working with Logs" and label it with today's date.

What is a log?

How are logarithms and exponential equations related to each other?

How can you find an equivalent exponential equation for an equation that is in log form?

How can you transform the graphs of log functions?

5-96. Last night, while on patrol, Agent 008 came upon a spaceship! He hid behind a tree and watched a group of little space creatures carry all sorts of equipment out of the ship. But suddenly, he sneezed. The creatures jumped back into their ship and sped off into the night. 008 noticed that they had dropped something, so he went to pick it up. It was a calculator! What a great find. He noticed that it had a LOG button, but he noticed something interesting: $\log 10$ did not equal 1! With this calculator, $\log 10 \approx 0.926628408$. He tried some more: $\log 100 \approx 1.853256816$ and $\log 1000 \approx 2.779885224$.

a. What base do the space creatures work in? Explain how you can tell.

b. How many fingers do you think the space creatures have?

5-97. Copy these equations and solve for x. You should be able to do all these problems without a calculator.

a. $\log_x(25) = 1$ b. $x = \log_3(9)$ c. $3 = \log_7(x)$

d. $\log_3(x) = \frac{1}{2}$ e. $3 = \log_x(27)$ f. $\log_{10}(10000) = x$

5-98. Is $\log(0.3)$ greater than or less than one? Justify your answer.

5-99. Solve $1.04^x = 2$. Your answer should be accurate to three decimal places.

5-100. This problem is a checkpoint for factoring quadratics. It will be referred to as Checkpoint 5B.

Factor each expression below.

a. $4x^2 - 1$

b. $4x^2 + 4x + 1$

c. $2y^2 + 5y + 2$

d. $3m^2 - 5m - 2$

Check your answers by referring to the Checkpoint 5B materials located at the back of your book.

If you needed help solving these problems correctly, then you need more practice. Review the Checkpoint 5B materials and try the practice problems. Also, consider getting help outside of class time. From this point on, you will be expected to do problems like these quickly and easily.

5-101. Solve the following inequalities.

a. $x^2 - 2x < 3$

b. $3x - x^2 \le 2$

5-102. Is it true that $\log_3(2) = \log_2(3)$? Justify your answer.

5-103. Consider the general form of an exponential function: $y = ab^x$.

a. Solve for a.

b. Solve for b.

5-104. Make a sketch of a graph that is a decreasing exponential function with the x-axis as the horizontal asymptote. Then make a similar sketch, but this time with the line $y = 5$ as the horizontal asymptote.

5.2.5 How can I build a new function?

Investigating Compositions of Functions

Today you will work with your team to create and analyze new, interesting functions that are compositions of functions with which you are already familiar.

5-105. Polly Parabola's first corporate venture, Professional Parabola Productions, was so successful that Felix's Famous Functions bought her out in a corporate takeover. With all of the money she made from the transaction, she has decided to start a new company, Creative Compositions. Creative Compositions plans to develop a line of composite functions designed to appeal to the imagination of the next generation of function groupies. She wants to market three new functions and is offering huge contracts to the winners of the competition. Your boss wants your company to enter this competition and has assigned your team to the development department.

CREATIVE COMPOSITIONS

Call for new and visually interesting compositions of functions

The Creative Composition Corporation announces an open competition for contracts to design new products. The products must be a composition of two or more functions whose parent functions are listed below:

$f(x)=x^2$ $g(x)=x^3$ $h(x)=2^x$ $i(x)=\frac{1}{x}$ $j(x)=\sqrt{x}$ $k(x)=|x|$ $l(x)=\log_3 x$

Competing teams will prepare a poster to display their composite function and respond to questions from a panel of judges. Three contracts will be awarded based on the evaluation of the judges.

The judges will base their review on the following:

Is the graph of the composition a new and interesting shape?

Are multiple representations used effectively to show key features of the new function?

Does the selection of examples show off a variety of ways the function will appear when it is transformed?

Problem continues on next page →

5-105. *Problem continued from previous page.*

Your Task: With your team, try out different ways to write compositions involving two or more of the given functions and check their graphs. Record everything you try as documentation for the report you will need to give your boss. When your team agrees on a function they like, investigate it thoroughly and prepare a poster for the competition.

Discussion Points

What does the graph of each function look like separately?

How does making the output of one function the input of the other change the original graph?

How do we have to adjust the domains and ranges?

Is the inverse a function?

Further Guidance

5-106. Consider $h(x)=2^x$ and $k(x)=|x|$. Write the equation for each composite function $k(h(x))$ and $h(k(x))$. Discuss what each graph will look like and then sketch it. For each graph, explain the effect of one parent function on the other.

5-107. Choose other pairs of parent functions from the list. Then write the composite functions in both directions. In other words, use one function as the input for the other and then switch. Check the graphs and decide whether either is a good candidate for the competition. Try out at least five different pairs and record your equations and sketches of their graphs.

5-108. As a team, decide which of the functions you created that you want to enter in the competition. Now do a thorough investigation of that function.

5-109. Prepare a poster to show off your new function. Be sure to include all of the important details from your investigation on your poster and be prepared to respond to the judges with your arguments for why this function should be selected as one of the new products of Creative Compositions.

Further Guidance section ends here.

5-110. Consider the functions $f(x)$ in parts (a) and (b) below. For each $f(x)$, find two functions $h(x)$ and $g(x)$, so that $h(g(x)) = f(x)$. Use numerical examples to demonstrate that your functions $h(x)$ and $g(x)$ work.

a. $f(x) = \sqrt{3x+6}$

b. $f(x) = \frac{5}{\sqrt{x}}$

c. **Additional Challenge:** Work with your team to find another possibility for $h(x)$ and $g(x)$ such that $h(g(x)) = f(x)$ for each function given in parts (a) and (b). Be prepared to share your ideas with the class.

5-111. LEARNING LOG

Create a Learning Log entry explaining what you have learned about compositions of functions. Use examples to illustrate your ideas. Title this entry "Compositions of Functions" and label it with today's date.

5-112. If $f(x) = \sqrt{7-x} - 6$ and $g(x) = -(x+6)^2 + 7$, find $f(g(x))$ and $g(f(x))$. What do the results tell you about $f(x)$ and $g(x)$?

5-113. For functions of the form $f(x) = mx$, it is true that $f(a) + f(b) = f(a+b)$? For example, when $f(x) = 5x$, $f(a) + f(b) = 5a + 5b = 5(a+b)$ and $f(a+b) = 5(a+b)$. Is $f(a) + f(b) = f(a+b)$ true for all linear functions? Explain why or show why not.

5-114. Find the value of x in the equation $2^x = 3$. Make your answer accurate to three decimal places.

5-115. Consider the following three sequences:

$t(n) = 50 - 7n$ $\qquad h(n) = 4 \cdot 3^n$ $\qquad q(n) = n^2 - 6n + 17$

a. Which, if any, is arithmetic? Geometric? Neither?

b. Are there any terms that all three sequences have in common? Justify how you know for sure.

c. Are there any terms that two of them share? Justify how you know for sure.

5-116. Using the sequences in the previous problem, suppose we define a new sequence, $s(n)$, defined as $s(n) = q(t(n))$, a composition of two sequences. Do you think the new sequence will be arithmetic? Geometric? Neither? Explain. Make a table of values. Does the table support your hypothesis, or do you want to change your guess? Explain.

5-117. Gary has his function $g(x) = 10^x$ and Amy has her function $a(m) = 10^m$.

a. Each person is going to choose a whole number at random from the numbers 1, 2, 3...10, and substitute it into his or her respective function. After they do this, what is the probability that $g(x) = a(m)$?

b. Find and simplify an expression for $g(x) \cdot a(m)$.

5-118. Sketch the graph of $y = 3\log(x+4) - 1$.

5-119. Solve the system of equations at right.

$$x + y = -3$$
$$2x - y = -6$$
$$3x - 2y + 5z = 16$$

5-120. Solve for m: $m^5 = 50$.

5-121. Consider two functions $f(x) = \log x$ and $g(x) = |x|$.

a. Use these two functions to write an equation for a composite function and sketch its graph.

b. Use these two functions to write a different composite function and sketch its graph.

c. What makes the two composite functions so different from each other?

d. **Challenge:** Now try graphing $g(f(g(x)))$.

5-122. Sketch square $ABCD$ on your paper, then randomly choose a point on $\overline{AB}$ and label it X. Draw $\overline{XC}$ and $\overline{XD}$ to form ΔXCD. If a dart is thrown and lands inside the square, what is the probability that it landed inside ΔXCD? Does it matter where you place X on $\overline{AB}$?

5-123. Solve $5^x = 15$ for x. Make your answer accurate to two decimal places.

5-124. Some of the following algebraic fractions have common denominators and some do not. Add or subtract the expressions and, if possible, simplify.

a. $\frac{3}{(x-4)(x+1)} + \frac{6}{x+1}$

b. $\frac{5}{2(x-5)} + \frac{3x}{x-5}$

c. $\frac{x}{x^2-x-2} - \frac{2}{x^2-x-2}$

d. $\frac{x+2}{x^2-9} - \frac{1}{x+3}$

5-125. Simplify each of the expressions in parts (a) through (c) below.

a. $ab(\frac{1}{a} + \frac{1}{b})$

b. $cd(\frac{3}{c} + \frac{2c}{d})$

c. $x(1 - \frac{1}{x})$

d. What expression would go in the box in order to make the equation $\square\left(\frac{5}{x} + \frac{8}{y}\right) = 5y + 8x$ true?

Chapter 5 Closure What have I learned?

Reflection and Synthesis

The activities below offer you a chance to reflect about what you have learned during this chapter. As you work, look for concepts that you feel very comfortable with, ideas that you would like to learn more about, and topics you need more help with. Look for connections between ideas as well as connections with material you learned previously.

① TEAM BRAINSTORM

What have you studied in this chapter? What ideas were important in what you learned? With your team, brainstorm a list. Be as detailed as you can. To help get you started, a list of Learning Log entries and Math Notes boxes are below.

What topics, ideas, and words that you learned *before* this chapter are connected to the new ideas in this chapter? Again, be as detailed as you can.

How long can you make your list? Challenge yourselves. Be prepared to share your team's ideas with the class.

Learning Log Entries

- Lesson 5.1.1 – Finding and Checking Inverse Equations
- Lesson 5.2.3 – The Family of Logarithmic Functions
- Lesson 5.2.4 – Working with Logs
- Lesson 5.2.5 – Composition of Functions

Math Notes

- Lesson 5.1.2 – Notation for Inverses
- Lesson 5.1.3 – Composition of Functions
- Lesson 5.2.2 – Logarithms and Their Notation

② MAKING CONNECTIONS

Below is a list of the vocabulary used in this chapter. Make sure that you are familiar with all of these words and know what they mean. Refer to the glossary or index for any words that you do not yet understand.

asymptote	composite function	domain
exponential equation	$f^{-1}(x)$	inverse function
inverse relation	line of symmetry	logarithm
range	undo	$y = x$

Make a concept map showing all of the connections you can find among the key words and ideas listed above. To show a connection between two words, draw a line between them and explain the connection. A word can be connected to any other word as long as you can justify the connection. For each key word or idea, provide an example or sketch that shows the idea.

While you are making your map, your team may think of related words or ideas that are not listed here. Be sure to include these ideas on your concept map.

③ PORTFOLIO: EVIDENCE OF MATHEMATICAL PROFICIENCY

This section gives you an opportunity to show growth in your understanding of key mathematical ideas over time as you complete this course.

Include your investigation from problem 5-81 INVESTIGATING THE FAMILY OF LOGARITHMIC FUNCTIONS in your portfolio. Copy it over neatly and enhance your explanations if necessary.

Then investigate the following problem. (If you completed Appendix B in this course, you may have seen this problem already at the end of that appendix. Now you should have new graphs to add to your list of examples. You should expect to be able to add even more when you revisit this problem again at the end of Chapter 8.)

How many different kinds of graphs can you create that have:

a. No x-intercepts?

b. One x-intercept?

c. Two x-intercepts?

d. Three or more x-intercepts?

For each type of graph, show a sketch, label the key points, and give its equation. Make sure that each graph you give as an example represents a different family and describe the family in words or with a general equation. Show how to calculate the x-intercepts of each of your sample graphs.

Your teacher may assign you the Chapter 5 Closure Resource Page: Inverses GO to include in your portfolio.

④ WHAT HAVE I LEARNED?

Most of the problems in this section represent typical problems found in this chapter. They serve as a gauge for you. You can use them to determine which types of problems you can do well and which types of problems require further study and practice. Even if your teacher does not assign this section, it is a good idea to try these problems and find out for yourself what you know and what you still need to work on.

Solve each problem as completely as you can. The table at the end of the closure section has answers to these problems. It also tells you where you can find additional help and practice with problems like these.

CL 5-126. Quinten and his sister Kelsey always make a habit of undoing each other's work. If Kelsey folds the laundry, Quinten unfolds it. If Quinten rakes the leaves in the yard, Kelsey "unrakes" them! While working on her math homework, Kelsey wrote the following equations. Help Quinten undo these equations by finding their inverse equations.

a. $y = 3x - 2$

b. $y = \frac{x+1}{4}$

c. $y = x^3 + 1$

d. $y = 1 + \sqrt{x+5}$

CL 5-127. Given the function $f(x) = 2 + \sqrt{x-1}$:

a. Graph $f(x)$ and state the domain and range.

b. Determine the equation for $f^{-1}(x)$, that is, the inverse of $f(x)$.

c. Graph $f^{-1}(x)$ using the appropriate new domain and range.

d. Compute $f^{-1}(f(5))$ and $f(f^{-1}(5))$ to show that your answer is correct.

CL 5-128. Use the definition of logarithms to compute each of the following *without using a calculator*.

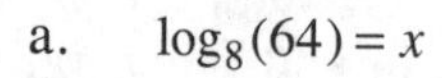

a. $\log_8(64) = x$

b. $\log_9(x) = \frac{1}{2}$

c. $\log_3(3^4) = x$

d. $10^{\log_{10}(4)} = x$

e. What do the answers to (c) and (d) demonstrate about logs and exponents with the same base?

CL 5-129. Use the graph at right to help answer the questions below.

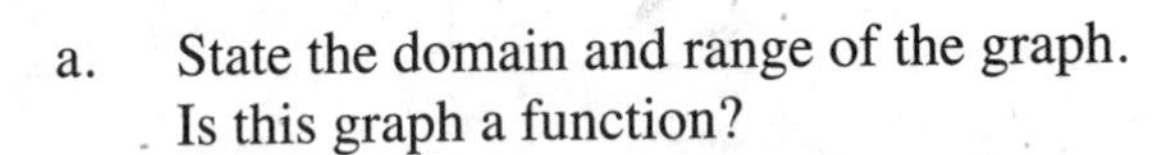

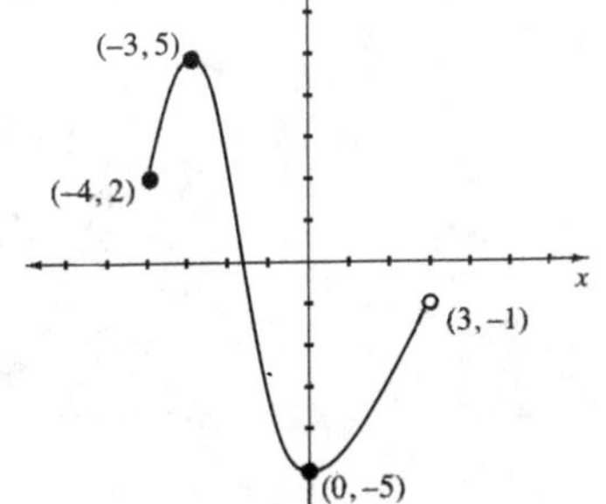

a. State the domain and range of the graph. Is this graph a function?

b. Draw the inverse of the graph. Is the inverse a function? Explain your answer.

c. State the domain and range of the inverse.

CL 5-130. A gallon of milk costs \$3.89. Inflation has steadily increased 4% per year.

a. What did a gallon of milk cost ten years ago?

b. How much longer will it be until it costs \$10?

CL 5-131. Perform the indicated operation on each of the following rational expressions. Be sure to state any values of the excluded variable and that your final answer is simplified. If a graphing tool is available, check the graph of the original problem to see if it coincides with the graph of your answer.

a. $\frac{5x}{x+3}+\frac{3+x}{x^2+9}$

b. $\frac{x}{x-1}-1$

c. $\frac{x^2+5x+6}{x^2-4x}\cdot\frac{4x}{x+2}$

d. $\frac{x^2-2x}{x^2-4x+4}\div\frac{4x^2}{x-2}$

CL 5-132. Graph the system of $y \geq x^2$ and $y \geq (x-4)^2+2$ and shade the inequalities' overlapping region. How is the graph of $y \geq (x-4)^2+2$ positioned in relation to the graph of $y \geq x^2$?

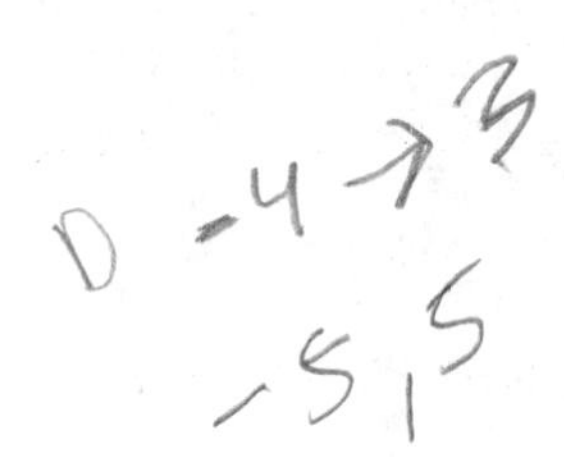

CL 5-133. Write possible equations for the graphs shown below.

a.

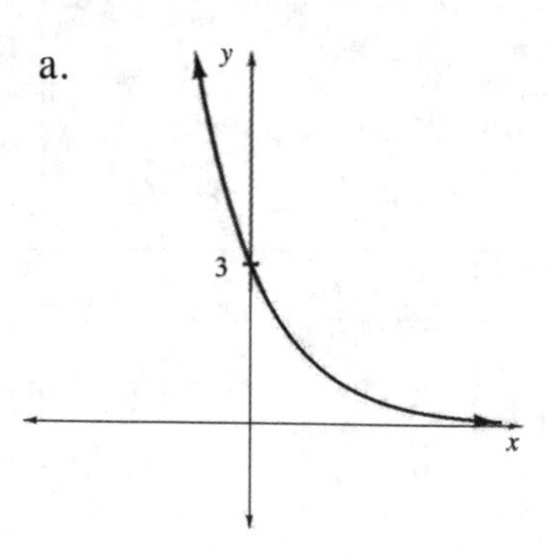

b.

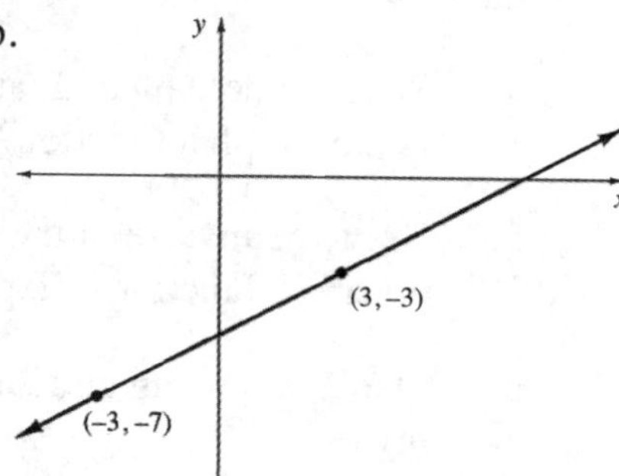

c.

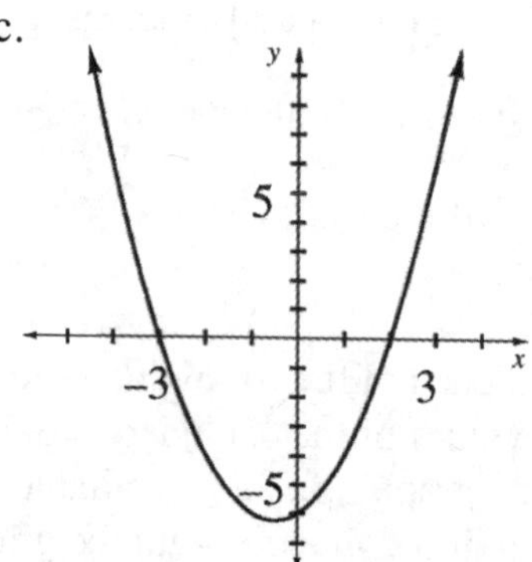

d.

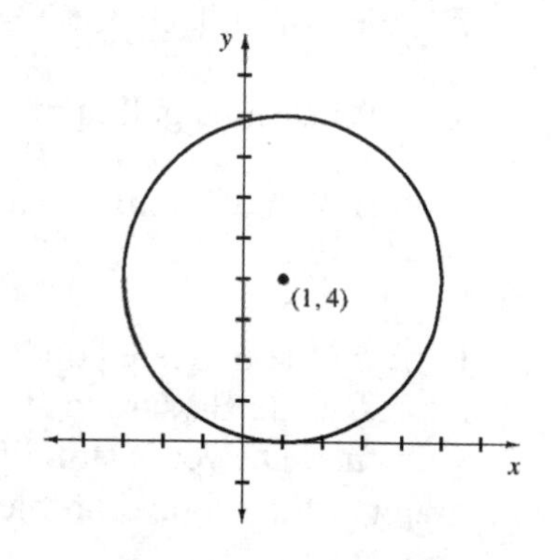

CL 5-134. Factor the expressions below.

a. $3x^2 + 11x + 10$

b. $6x^3 - 31x^2 + 5x$

c. $6ab^2 + 15ab - 21a$

d. $y^2 + 5y - 24$

CL 5-135. Check your answers using the table at the end of this section. Which problems do you feel confident about? Which problems were hard? Have you worked on problems like these in previous math classes? Use the table to make a list of topics you need to learn more about and a list of topics you just need to practice more.

Answers and Support for Closure Activity #4

What Have I Learned?

Note: MN = Math Note, LL = Learning Log

Problem	Solutions	Need Help?	More Practice
CL 5-126.	a. $y = \frac{x+2}{3}$ b. $y = 4x - 1$ c. $y = \sqrt[3]{x-1}$ d. $y = (x-1)^2 - 5$	Lessons 5.1.1 and 5.1.3	Problems 5-2, 5-3, 5-5, 5-40, and 5-41
CL 5-127.	a. domain $x \geq 1$; range $y \geq 2$ 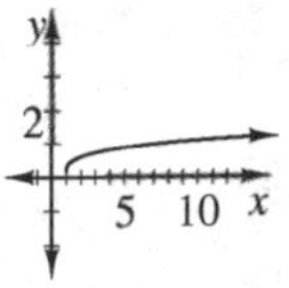 b. $f^{-1}(x) = (x-2)^2 + 1$ c. domain $x \geq 2$; range $y \geq 1$ 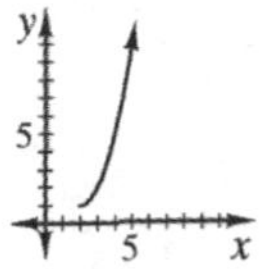 d. $f^{-1}(f(5)) = f(f^{-1}(5)) = 5$	Lessons 5.1.2 and 5.1.3 MN: 5.1.2 and 5.1.3	Problems 5-21, 5-22, 5-24, 5-26, 5-41, 5-42, 5-43, 5-45, 5-44, 5-33, 5-62, and 5-112
CL 5-128.	a. 2 b. 3 c. 4 d. 4	Lesson 5.2.2 MN: 5.2.2	Problems 5-70, 5-72, 5-74, and 5-97
CL 5-129.	a. domain: $-4 \leq x < 3$ range: $-5 \leq y \leq 5$ b. See graph at right. No, there are 2 outputs when $-5 < x < -1$ and $2 < x \leq 5$ c. domain: $-5 \leq x \leq 5$ 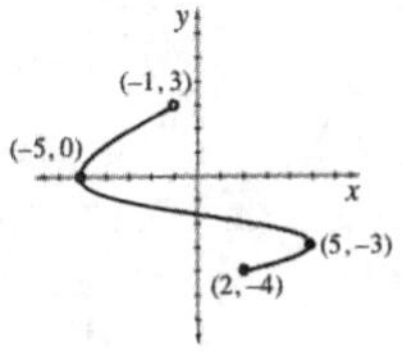 range: $-4 \leq y < 3$	Lesson 5.1.2	Problems 5-16, 5-21, 5-24, 5-44, 5-33, and 5-46

Problem	Solutions	Need Help?	More Practice
CL 5-130.	a. \$2.63 b. ≈ 24 years (by guess and check)	Lessons A.3.2 and B.2.3	Problems A-116, B-36, and B-46
CL 5-131.	a. $\frac{5x^2-14x+3}{(x-3)(x+3)}$, $x \neq \pm 3$ b. $\frac{1}{x-1}$, $x \neq 1$ c. $\frac{4(x+3)}{x-4}$, $x \neq -2, 0,$ or 4 d. $\frac{1}{4x}$, $x \neq 0, 2$	Lessons 3.2.3, 3.2.4, and 3.25 MN: 3.2.5 LL: 3.2.3 and 3.2.4	Problems 5-31, 5-54, 5-124, and 5-92
CL 5-132.	See graph below. It is shifted to the right 4 units and up 2 units. 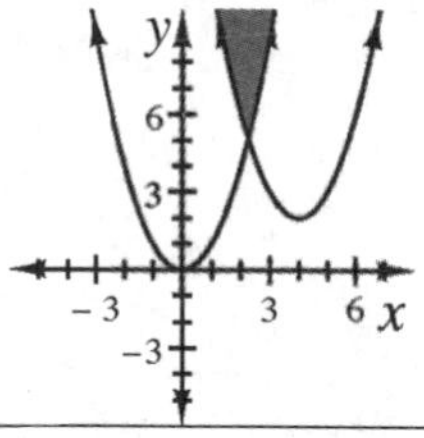	Lesson 4.2.1 MN: 4.2.3 LL: 4.2.1	Problems 4-93, 4-100, CL 4-109, 5-13, and 5-67
CL 5-133.	Possibilities include: a. $y = 3(\frac{1}{2})^x$ or $y = 3(2)^{-x}$ b. $y = \frac{2}{3}x - 5$ c. $y = (x-2)(x+3)$ or $y = x^2 + x - 6$ d. $(x-1)^2 + (y-4)^2 = 16$	Lessons B.1.5, 2.1.3, 2.2.1, and 2.2.2 MN: 1.1.2, 2.1.3, 2.2.2, 2.2.3	Problems B-60, B-89, 2-95, and 2-107
CL 5-134.	a. $(3x+5)(x+2)$ b. $x(6x-1)(x-5)$ c. $3a(2b+7)(b-1)$ d. $(y-3)(y+8)$	MN: 1.1.4 Checkpoint 5B	Problems 1-13, 2-98, 2-169, and CL 2-178

SEQUENCES

Appendix A

Sequences

Appendix A provides you an opportunity to review and strengthen your algebra skills while you learn about arithmetic and geometric sequences.

Early in this chapter, you will use familiar strategies such as looking for patterns and making tables to write algebraic equations describing sequences of numbers.

Later in this chapter, you will develop shortcuts for writing equations for certain kinds of sequences.

Guiding Question

Mathematically proficient students look for and express regularity in repeated reasoning.

Think about this question throughout the chapter:

When patterns are repeated, can I find shortcuts that lead to equations?

Chapter Outline

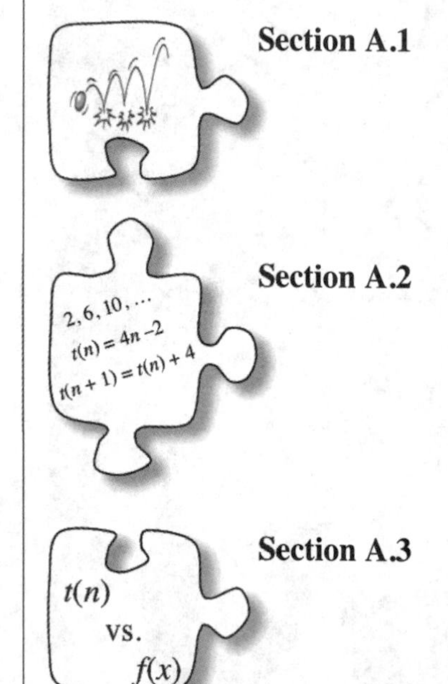

Section A.1 This section begins with lessons that ask you to describe the growth of a rabbit population and the decreasing rebound height of a bouncing ball. You will use tables, graphs, and equations to represent the growth.

Section A.2 You will do an investigation where you categorize several sequences. You will also learn some of the specialized vocabulary used when discussing sequences. You will create multiple representations of arithmetic sequences, including equations for sequences that depend on previous terms.

Section A.3 In this section you will compare the growth of various sequences and recognize growth by multiplication and growth by addition. Then you will create multiple representations of geometric sequences and compare sequences to functions.

A.1.1 How does the pattern grow?

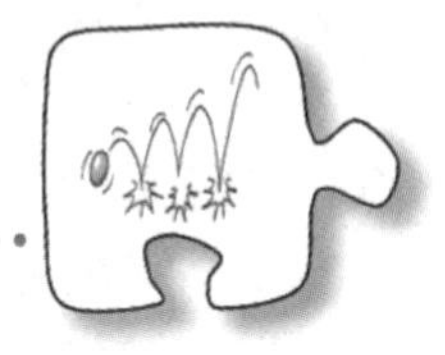

Representing Exponential Growth

So far in this course, you have been investigating the family of linear functions using multiple representations (especially $x \rightarrow y$ tables, graphs, and equations). In this chapter, you will learn about a new family of functions and the type of growth it models.

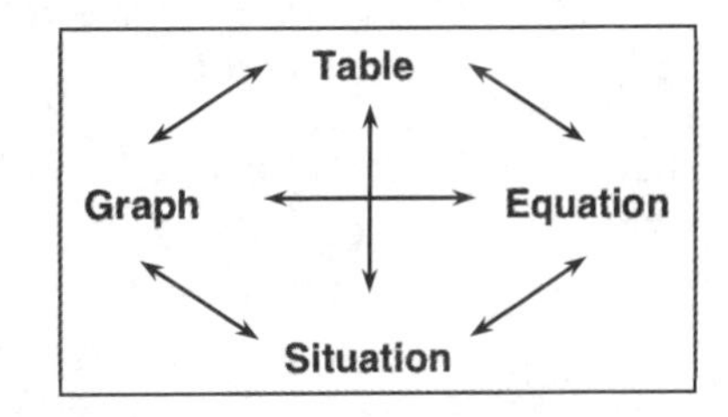

A-1. MULTIPLYING LIKE BUNNIES

In the book *Of Mice and Men* by John Steinbeck, two good friends named Lenny and George dream of raising rabbits and living off the land. What if their dream came true?

Suppose Lenny and George started with two rabbits and that in each following month those rabbits have two babies. Also suppose that every month thereafter, each pair of rabbits has two babies.

Your Task: With your team, determine how many rabbits Lenny and George would have after one year (12 months). Represent this situation with a written description of the growth pattern, a diagram, and a table. What patterns can you find and how do they compare to other patterns that you have investigated previously?

Discussion Points

What strategies could help us keep track of the total number of rabbits?

What patterns can we see in the growth of the rabbit population?

How can we predict the total number of rabbits after many months have passed?

Further Guidance

A-2. How can you determine the number of rabbits that will exist at the end of one year? Consider this as you answer the questions below.

a. Draw a diagram to represent how the total number of rabbits is growing each month. How many rabbits will Lenny and George have after three months?

b. As the number of rabbits becomes larger, a diagram becomes too cumbersome to be useful. A table might work better. Organize your information in a table showing the total number of rabbits for the first several months (at least 6 months). What patterns can you find in your table? Describe the pattern of growth in words.

c. If you have not done so already, use your pattern to determine the number of rabbits that Lenny and George would have after one year (12 months) has passed.

d. How does the growth in the table that you created compare to the growth patterns that you have investigated previously? How is it similar and how is it different?

Further Guidance section ends here.

A-3. Lenny and George want to raise as many rabbits as possible, so they have a few options to consider. They could start with a larger number of rabbits, or they could raise a breed of rabbits that reproduces faster. How do you think that each of these options would change the pattern of growth you observed in the previous problem? Which situation might yield the largest rabbit population after one year?

a. To help answer these questions, model each case below with a table for the first five months.

Case 2: Start with 10 rabbits; each pair has 2 babies per month.

Case 3: Start with 2 rabbits; each pair has 4 babies per month.

Case 4: Start with 2 rabbits; each pair has 6 babies per month.

b. Which case would appear to give Lenny and George the most rabbits after one year? How many rabbits would they have in that case?

A-4. A NEW FAMILY

Look back at the tables you created in problems A-1 and A-3.

a. What pattern do they all have in common? Functions that have this pattern are called **exponential functions**.

b. Obtain the Lesson A.1.1 Resource Page from your teacher. Graph the data for Case 2. Give a complete description of the graph.

A-5. LEARNING LOG

To represent the growth in number of rabbits in problems A-1 and A-3, you discovered a new function family that is not linear. Functions in this new family are called exponential functions. Throughout this chapter and later in Appendix B, you will learn more about this special family of functions.

Write a Learning Log entry to record what you have learned so far about exponential functions. For example, what do their graphs look like? What patterns do you observe in their tables? Title this entry "Exponential Functions" and include today's date.

A-6. What if the data for Lenny and George (from problem A-1) matched the data in each table below? Assuming that the growth of the rabbits continues as it did in problem A-1, complete each of the following tables. Show your thinking or give a brief explanation of how you found the missing entries.

a.

Months	Rabbits
0	4
1	12
2	36
3	
4	

b.

Months	Rabbits
0	6
1	
2	24
3	
4	96

A-7. Solve the following systems of equations algebraically. Then graph each system to confirm your solution.

a. $x + y = 3$
$x = 3y - 5$

b. $x - y = -5$
$y = -2x - 4$

A-8. For the function $f(x)=\frac{6}{2x-3}$, find the value of each expression below.

a. $f(1)$ b. $f(0)$ c. $f(-3)$ d. $f(1.5)$

e. What value of x would make $f(x)=4$?

A-9. Benjamin is taking Algebra 1 and is stuck on the problem shown below. Examine his work so far and help him by showing and explaining the remaining steps.

Original problem: Simplify $(3a^{-2}b)^3$.

He knows that $(3a^{-2}b)^3=(3a^{-2}b)(3a^{-2}b)(3a^{-2}b)$. Now what?

A-10. Simplify each expression below. Assume that the denominator in part (b) is not equal to zero.

a. $(x^3)(x^{-2})$ b. $\frac{y^5}{y^{-2}}$ c. 4^{-1} d. $(4x^2)^3$

A-11. The equation of a line describes the relationship between the x- and y-coordinates of the points on the line.

a. Plot the points $(3,-1)$, $(3,2)$, and $(3,4)$ and draw the line that passes through them. State the coordinates of two more points on the line. Then answer this question: What will be true of the coordinates of any other point on this line? Now write an equation that says exactly the same thing. (Do not worry if it is very simple! If it accurately describes all the points on this line, it is correct.)

b. Plot the points $(5,-1)$, $(1,-1)$, and $(-3,-1)$. What is the equation of the line that goes through these points?

c. Choose any three points on the y-axis. What must be the equation of the line that goes through those points?

A-12. Jill is studying a strange bacterium. When she first looks at the bacteria, there are 1000 cells in her sample. The next day, there are 2000 cells. Intrigued, she comes back the next day to find that there are 4000 cells!

a. Should the graph of this situation be linear or curved?

b. Create a table and graph for this situation. The inputs are the days that have passed after she first began to study the sample, and the outputs are the number of cells of bacteria.

A-13. Write each expression below in a simpler form.

a. $\frac{5^{723}}{5^{721}}$ b. $\frac{3^{300}}{3^{249}}$ c. $\left(\frac{3 \cdot 4^3}{3^{-2} \cdot 4^{-7}}\right)^0$ d. $\left(\frac{4 \times 10^3}{10^{-2}}\right)^2$

A-14. Jackie and Alexa were working on homework together when Jackie said, *"I got $x = 5$ as the solution, but it looks like you got something different. Which solution is right?"*

"I think you made a mistake," said Alexa. Did Jackie make a mistake? Help Jackie figure out whether she made a mistake and, if she did, explain her mistake and show her how to solve the equation correctly. Jackie's work is shown above right.

$$(x+4)^2 - 2x - 5 = (x-1)^2$$
$$x^2 + 16 - 2x - 5 = x^2 + 1$$
$$16 - 2x - 5 = 1$$
$$11 - 2x = 1$$
$$-2x = -10$$
$$x = 5$$

A-15. Solve each of the following equations.

a. $\frac{m}{6} = \frac{15}{18}$ b. $\frac{\pi}{7} = \frac{a}{4}$

A-16. Write the equation of each line described below.

a. A line with slope -2 and y-intercept 7.

b. A line with slope $-\frac{3}{2}$ and x-intercept $(4, 0)$.

A-17. The dartboard shown at right is in the shape of an equilateral triangle. It has a smaller equilateral triangle in the center, which was made by joining the midpoints of the three edges. If a dart hits the board at random, what is the probability that:

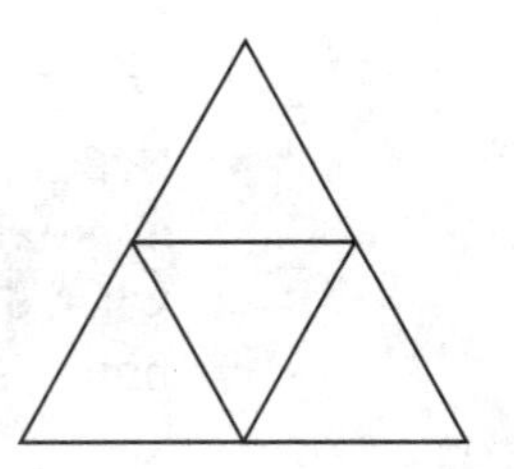

a. The dart hits the center triangle?

b. The dart misses the center triangle but hits the board?

A.1.2 How high will it bounce?

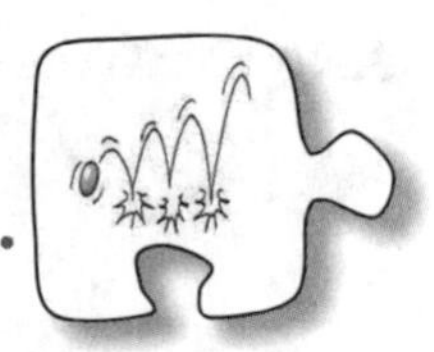

Rebound Ratios

Many games depend on how a ball bounces. For example, if different basketballs rebounded differently, one basketball would bounce differently off of a backboard than another would, and this could cause basketball players to miss their shots. For this reason, manufacturers have to make balls' bounciness conform to specific standards. In this lesson, you will investigate the relationship between the height from which you drop a ball and the height to which it rebounds.

A-18. Listed below are "bounciness" standards for different kinds of balls.

- Tennis balls: Must rebound approximately 111 cm when dropped from 200 cm.
- Soccer balls: Must rebound approximately 120 cm when dropped from 200 cm onto a steel plate.
- Basketballs: Must rebound approximately 53.5 inches when dropped from 72 inches onto a wooden floor.
- Squash balls: Must rebound approximately 29.5 inches when dropped from 100 inches onto a steel plate at 70° F.

Discuss with your team how you can measure a ball's bounciness. Which ball listed above is the bounciest? Justify your answer.

A-19. THE BOUNCING BALL

How can you determine if a ball meets expected standards?

Your Task: With your team, find the rebound ratio for a ball. Your teacher will provide you with a ball and a measuring device. You will be using the same ball again later, so make sure you can identify which ball your team is using. Before you start your experiment, discuss the following questions with your team.

Discussion Points

What do we need to measure?

How should we organize our data?

How can we be confident that our data is accurate?

You should choose one person in your team to be the recorder, one to be the ball dropper, and two to be the spotters. When you are confident that you have a good plan, ask your teacher to come to your team and approve it.

A-20. MODELING YOUR DATA

Work with your team to model the data you collected in problem A-19 by considering parts (a) through (c) below.

a. In problem A-19, does the height from which the ball is dropped depend on the rebound height, or is it the other way around? With your team, decide which is the independent variable and which is the dependent variable.

b. Graph your results on a full sheet of graph paper. Draw a line that best fits your data. Should this line go through the origin? Why or why not? Justify your answer in terms of what the origin represents in this problem situation.

c. Find an equation for your line.

A-21. What is the rebound ratio for your team's ball? How is the rebound ratio reflected in the graph of your line of best fit? Where is it reflected in the equation for your data? Where is it reflected in your table?

Save your data and your graph in a safe place. You will need them for the next lesson.

MATH NOTES

METHODS AND MEANINGS

Continuous and Discrete Graphs

When the points on a graph are connected, and it *makes sense* to connect them, the graph is said to be **continuous**. If the graph is not continuous, and is just a sequence of separate points, the graph is called **discrete**.

For example, the graph on the left represents the cost of buying x shirts and is discrete because you can only buy whole numbers of shirts. The graph on the right represents the cost of buying x gallons of gasoline and is continuous because you can buy any (non-negative) amount of gasoline.

Discrete Graph

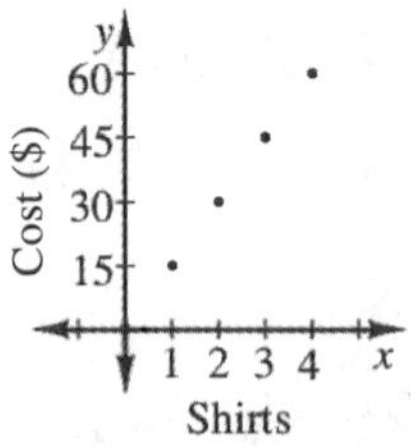

Cost ($)
60
45
30
15
1 2 3 4 x
Shirts

Continuous Graph

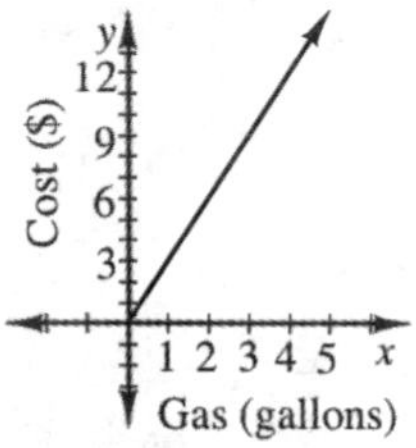

Cost ($)
12
9
6
3
1 2 3 4 5 x
Gas (gallons)

Review & Preview

A-22. Solve each system of equations below.

a. $y = 3x + 1$
$x + 2y = -5$

b. $2x + 3y = 9$
$x - 2y = 1$

A-23. Solve each equation for the indicated variable.

a. $t = an + b$ (for b)

b. $\frac{y}{3} - a = b$ (for y)

c. $m = \frac{y}{x}$ (for y)

d. $m = \frac{y}{x}$ (for x)

A-24. Simplify each expression below.

a. $\frac{6x^2y^3}{3xy}$

b. $(-mn)^3$

c. $(mn)^{-3}$

d. $\frac{3.2\times10^{-2}}{8\times10^3}$

A-25. Determine the domain and range of each of the following graphs.

a.

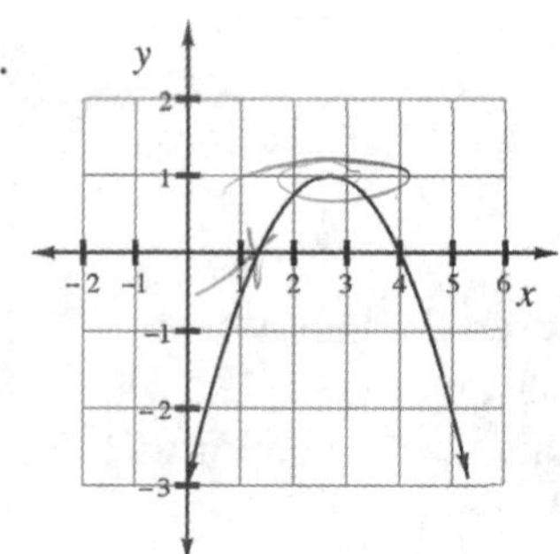

b.

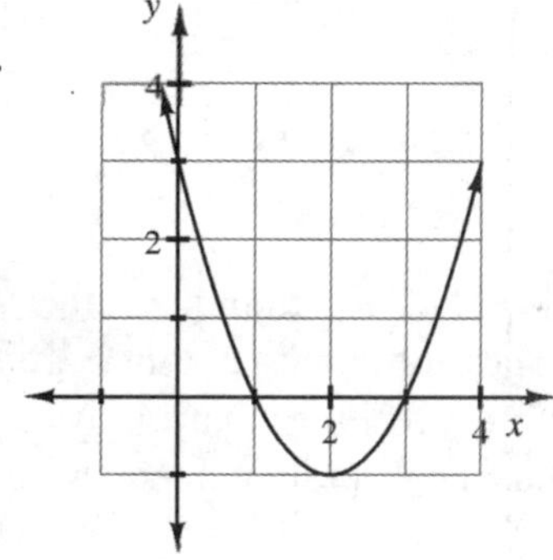

c.

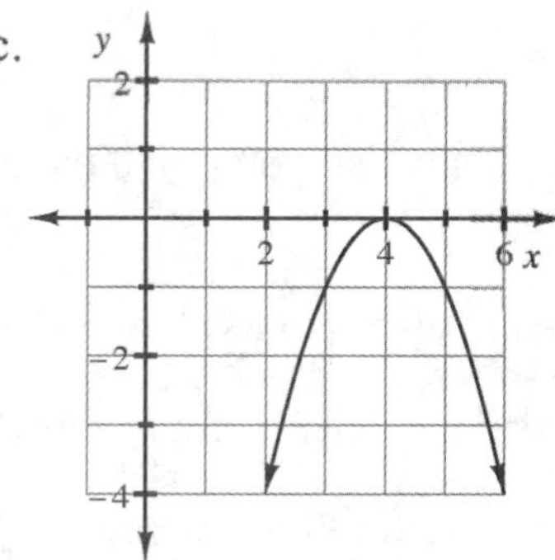

d.

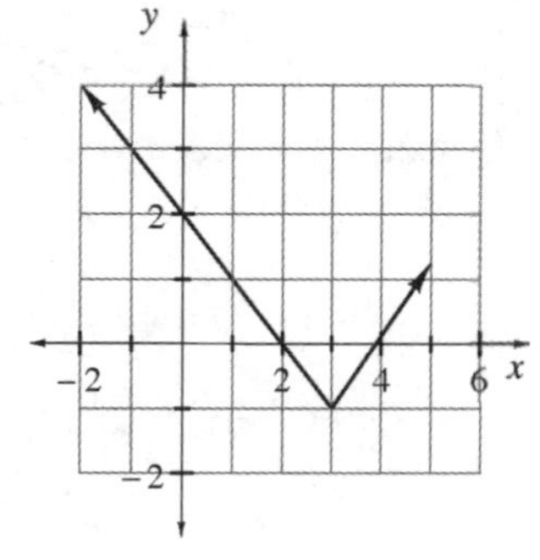

A-26. The graph at right compares the age and the number of pets for a certain population.

Describe the association for this population.

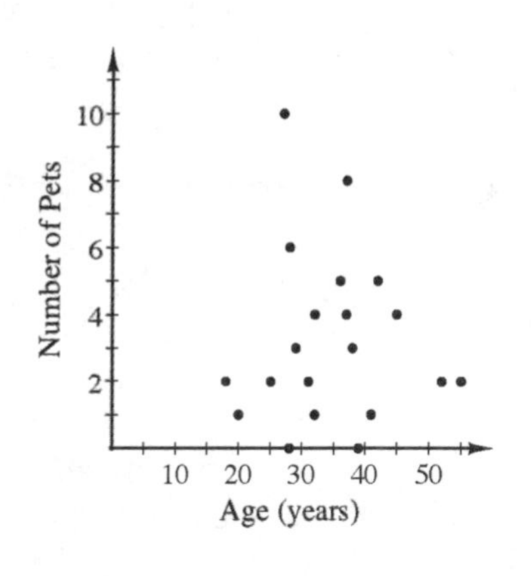

A-27. At his aunt's wedding, Nicolas collected data about an ice sculpture that was slowly melting. A graph of his data is shown at right.

a. Calculate the equation of a line of best fit.

b. Based on your equation, how tall was the ice sculpture one hour before Nicolas started measuring?

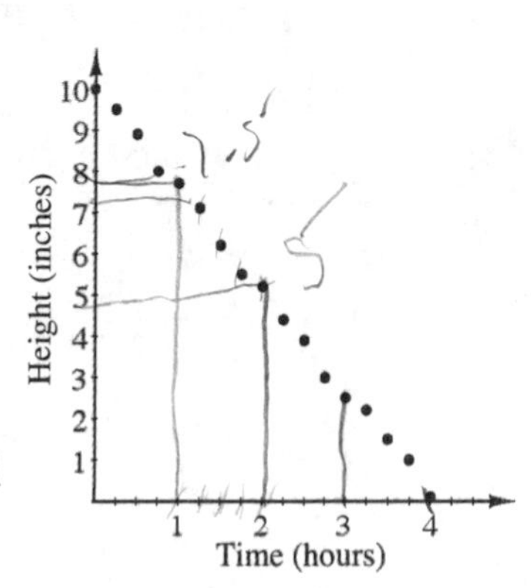

A.1.3 What is the pattern?

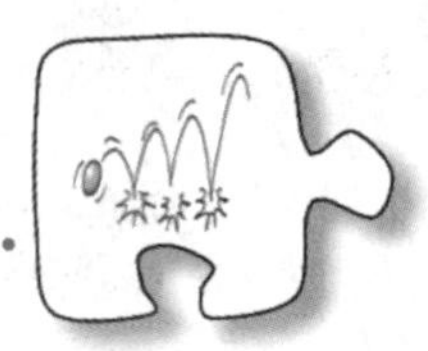

The Bouncing Ball and Exponential Decay

In Lesson A.1.2, you found that the relationship between the height from which a ball is dropped and its rebound height is determined by a constant multiplier. In this lesson, you will continue this investigation by exploring the mathematical relationship between how many times a ball has bounced and the height of each bounce.

A-28. Consider the work you did in Lesson A.1.2, in which you found the rebound ratio for a ball.

a. What was the rebound ratio for the ball your team used?

b. Did the height from which you dropped the ball affect this ratio?

c. If you were to use the same ball again and drop it from *any* height, could you predict its rebound height? Explain how you would do this.

A-29. A MODEL FOR MANY BOUNCES

Imagine that you drop the same ball that you used in problem A-19 from a height of 200 cm, but this time you let it bounce repeatedly.

a. As a team, discuss this situation. Then sketch a picture showing what this situation would look like. Your sketch should show a minimum of 6 bounces after you release the ball.

b. Predict your ball's rebound height after each successive bounce if its starting height is 200 cm. Create a table with these predicted heights.

c. What are the independent and dependent variables in this situation?

d. Graph your predicted rebound heights.

e. Should the points on your graph be connected? How can you tell?

A-30. TESTING THE MANY-BOUNCE MODEL

Now you will test the accuracy of the predictions you made in problem A-29.

Your Task: Test your predictions by collecting experimental data. Use the same Team Roles as you used in problem A-19. Drop your ball, starting from an initial height of 200 cm, and record your data in a table. Then compare your experimental data to your predictions using your table and your graph. How do they compare? What might cause your experimental data to be different from your predictions? Do you think that your table and graph model the situation appropriately? Why or why not?

These suggestions will help you gather accurate data:

- Have a spotter catch the ball just as it reaches the top of its first rebound and have the spotter "freeze" the ball in place.
- Record the first rebound height and then drop the ball again from that new height.
- Catch and "freeze" it again at the second rebound height.
- Repeat this process until you have collected at least 6 data points (or until the height of the bounce is so small that it is not reasonable to continue).

A-31. Compare your graph for the height of successive bounces in problem A-29 to the graph for drop height versus bounce height that you investigated in Lesson A.1.2.

a. Can you use the same kind of equation to model the two situations? That is, what family of functions do you think would make the best fit for each data set? Discuss this with your team and be ready to report and justify your choice.

b. Describe how the pattern of growth for successive bounces is the same as or different from other models that you have looked at previously.

A-32. If you continued to let your ball bounce uninterrupted, how high would the ball be after 12 bounces? Would the ball ever stop bouncing? Explain your answer in terms of both your experimental data and your equation.

34-36, 40

A-33. Notice that your investigations of rebound patterns in Lessons A.1.2 and A.1.3 involved both a linear and an exponential model. Look back over your work and discuss with your team why each model was appropriate for its specific purpose. Be prepared to share your ideas with the class.

A-34. DeShawna and her team gathered data for their ball and recorded it in the table shown at right.

Drop Height	Rebound Height
150 cm	124 cm
70 cm	59 cm
120 cm	100 cm
100 cm	83 cm
110 cm	92 cm
40 cm	33 cm

a. What is the rebound ratio for their ball?

b. Predict how high DeShawna's ball will rebound if it is dropped from 275 cm. Look at the precision of DeShawna's measurements in the table. Round your calculation to a reasonable number of decimal places.

c. Suppose the ball is dropped and you notice that its rebound height is 60 cm. From what height was the ball dropped? Use appropriate precision for your answer.

d. Suppose the ball is dropped from a window 200 meters up the Empire State Building. What would you predict the rebound height to be after the first bounce?

e. How high would the ball in part (d) rebound after the second bounce? After the third bounce?

A-35. Look back at the data given in problem A-18 that describes the rebound ratio for an official tennis ball. Suppose you drop such a tennis ball from an initial height of 10 feet.

a. How high would it rebound after the first bounce?

b. How high would it rebound after the second bounce?

c. How high would it rebound after the fifth bounce?

A-36. Solve the following systems of equations algebraically and then confirm your solutions by graphing.

a. $y = 3x - 2$
$4x + 2y = 6$

b. $x = y - 4$
$2x - y = -5$

A-37. Lona received a stamp collection from her grandmother. The collection is in a leather book and currently has 120 stamps. Lona joined a stamp club, which sends her 12 new stamps each month. The stamp book holds a maximum of 500 stamps.

a. Complete the table at right.

Month	Stamps
0	120
1	132
2	
3	
4	
5	

b. How many stamps will Lona have in one year from now?

c. Write an equation using function notation to represent the total number of stamps that Lona has in her collection after n months. Let the total be represented by $t(n)$.

d. Solve your equation from part (c) for n when $t(n) = 500$. Will Lona be able to fill her book exactly with no stamps remaining? How do you know? When will the book be filled?

A-38. Use slope to determine whether the points $A(3,5)$, $B(-2,6)$, and $C(-5,7)$ are on the same line. Justify your conclusion algebraically.

A-39. Serena wanted to examine the graphs of the equations below on her graphing calculator. Rewrite each of the equations in $y=$ form (when the equation is solved for y) so that she can enter them into the calculator.

a. $5-(y-2)=3x$

b. $5(x+y)=-2$

A-40. The graph at right shows a comparison of the length of several gold chain necklaces (including the clasp) to the total mass.

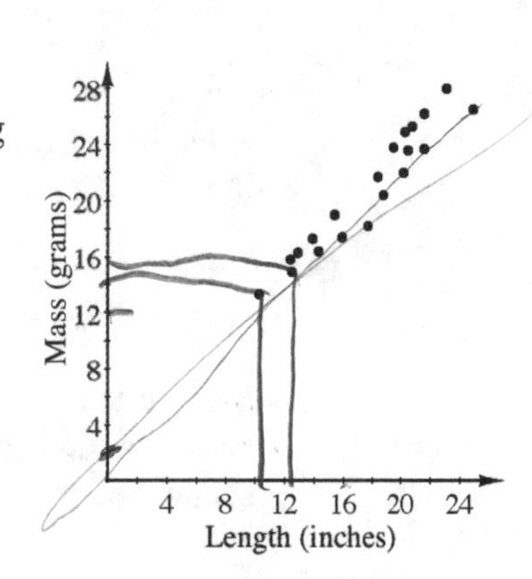

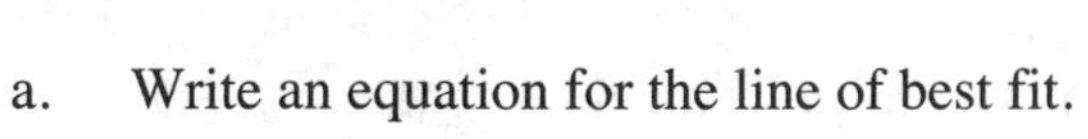

a. Write an equation for the line of best fit.

b. Based on your equation, what would you expect to be the mass of a 26-inch chain?

A.2.1 How can I describe a sequence?

Generating and Investigating Sequences

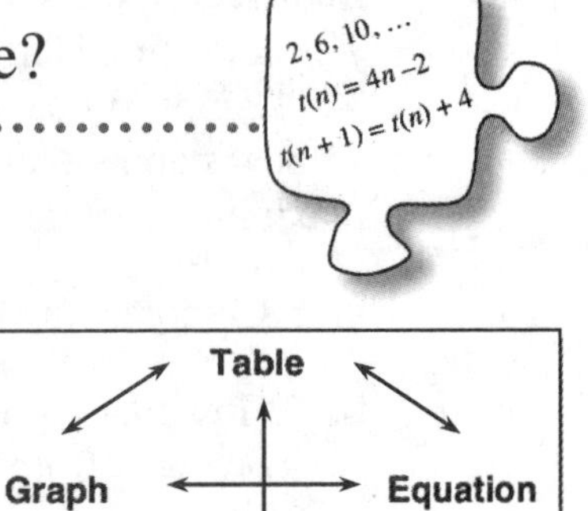

In the bouncing ball activity from Lessons A.1.2 and A.1.3, you used multiple representations (an $x \to y$ table, an equation, and a graph) to represent a discrete situation involving a bouncing ball (a situation). Today you will learn about a new way to represent a discrete pattern, also called a sequence.

Table / Graph / Equation / Situation

A-41. Samantha was thinking about George and Lenny and their rabbits. When she listed the number of rabbits George and Lenny could have each month, she ended up with the ordered list below, called a **sequence**.

$$2, 6, 18, 54, \ldots$$

She realized that she could represent this situation using a sequence-generating machine that would generate the number of rabbits each month by doing something to the previous month's number of rabbits. She tested her generator by putting in a **first term** of 2 and she recorded each output before putting it into the next machine. Below is the diagram she used to explain her idea to her teammates.

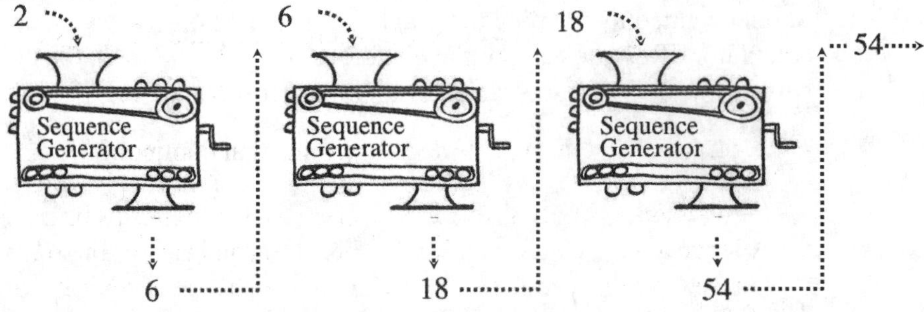

a. What does Samantha's **sequence generator** seem to be doing to each input?

b. What are the next two terms of Samantha's sequence? Show how you got your answer.

c. Samantha decided to use the same sequence generator, but this time she started with a first term of 5. What are the next four terms in this new sequence?

A-42. SEQUENCE FAMILIES

Samantha and her teacher have been busy creating new sequence generators and the sequences they produce. Below are the sequences Samantha and her teacher created.

a. $-4, -1, 2, 5, \ldots$

b. $1.5, 3, 6, 12, \ldots$

c. $0, 1, 4, 9, \ldots$

d. $2, 3.5, 5, 6.5, \ldots$

e. $1, 1, 2, 3, 5, 8, \ldots$

f. $9, 7, 5, 3, \ldots$

g. $48, 24, 12, \ldots$

h. $27, 9, 3, 1, \ldots$

i. $8, 2, 0, 2, 8, 18, \ldots$

j. $\frac{5}{4}, \frac{5}{2}, 5, 10, \ldots$

Your teacher will give your team a set of Lesson A.2.1A Resource Pages with the above sequences on strips so that everyone in your team can see and work with them in the middle of your workspace.

Your Task: Working together, organize the sequences into families of similar sequences. Your team will need to decide how many families to make, what common features make the sequences a family, and what characteristics make each family different from the others. Read and carry out the directions that follow. As you work, use the following questions to help guide your team's discussion.

Discussion Points

How can we describe the pattern?

How does it grow?

What do the patterns have in common?

(1) As a team, initially sort the sequence strips into groups based on your first glance at the sequences. Remember that you can sort the sequences into more than two families. You will have a chance to revise your groups of sequences throughout this activity, so just sort them in a way that makes sense to start out with. Which seem to behave similarly? Record your groupings and what they have in common before proceeding.

(2) If one exists, find a sequence generator (growth pattern) for each sequence and write it on the strip. You can express the sequence generator either in symbols or in words. Also record the next three terms in each sequence on the strips. Do your sequence families still make sense? If so, what new information do you have about your sequence families? If not, reorganize the strips and explain how you decided to group them.

Problem continues on next page. →

A-42. *Problem continued from previous page.*

(3) Get a set of Lesson A.2.1B Resource Pages for your team. Then record each sequence in a table. Your table should compare the **term number**, n, to the value of each **term**, $t(n)$. This means that your sequence itself is a list of *outputs* of the relationship and the *inputs* are a list of integers! The first term in a sequence is always $n=1$. Attach each table to the sequence strip it represents. Do your sequence families still make sense? Record any new information or reorganize your sequence families if necessary.

(4) Now graph each sequence on a Lesson A.2.1C Resource Page. Include as many terms as will fit on the existing set of axes. Be sure to decide whether your graphs should be discrete or continuous. Use color to show the growth between the points on each graph. Attach each graph to the sequence strip it represents. Do your sequence families still make sense? Record any new information and reorganize your sequence families if necessary.

A-43. Choose one of the families of sequences you created in problem A-42. With your team, write clear summary statements about this family of sequences. Refer to the Discussion Points in problem A-42 to help you write summary statements. Be sure to use multiple representations to justify each statement. Be prepared to share your summary statements with the class.

A-44. Some types of sequences have special names.

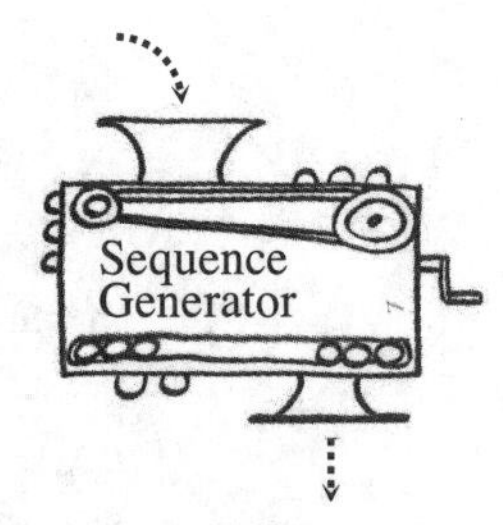

a. When the sequence generator *adds* a constant to each previous term, it is called an **arithmetic sequence**. Which of your sequences from problem A-42 fall into this family? Should you include the sequence labeled (f) in this family? Why or why not?

b. When the sequence generator *multiplies* a constant times each previous term, it is called a **geometric sequence**. Which of the sequences from problem A-42 are geometric? Should sequence (h) be in this group? Why or why not?

A-45. Find the slope of the line you would get if you graphed each sequence listed below and connected the points.

a. $5, 8, 11, 14, \ldots$

b. $3, 9, 15, \ldots$

c. $26, 21, 16, \ldots$

d. $7, 8.5, 10, \ldots$

A-46. For the line passing through the points $(-2,1)$ and $(2,-11)$,

a. Calculate the slope of the line.

b. Find an equation of the line.

A-47. Allie is making 8 dozen chocolate chip muffins for the Food Fair at school. The recipe she is using makes 3 dozen muffins. If the original recipe calls for 16 ounces of chocolate chips, how many ounces of chocolate chips does she need for her new amount? (Allie buys her chocolate chips in bulk and can measure them to the nearest ounce.)

A-48. The area of a square is 225 square centimeters.

a. Make a diagram and determine the length of each side.

b. Use the Pythagorean theorem to find the length of its diagonal.

A-49. Refer to sequences (c) and (i) in problem A-42.

a. How are these two sequences similar?

b. The numbers in the sequence in part (e) of problem A-42 are called **Fibonacci numbers**. They are named after an Italian mathematician who discovered the sequence while studying how fast rabbits could breed. What is different about this sequence than the other three you discovered?

A-50. Chelsea dropped a bouncy ball off the roof while Nery recorded its rebound height. The table at right shows their data. Note that the 0 in the "Bounce" column represents the starting height.

Bounce	Rebound Height
0	800 cm
1	475 cm
2	290 cm
3	175 cm
4	100 cm
5	60 cm

a. To what family does the function belong? Explain how you know.

b. Show the data as a sequence. Is the sequence arithmetic, geometric, quadratic, or something else? Justify your answer.

A-51. For the function $f(x)=\sqrt{3x-2}$, find the value of each expression below.

a. $f(1)$ b. $f(9)$ c. $f(4)$ d. $f(0)$

e. What value of x makes $f(x)=6$?

A-52. Simplify each expression below.

a. $y+0.03y$ b. $z-0.2z$ c. $x+0.002x$

A-53. A tank contains 8000 liters of water. Each day, half of the water in the tank is removed. How much water will be in the tank at the end of:

a. The 4th day?   b. The 8th day?

A-54. Solve each system.

a. $y+3x=-10$
$5x-y=2$

b. $6x=7-2y$
$4x+y=4$

A-55. Draw a slope triangle and use it to find the equation of the line shown in the graph at right.

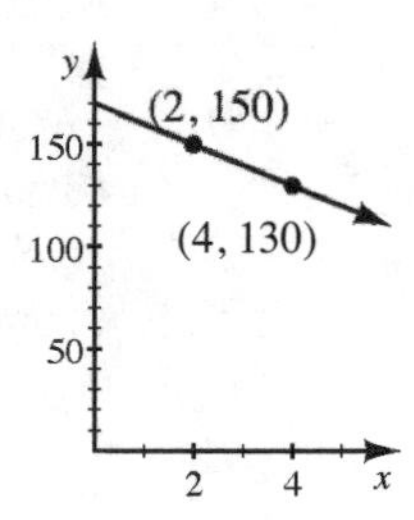

A-56. Simplify each expression. In parts (e) through (f) write the final answer in scientific notation.

a. $4^2 \cdot 4^5$ b. $(5^0)^3$ c. $x^{-5} \cdot x^3$

d. $(x^{-1} \cdot y^2)^3$ e. $(8\times10^5)\cdot(1.6\times10^{-2})$ f. $\frac{4\times10^3}{5\times10^5}$

A.2.2 How do arithmetic sequences work?

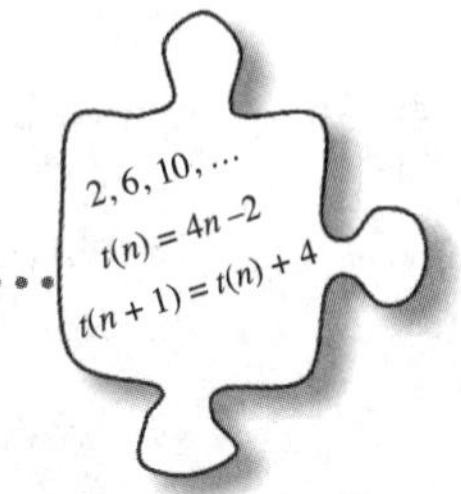

Generalizing Arithmetic Sequences

In Lesson A.2.1, you learned how to identify arithmetic and geometric sequences. Today you will solve problems involving arithmetic sequences. Use the questions below to help your team stay focused and start mathematical conversations.

What type of sequence is this? How do we know?

How can we find the equation?

Is there another way to see it?

A-57. LEARNING THE LANGUAGE OF SEQUENCES

Sequences have their own notation and vocabulary that help describe them, such as "term" and "term number." The questions below will help you learn more of this vocabulary and notation.

Consider the sequence $-9, -5, -1, 3, 7, \ldots$ as you complete parts (a) through (f).

a. Is this sequence arithmetic, geometric, or neither? How can you tell?

b. What is the first term of the sequence?

c. When the sequence generator adds a number to each term, the value that is added is known as the **common difference**. It is the difference between each term and the term before it.

   What is the sequence generator?

d. Record the sequence in a table. Remember a sequence table compares the term number, n, to the value of each term, $t(n)$.

e. What is $t(n)$ when $n = 0$?

f. Graph the sequence. Should the graph be continuous or discrete? Why?

g. Write an equation (beginning $t(n) =$) for the nth term of this sequence.

h. What is the domain for the sequence equation that you have written?

i. How is the common difference related to the graph and the equation? Why does this make sense?

A-58. Consider the sequence $t(n) = -4, -1, 2, 5, \ldots$

a. If the first term is $t(1)$, what is $t(0)$ for this sequence? What is the common difference?

b. Write an equation for $t(n)$. Verify that your equation works for each of the first 4 terms of the sequence.

c. Is it possible for $t(n)$ to equal 42? Justify your answer.

d. For the function $f(x) = 3x - 7$, is it possible for $f(x)$ to equal 42? Explain.

e. Explain the difference between $t(n)$ and $f(x)$ that makes your answers to parts (b) and (c) different.

A-59. Trixie wants to create an especially tricky arithmetic sequence. She wants the 5th term of the sequence to equal 11 and the 50th term to equal 371. That is, she wants $t(5) = 11$ and $t(50) = 371$. Is it possible to create an arithmetic sequence to fit her information? If it is possible, find the sequence generator, the initial value $t(0)$, and then find the equation for the arithmetic sequence. If it is not possible, explain why not.

A-60. Seven years ago, Kodi found a box of old baseball cards in the garage. Since then, he has added a consistent number of cards to the collection each year. He had 52 cards in the collection after 3 years and now has 108 cards.

a. How many cards were in the original box? Is this $t(0)$ or $t(1)$? Write the first few terms of the sequence.

b. Kodi plans to keep the collection for a long time. How many cards will the collection contain 10 years from now?

c. Write an equation that determines the number of cards in the collection after n years. What does each number in your equation represent?

A-61. Trixie now wants an arithmetic sequence with a sequence generator of -17 and a 16th term of 93. (In other words, $t(16) = 93$.) Is it possible to create an arithmetic sequence to fit her information? If it is possible, find the equation. If it is not possible, explain why not.

A-62. Your favorite radio station, WCPM, is having a contest. The DJ poses a question to the listeners. If the caller answers correctly, he or she wins the prize money. If the caller answers incorrectly, \$20 is added to the prize money and the next caller is eligible to win. The current question is difficult, and no one has won for two days.

a. Lucky you! Fourteen people already called in today with incorrect answers, so when you called (with the right answer, of course) you won \$735! How much was the prize worth at the beginning of the day today?

b. Suppose the contest always starts with \$100. How many people would have to guess incorrectly for the winner to get \$1360?

A-63. Trixie is at it again. This time she wants an arithmetic sequence that has a graph with a slope of 22. She also wants $t(8) = 164$ and the 13th term to have a value of 300. Is it possible to create an arithmetic sequence to fit her information? If it is possible, find the equation. If it is not possible, explain why not.

A-64. Find the equation for each arithmetic sequence represented by the tables below.

a.

n	$t(n)$
7	54
3	10
19	186
16	153
40	417

b.

n	$t(n)$
100	10
70	100

A-65. Trixie exclaimed, *"Hey! Arithmetic sequences are just another name for linear functions."* What do you think? Justify your idea based on multiple representations.

A-66. Determine whether 447 is a term of each sequence below. If so, which term is it?

a. $t(n) = 5n - 3$

b. $t(n) = 24 - 5n$

c. $t(n) = -6 + 3(n-1)$

d. $t(n) = 14 - 3n$

e. $t(n) = -8 - 7(n-1)$

A-67. Choose one of the sequences in problem A-66 for which you determined that 447 is *not* a term. Write a clear explanation describing how you can be sure that 447 is not a term of the sequence.

A-68. Find the sequence generator for each sequence listed below. Write an equation for the nth term in each sequence below, keeping in mind that the first term of each sequence is $t(1)$.

a. $4, 7, 10, 13, \ldots$

b. $3, 8, 13, \ldots$

c. $24, 19, 14, \ldots$

d. $7, 9.5, 12, \ldots$

A-69. Great Amusements Park has been raising its ticket prices every year, as shown in the table at right.

Year	Price
0	\$50
1	\$55
2	\$60.50
3	\$66.55

a. Describe how the ticket prices are growing.

b. What will the price of admission be in year 6?

A-70. Solve the system at right for m and b.

$$1239 = 94m + b$$
$$810 = 61m + b$$

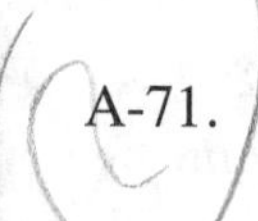

A-71. Write an equation or system of equations and then solve the problem below.

The French club sold rose bouquets and chocolate hearts for Valentine's Day. The roses sold for \$5 and the hearts sold for \$3. The number of bouquets sold was 15 more than the number of hearts sold. If the club collected a total of \$339, how many of each gift was sold.

A.2.3 How else can I write the equation?

Recursive Sequences

2, 6, 10, ...
$t(n) = 4n - 2$
$t(n + 1) = t(n) + 4$

In this chapter you have been writing equations for arithmetic sequences so that you could find the value of any term in the sequence, such as the 100th term, directly. Today you will investigate recursive sequences. A term in a recursive sequence depends on the term(s) before it.

A-72. Look at the following sequence:

$$-8, -2, 4, 10, \ldots$$

a. What are two ways that you could find the 10th term of the sequence? What is the 10th term?

b. If you have not done so already, write an equation that lets you find the value of any term $t(n)$. This kind of equation is called an **explicit equation**.

c. The next term after $t(n)$ is called $t(n+1)$. Write an equation to find $t(n+1)$ if you know what $t(n)$ is. An equation that depends on knowing other terms is called a **recursive equation**.

A-73. Alejandro used the recursive equation from part (c) of problem A-72 to write a sequence and came up with the following:

$$0, 6, 12, 18, 24$$

a. Does Alejandro's sequence match the recursive equation from problem A-72?

b. Why did Alejandro get a different sequence than the one from problem A-72? How can you mathematically write down the information he needs so that he can write the correct sequence?

A-74. Avery and Collin were trying to challenge each other with equations for sequences. Avery wrote:

$$t(n+1) = t(n)^2 - 1$$
$$t(1) = 3$$

a. Help Collin write the first 4 terms of this sequence.

b. Is Avery's sequence arithmetic, geometric, or some other kind of sequence? How do you know?

c. Describe to Collin how he could find the 10th term of this sequence. You do not need to actually find the 10th term.

A-75. Avery and Collin were still at it.

a. Collin wrote: $t(2) = 19$
$$t(n+1) = t(n) - 2$$

Help Avery write an explicit equation. Is the sequence arithmetic, geometric, or neither?

b. Then Avery wrote $t(n) = 6n + 8$. Help Collin write a recursive equation.

A-76. The Fibonacci sequence is a famous sequence that appears many times in mathematics. It can describe patterns found in nature, such as the number of petals on flowers, the arrangements of seeds in sunflowers, or scales on pinecones. It is named after Leonardo of Pisa, who was known as Fibonacci. He introduced the sequence to Western European mathematicians in 1202, though it had been described earlier by others including mathematicians in India.

The equation that describes the Fibonacci sequence can be written as:

$$t(1) = 1$$
$$t(2) = 1$$
$$t(n+1) = t(n) + t(n-1)$$

a. Write the first 10 terms of the Fibonacci sequence.

b. Is the Fibonacci sequence arithmetic, geometric, or neither?

c. Describe what you would need to do in order to find the 100th term of the Fibonacci sequence. Do not actually calculate the 100th term.

A-77. Avery and Collin were challenging each other with more equations for sequences. Avery was looking at an explicit equation that Collin wrote.

$$t(n) = 4.5n - 8$$

a. Write the first 4 terms for the sequence.

b. What would Avery do to write the 15th term of this sequence?

A-78. Write both an explicit equation and a recursive equation for the sequence: 5, 8, 11, 14, 17, ...

A-79. Draw a slope triangle and use it to find the equation of the line shown in the graph at right.

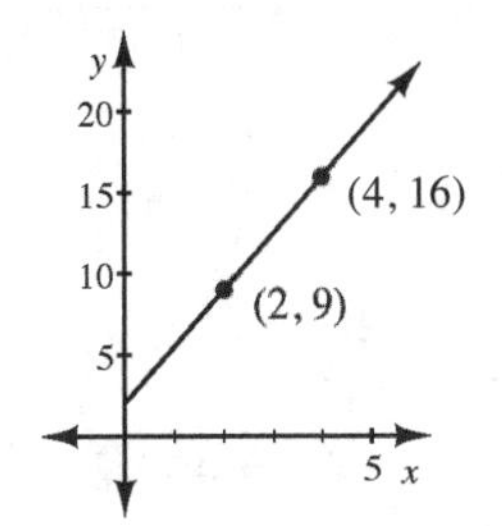

A-80. Find the following products.

a. $(4x+5)(4x-5)$

b. $(4x+5)^2$

A-81. Write an equation or system of equations to solve the problem below.

Apollo and Zeus are both on diets. Apollo currently weighs 105 kg and is gaining 2 kg per month. Zeus currently weighs 130 kg and is losing 3 kg per month. In how many months will they weigh the same?

A-82. Solve each system.

a. $6x - 2y = 10$
$3x - 2 = y$

b. $3x - 9y = 3$
$2x = 16 - y$

A-83. For each sequence defined recursively, write the first 5 terms and then define it explicitly.

a. $t(1) = 12$
$t(n+1) = t(n) - 5$

b. $a_1 = 32$
$a_{n+1} = \frac{1}{2} a_n$

A.3.1 What is the rate of change?

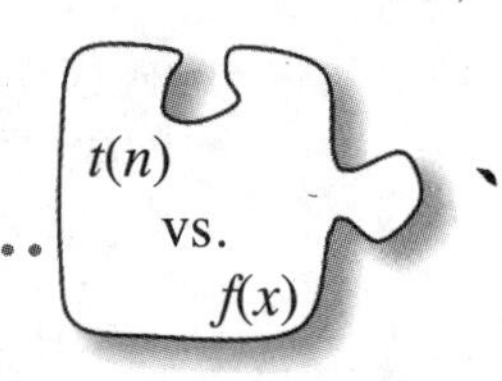

Patterns of Growth in Tables and Graphs

So far in this chapter you have looked at several types of sequences and compared linear and exponential growth patterns in situations, tables, and graphs. In this lesson you will compare patterns of growth rates to each other. This work will also help you write equations for exponential sequences in the next lesson.

A-84. PATTERNS OF GROWTH

Sequence A

n	$t(n)$
1	27
2	54
3	81
4	108

Sequence B

n	$t(n)$
1	9
2	36
3	81
4	144

Sequence C

n	$t(n)$
1	6
2	12
3	24
4	48

Your Task:

- Represent these three sequences on a graph (the Lesson A.3.1A Resource Page). Use a different color for each sequence. Although the graph should be discrete, connect the lines so you can see the trends easier.
- Consider the discussion points below for each sequence as you investigate the growth of these three sequences. You can discuss the sequences in any order.
- Be prepared to share your results with the class.

Discussion Points

How do the inputs, n, and the outputs of the sequence generator, $t(n)$, increase?

How does the sequence grow? Is the rate of change constant or changing? How? (You can make growth triangles to help answer this question.)

If we know a specific term, how would we find the next term? For example, if we knew the 10th term, could we find the 11th term?

Which family of functions best models each sequence?

A-85. GROWTH RATES IN SEQUENCES

Consider how fast each of the sequences is growing by looking at the tables and the graph. Do not make any additional computations. Instead make conjectures based on the tables and graphs.

a. If n represents the number of years, and $t(n)$ represents the amount of money in your savings account, which account would you want, Sequence A, B, or C?

b. Would your answer change if you kept the account for many years?

c. Obtain the Lesson A.3.1C Resource Page from your teacher. Extend the tables and the graph to $n = 7$. The table for Sequence B has been completed for you.

d. Based on your new graph, do you want to change your answer to part (b)? Why or why not?

A-86. WHICH GROWS THE MOST?

a. Will an exponentially growing bank account eventually contain more money than a linearly growing bank account for the same amount of initial savings, no matter how fast (steep) the rate of growth of the linear account? Use the slope triangles on your graph from problem A-85 to help you explain.

b. Sequence B shows quadratic growth. How does the growth of a quadratic sequence, like Sequence B, compare to exponential growth?

A-87. Identify the following sequences as linear, exponential, or other. For the linear and exponential sequences, identify the rate of change and whether it is a constant that is added or multiplied.

a. 12, 144, 1728, ...

b. 0, 5, 10, 15, 20, 25, ...

c. 0, 4, 16, 36, 64, ...

d. 1.5, 2.25, 3.375, 5.0625, ...

A-88. Solve the system of equations at right.

$$y = -x - 2$$
$$5x - 3y = 22$$

A-89. Write the first five terms of each sequence.

a. $t(1)=-3$
$t(n+1)=-2\cdot t(n)$

b. $t(1)=8$
$t(n+1)=t(n)-5$

c. $t(1)=2$
$t(n+1)=(t(n))^{-1}$

A-90. The graph at right compares the gas mileage to the weight of numerous vehicles.

Describe the association between these two quantities.

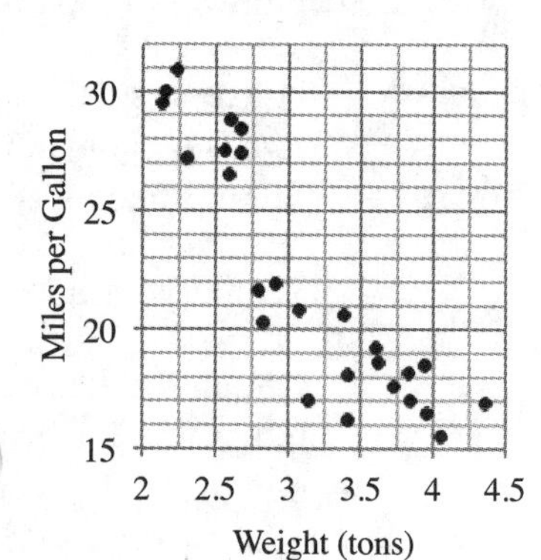

A-91. **Multiple Choice:** Which line below is parallel to $y=-\frac{2}{3}x+5$?

a. $2x-3y=6$

b. $2x+3y=6$

c. $3x-2y=6$

d. $3x+2y=6$

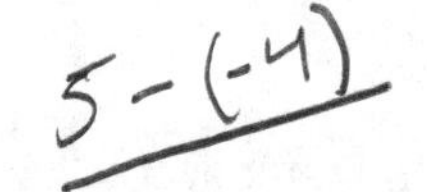

A-92. Use the given information to find an equation of the line.

a. Slope 2 and passing through $(10,17)$.

b. Passing through $(1,-4)$ and $(-2,5)$.

c.

x	−6	−3	0	3	6
y	−6	−4	−2	0	2

d.

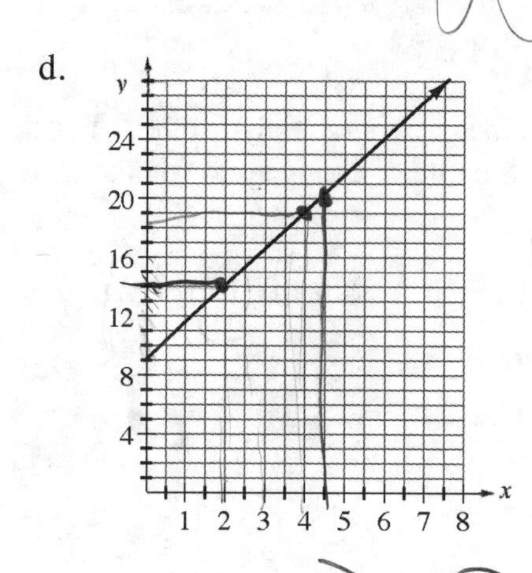

A.3.2 How can I use a multiplier?

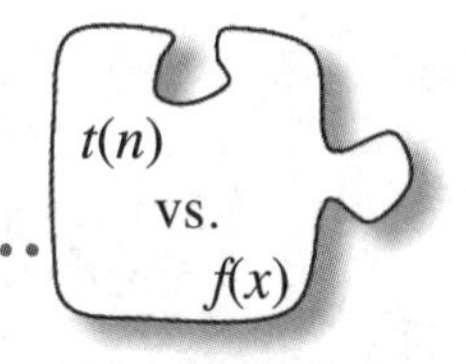

Using Multipliers to Solve Problems

In the past few lessons, you have investigated sequences that grow by adding (arithmetic) and sequences that grow by multiplying (geometric). In today's lesson, you will learn more about growth by multiplication as you use your understanding of geometric sequences and multipliers to solve problems. As you work, use the following questions to move your team's discussion forward:

What type of sequence is this? How do we know?

How can we describe the growth?

How can we be sure that our multiplier is correct?

A-93. Thanks to the millions of teens around the world seeking to be just like their math teachers, industry analysts predict that sales of the new πPhone will skyrocket!

πPHONES SWEEP THE NATION

Millions demand one!

(API) – Teenagers and Hollywood celebrities flocked to an exclusive shop in Beverly Hills, California yesterday, clamoring for the new πPhone. The store expects to start by selling 100 and expects to sell an average of 15% more each week after that.

"I plan to stand in line all night!" said Nelly Hillman. "As soon as I own one, I'll be cooler than everyone else."

Across the globe, millions of fans

a. The article provides a model for how many πPhones the store expects to sell. They start by selling 100 πPhone pre-orders in week zero. Predict the number sold in the 4th week.

b. If you were to write the number of πPhones the store received each week as a sequence, would your sequence be arithmetic, geometric, or something else? Justify your answer.

c. The store needs to know how many phones to order for the last week of the year. If you knew the number of πPhones sold in week 51, how could you find the sales for week 52? Write a recursive equation to show the predicted sales of πPhones in the nth week.

d. Write an explicit equation that starts with "$t(n) =$" to find the number of πPhones sold during the nth week without finding all of the weeks in between.

e. How many πPhones will the store predict it sells in the 52nd week?

A-94. A new πRoid, a rival to the πPhone, is about to be introduced. It is cheaper than the πPhone, so more are expected to sell. The manufacturer plans to make and then sell 10,000 pre-orders in week zero and expects sales to increase by 7% each week.

a. Write an explicit and a recursive equation for the number of πRoids sold during the nth week.

b. What if the expected weekly sales increase were 17% instead of 7%? Now what would the new explicit equation be? How would it change the recursive equation?

A-95. Oh no! Thanks to the lower price, 10,000 πRoid were made and sold initially, but after that, weekly sales actually decreased by 3%.

Find an explicit and a recursive equation that models the product's actual weekly sales.

A-96. In a geometric sequence, the sequence generator is the number that one term is multiplied by to generate the next term. Another name for this number is the **multiplier** or the **common ratio**.

a. Look back at your work for problems A-94, and A-95. What is the multiplier in each of these three situations?

b. What is the multiplier for the sequence 8, 8, 8, 8, ... ?

c. Explain what happens to the terms of the sequence when the multiplier is less than 1, but greater than zero. What happens when the multiplier is greater than 1? Add this description to your Learning Log. Title this entry "Multipliers" and add today's date.

A-97. MULTIPLE REPRESENTATIONS ON THE GRAPHING CALCULATOR

a. According to the model in problem A-95, how many weeks will it take for the weekly sales to drop to only one πRoid per week? Make a conjecture.

b. Before calculating the exact answer to the question in part (a), become comfortable with using your graphing calculator. On your calculator, make a graph for the sales of πPhones (problem A-93) for the first year. Sketch the graph on your paper. Make sure you show the scale of the axes on your sketch.

c. Use the table on your calculator to determine where, if at all, the graph in part (b) crosses the x-axis.

d. Enter the explicit equations for both problems A-93, $t(n) = 100 \cdot 1.15^n$, and problem A-94, $t(n) = 10\,000 \cdot 1.07^x$, in your calculator. Use your table to find the number of weeks it takes for sales in the first equation to exceed the sales in the second equation.

e. Make a sketch of the graph of both equations in part (d). Be sure to show the point of intersection. Label the scale on both axes.

f. Now use your calculator to answer the question in part (a). How close was your conjecture?

A-98. Write an explicit and a recursive equation for each table below. Be sure to check that your equations work for all of the entries in the table.

a.

n	$t(n)$
0	1600
1	2000
2	2500
3	3125
4	3906.25

b.

n	$t(n)$
0	3906.25
1	3125
2	2500
3	2000
4	1600

c.

n	$t(n)$
0	50
1	72
2	103.68
3	149.2992

d.

n	$t(n)$
0	
1	50
2	
3	72
4	
5	103.68
6	
7	149.2992

Problem continues on next page.→

A-98. *Problem continued from previous page.*

e. How are the tables in (a) and (b) related? How are the multipliers for (a) and (b) related? Why does this make sense?

f. What strategies did you use to find the equation for part (d)? How is the table in part (d) related to the one in part (c)?

g. In part (d), why is term 2 *not* 61?

METHODS AND MEANINGS

Types of Sequences

An **arithmetic sequence** is a sequence with an addition (or subtraction) **sequence generator**. The number added to each term to get the next term is called the **common difference**.

A **geometric sequence** is a sequence with a multiplication (or division) generator. The number multiplied by each term to get the next term is called the **common ratio** or the **multiplier**.

A multiplier can also be used to increase or decrease by a given percentage. For example, the multiplier for an increase of 7% is 1.07. The multiplier for a decrease of 7% is 0.93.

A **recursive sequence** is a sequence in which each term depends on the term(s) before it. The equation of a recursive sequence requires at least one term to be specified. A recursive sequence can be arithmetic, geometric, or neither.

For example, the sequence –1, 2, 5, 26, 677, ... can be defined by the **recursive equation**:

$$t(1) = -1, \quad t(n+1) = \left(t(n)\right)^2 + 1$$

An alternative notation for the equation of the sequence above is:

$$a_1 = -1, \quad a_{n+1} = (a_n)^2 + 1$$

A-99. For each table below, find the missing entries and write an equation.

a.

Month (x)	0	1	2	3	4	5	6
Population (y)	2	8	32				

b.

Year (x)	0	1	2	3	4	5	6
Population (y)	5	6	7.2				

A-100. Convert each percent increase or decrease into a multiplier.

a. 3% increase

b. 25% decrease

c. 13% decrease

d. 2.08% increase

A-101. Mr. C is such a mean teacher! The next time Mathias gets in trouble, Mr. C has designed a special detention for him. Mathias will have to go out into the hall and stand exactly 100 meters away from the exit door and pause for a minute. Then he is allowed to walk exactly halfway to the door and pause for another minute. Then he can again walk exactly half the remaining distance to the door and pause again, and so on. Mr. C says that when Mathias reaches the door he can leave, *unless* he breaks the rules and goes more than halfway, even by a tiny amount. When can Mathias leave? Prove your answer using multiple representations.

A-102. Simplify each expression.

a. $(2m^3)(4m^2)$

b. $\frac{6y^5}{3y^2}$

c. $\frac{-4y^2}{6y^7}$

d. $(-2x^2)^3$

A-103. For this problem, refer to the sequences graphed below.

#1

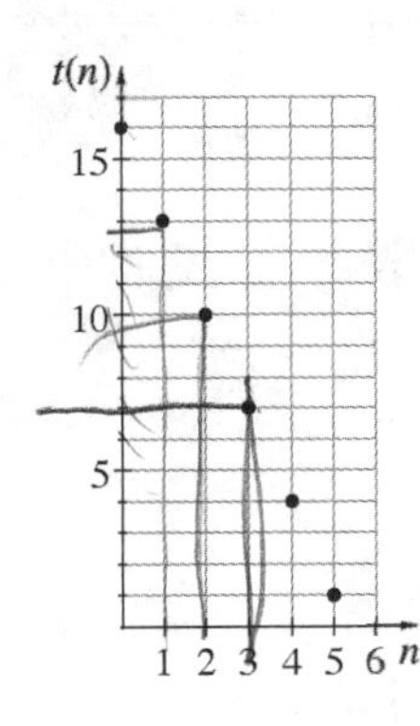

#2

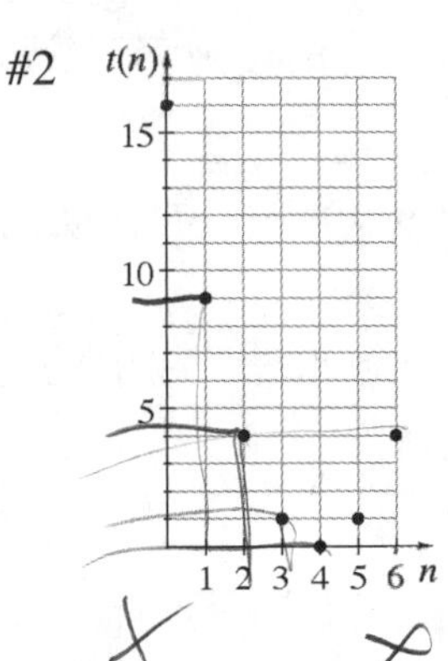

#3

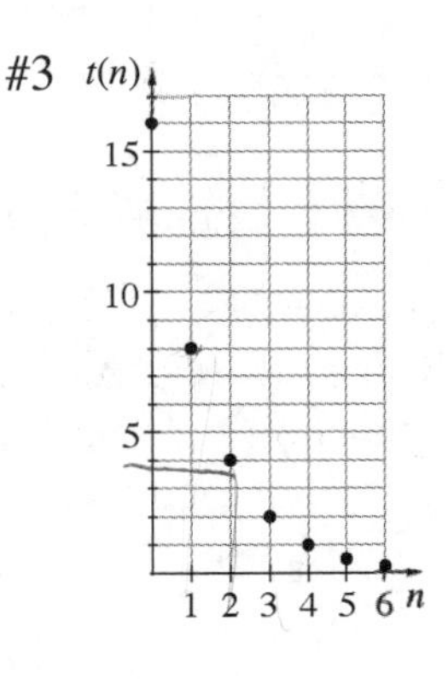

a. Identify each sequence as arithmetic, geometric, or neither.

b. If it is arithmetic or geometric, describe the sequence generator.

A-104. Read the Math Notes box in this lesson for information about an alternative notation for sequences and write the first 5 terms of these sequences.

a. $a_n = 2n - 5$

b. $a_1 = 3$
$a_{n+1} = -2 \cdot a_n$

A-105. Solve each equation.

a. $(x+2)(x+3) = x^2 - 10$

b. $\frac{1}{2}x + \frac{1}{3}x - 7 = \frac{5}{6}x$

c. $|2x - 1| = 9$

d. $\frac{x+1}{3} = \frac{x}{2}$

A.3.3 Is it a function?

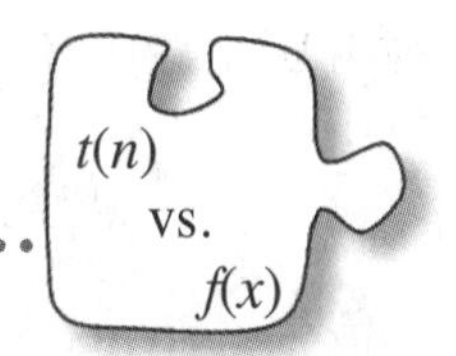

Comparing Sequences to Functions

Throughout this chapter, you have been learning about sequences. In Chapter 1, you worked with various function families. But what is the difference between a sequence and a function? In this lesson, you will compare and contrast sequences with functions. By the end of the lesson, you will be able to answer these questions:

Is a sequence different from a function?

What is the difference between a sequence $t(n)$ and the function $f(x)$ with the same equation?

A-106. Consider sequence $t(n)$ below.

$$-5, -1, 3, 7, \ldots$$

a. Create multiple representations, including a table, a graph, and an equation (recursive or explicit), for the sequence $t(n)$.

b. Is it possible for the equation representing $t(n)$ to equal 400? Justify your answer.

c. Create the same multiple representations as you did in part (a) for the function $f(x)=4x-9$. How are $f(x)$ and $t(n)$ different? How can you see their differences in each of the representations?

d. For the function $f(x)=4x-9$, is it possible for $f(x)$ to equal 400? Explain why or why not.

A-107. Let us consider the difference between $t(n)=2\cdot 3^n$ and $f(x)=2\cdot 3^x$.

a. Is $f(x)=2\cdot 3^x$ a function? Why or why not? Is $t(n)=2\cdot 3^n$ a function?

b. Is it possible for $t(n)$ to equal 1400? If so, find the value of n that makes $t(n)=1400$. If not, justify why not.

c. Is it possible for $f(x)$ to equal 1400? Be prepared to share your justification with the class.

d. How are the functions similar? How are they different?

A-108. LEARNING LOG

Is a sequence a function? Justify your answer completely. If so, what makes it different from the functions that are usually written in the form $f(x) =$ ________ ? If it is not a function, why not? Be prepared to share your ideas with the class. After a class discussion about these questions, answer the questions in your Learning Log. Title this entry "Sequences vs. Functions" and label it with today's date.

A-109. Janine was working on her homework but lost part of it. She knew that one output of $p(r) = 2 \cdot 5^r$ is 78,000, but she could not remember if $p(r)$ is a sequence or if it is a regular function. With your team, help her figure it out. Be sure to justify your decision.

A-110. **Additional Challenge:** Khalil is working with a geometric sequence. He knows that $t(0) = 3$ and that the sum of the first three terms ($t(0)$, $t(1)$, and $t(2)$) is 63. Help him figure out the sequence. Be prepared to share your strategies with the class.

A-111. **Additional Challenge:** Discuss with your team how you can use your graphing calculator to solve each of the following equations for x, accurate to the nearest 0.01.

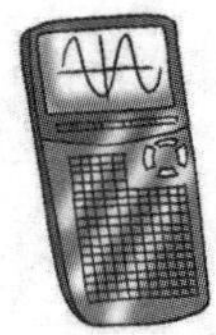

a. $200(0.5)^x = 3.125$

b. $318 = 6 \cdot 3^x$

A-112. Is it possible for the sequence $t(n) = 5 \cdot 2^n$ to have a term with the value of 200? If so, which term is it? If not, justify why not.

A-113. Is it possible for the function $f(x) = 5 \cdot 2^x$ to have an output of 200? If so, what input gives this output? If not, justify why not.

A-114. Consider the following sequences as you complete parts (a) through (c) below.

Sequence 1	Sequence 2	Sequence 3
2, 6, ...	24, 12, ...	1, 5, ...

a. Assuming that the sequences above are arithmetic with $t(1)$ as the first term, find the next four terms for each sequence. For each sequence, write an explanation of what you did to get the next term and write an equation for $t(n)$.

b. Would your terms be different if the sequences were geometric? Find the next four terms for each sequence if they are geometric. For each sequence, write an explanation of what you did to get the next term and write an equation for $t(n)$.

c. Create a totally different type of sequence for each pair of values shown above, based on your own equation. Write your equation clearly (using words or algebra) so that someone else will be able to find the next three terms that you want.

A-115. For the function $g(x) = x^3 + x^2 - 6x$, find the value of each expression below.

a. $g(1)$ b. $g(-1)$ c. $g(-2)$ d. $g(10)$

e. Find at least one value of x for which $g(x) = 0$.

f. If $f(x) = x^2 - x + 3$, find $g(x) - f(x)$.

A-116. Write equations to solve each of the following problems.

a. When the Gleo Retro (a trendy commuter car) is brand new, it costs \$23,500. Each year it loses 15% of its value. What will the car be worth when it is 15 years old?

b. Each year the population of Algeland increases by 12%. The population is currently 14,365,112. What will the population be 20 years from now?

A-117. An arithmetic sequence has $t(8) = 1056$ and $t(13) = 116$. Write an equation for the sequence. What is $t(5)$?

A-118. Describe the domain of each function or sequence below.

a. The function $f(x) = 3x - 5$. b. The sequence $t(n) = 3n - 5$.

c. The function $f(x) = \frac{5}{x}$. d. The sequence $t(n) = \frac{5}{n}$.

Appendix A Closure What have I learned?

Reflection and Synthesis

The activities below offer you a chance to reflect about what you have learned during this chapter. As you work, look for concepts that you feel very comfortable with, ideas that you would like to learn more about, and topics you need more help with. Look for connections between ideas as well as connections with material you learned previously.

① TEAM BRAINSTORM

What have you studied in this chapter? What ideas were important in what you learned? With your team, brainstorm a list. Be as detailed as you can. To help get you started, a list of Learning Log entries and Math Notes boxes are below.

What topics, ideas, and words that you learned *before* this chapter are connected to the new ideas in this chapter? Again, be as detailed as you can.

How long can you make your list? Challenge yourselves. Be prepared to share your team's ideas with the class.

Learning Log Entries

- Lesson A.1.1 – Exponential Functions
- Lesson A.3.2 – Multipliers
- Lesson A.3.3 – Sequence vs. Functions

Math Notes

- Lesson A.1.2 – Continuous and Discrete Graphs
- Lesson A.3.2 – Types of Sequences

② MAKING CONNECTIONS

Below is a list of the vocabulary used in this chapter. Make sure that you are familiar with all of these words and know what they mean. Refer to the glossary or index for any words that you do not yet understand.

arithmetic sequence	common difference	common ratio
continuous	discrete	domain
exponential function	first term	geometric sequence
initial value	linear function	multiplier
recursive sequence	sequence	sequence generator
$t(0)$	term	term number
y-intercept		

Make a concept map showing all of the connections you can find among the key words and ideas listed above. To show a connection between two words, draw a line between them and explain the connection, as shown in the model below. A word can be connected to any other word as long as you can justify the connection. For each key word or idea, provide an example or sketch that shows the idea.

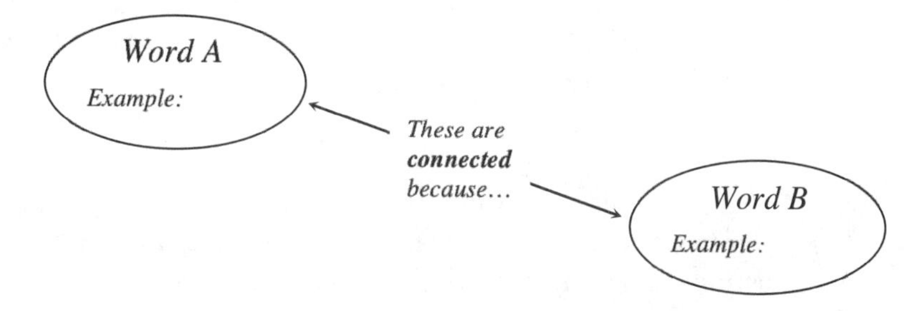

Your teacher may provide you with vocabulary cards to help you get started. If you use the cards to plan your concept map, be sure either to re-draw your concept map on your paper or to glue the vocabulary cards to a poster with all of the connections explained for others to see and understand.

While you are making your map, your team may think of related words or ideas that are not listed here. Be sure to include these ideas on your concept map.

③ PORTFOLIO: EVIDENCE OF MATHEMATICAL PROFICIENCY

Four members of a study team were analyzing the sequence $3, 7, 11, \ldots$ They found the equation for the sequence to be $t(n) = 4n - 1$, and they were trying to figure out if 200 could be a term of their sequence.

They made the following statements. Which students justified their statements? Are the justifications convincing? Explain why or why not.

Shinna: "I think it's not, because all the terms in the sequence are odd and 200 is an even number."

Aldo: "I think it is, because the equation $200 = 4n - 1$ has a solution."

James: "It can't be, because the solution to $200 = 4n - 1$ is $n = 50.25$, which is not a whole number. There can't be a 50.25^{th} term!"

Leslie: "I think 199 and 203 are terms of the sequence, but not 200."

Now create your own sequence. Then figure out what the 110th term of your sequence would be and whether the number 419 is a term in your sequence. Use multiple representations to justify your answers thoroughly.

Alternatively your portfolio entry could showcase your early understanding of an exponential function by explaining everything you know about the function $f(x) = 2^x - 3$. Provide one or two representative example problems.

Obtain the Appendix A Closure Resource Page: Sequence vs. Function Graphic Organizer from your teacher. Use this page to compare and contrast sequences and functions in their multiple representations. How are they similar? How are they different?

④ WHAT HAVE I LEARNED?

Most of the problems in this section represent typical problems found in this chapter. They serve as a gauge for you. You can use them to determine which types of problems you can do well and which types of problems require further study and practice. Even if your teacher does not assign this section, it is a good idea to try these problems and find out for yourself what you know and what you need to work on.

Solve each problem as completely as you can. The table at the end of the closure section has answers to these problems. It also tells you where you can find additional help and practice with problems like these.

CL A-119. Determine if the following sequences are arithmetic, geometric, or neither:

a. $-7, -3, 1, 5, 9, \ldots$

b. $-64, -16, -4, -1, \ldots$

c. $1, 0, 1, 4, 9, \ldots$

d. $0, 2, 4, \ldots$

CL A-120. Find an equation to represent each table as a sequence.

a.

n	$t(n)$
1	4
2	1
3	–2
4	

b.

n	$t(n)$
1	6
2	7.2
3	8.64
4	

CL A-121. Solve the following systems algebraically.

a. $x + 2y = 17$
$x - y = 2$

b. $4x + 5y = 11$
$2x + 6y = 16$

c. $4x - 3y = -10$
$x = \frac{1}{4}y - 1$

d. $2x + y = -2x + 5$
$3x + 2y = 2x + 3y$

CL A-122. Solve each equation after first rewriting it in a simpler equivalent form.

a. $3(2x-1)+12=4x-3$

b. $\frac{3x}{7}+\frac{2}{7}=2$

c. $\frac{x-3}{x}=\frac{3}{5}$

d. $4x(x-2)=(2x+1)(2x-3)$

CL A-123. Simplify each expression.

a. $(-3x)^2$

b. $(3x)^{-2}$

c. $\frac{2(3x)^2}{3x^3}$

d. $\frac{2(3x)^2}{(3x)^{-2}}$

CL A-124. Create multiple representations of each line described below.

a. A line with slope 4 and y-intercept –6.

b. A line with slope $\frac{3}{2}$ that passes through the point $(5,7)$.

CL A-125. Create an explicit equation for each recursively-defined sequence below.

a. $a_1=17,\ a_{n+1}=a_n-7$

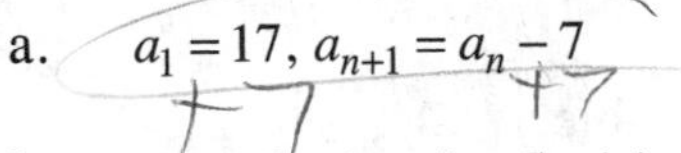

b. $t(1)=3,\ t(n+1)=5\cdot t(n)$

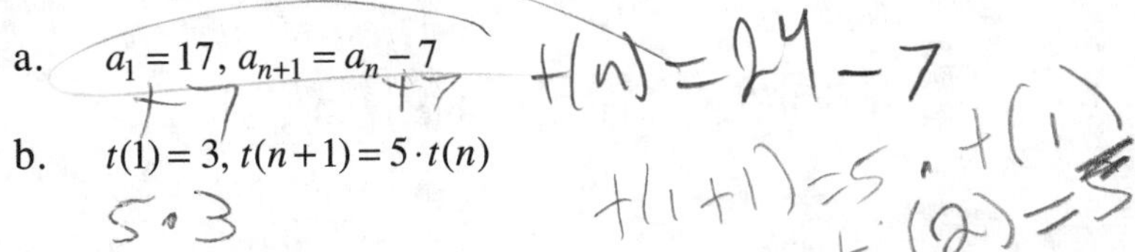

CL A-126. Use a graph to describe the domain and range of each function or sequence below.

a. The function $f(x)=(x-2)^2$.

b. The sequence $t(n)=3n-5$.

CL A-127. When a family with two adults and three children bought tickets for an amusement park, they paid a total of \$56.50. The next family in line, with four children and one adult, paid \$49.50. Find the adult and child ticket prices by writing and solving a system of equations.

CL A-128. Check your answers using the table at the end of this section. Which problems do you feel confident about? Which problems were hard? Have you worked on problems like these in previous math classes? Use the table to make a list of topics you need to learn more about, and a list of topics you just need to practice more.

Answers and Support for Closure Activity #4

What Have I Learned?

Note: MN = Math Note, LL = Learning Log

Problem	Solutions	Need Help?	More Practice
CL A-119.	a. arithmetic b. geometric c. neither d. arithmetic	Section A.2 MN: A.3.2	Problems A-42, A-44, A-50, A-87, and A-114
CL A-120.	a. $t(n) = -3n + 7$ b. $t(n) = 5(1.2)^n$ or $t(n) = 6(1.2)^{n-1}$	Lessons A.2.2 and A.3.2	Problems A-37, A-64, A-68, A-83, A-87, and A-99
CL A-121.	a. $(7, 5)$ b. $(-1, 3)$ c. $(-\frac{1}{4}, 3)$ d. $(1, 1)$	Explanations and practice of topics from previous courses are available in the *Core Connections Algebra Parent Guide with Extra Practice,* available free at www.cpm.org.	Problems A-7, A-22, A-36, A-54, A-70, and A-88
CL A-122.	a. -6 b. 4 c. 7.5 d. $\frac{3}{4}$	Topic from previous course	Problems 1-40, 1-52, A-15, A-87, and A-105
CL A-123.	a. $9x^2$ b. $\frac{1}{9x^2}$ c. $\frac{6}{x}$ d. $162x^4$	Topic from previous course	Problems A-9, A-10, A-13, A-24, A-56, and A-102

Problem	Solutions	Need Help?	More Practice
CL A-124.	a. $y = 4x - 6$ (table and graph below)	Topic from previous course	Problems A-11, A-16, A-37, A-46, and A-92

x	y
–3	–18
–2	–14
–1	–10
0	–6
1	–2
2	2
3	6

b. $y = \frac{3}{2}x - \frac{1}{2}$

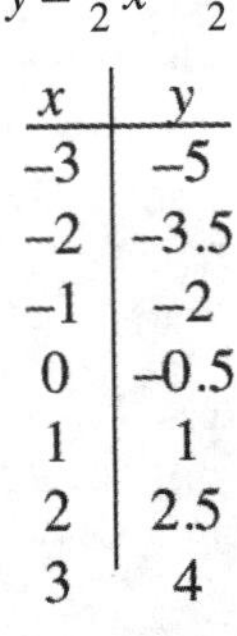

x	y
–3	–5
–2	–3.5
–1	–2
0	–0.5
1	1
2	2.5
3	4

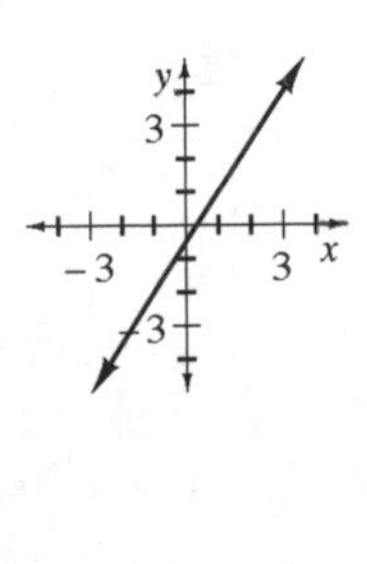

Problem	Solutions	Need Help?	More Practice
CL A-125.	a. $t(n) = 24 - 7n$ b. $t(n) = \frac{3}{5}(5)^n$	Lesson A.2.3 MN: A.3.2	Problems A-72, A-78, A-83, A-89, and A-104
CL A-126.	a. Domain: all real numbers Range: $y \geq 0$ b. Domain: all positive integers; Range: all real numbers of the form $3n - 5$	Lesson A.3.3 LL: A.3.3	Problems A-25 and A-118
CL A-127.	$2a + 3c = 56.5$, $a + 4c = 49.5$ adults cost $15.50, children cost $8.50	Topic from previous course	Problems A-71 and A-81

EXPONENTIAL FUNCTIONS
B
FAMILY of FUNCTIONS
$f(x)=b^x$
INVESTIGATE
MULTIPLIER
$m>0$
VARIABLES AND PARAMETERS

Appendix B Exponential Functions

Appendix B provides an opportunity for you to learn more about the family of exponential functions. As you do this you will build more advanced algebra skills, such as solving for an indicated variable, simplifying or rewriting exponential expressions, working with fractional exponents, and finding the exponential function that passes exactly through any pair of given points.

You will also learn about several important applications of exponential functions.

Guiding Question

Mathematically proficient students make sense of problems and persevere in solving them.

As you work through this chapter, ask yourself:

Am I making connections between the multiple representations and making sense of the situations?

Chapter Outline

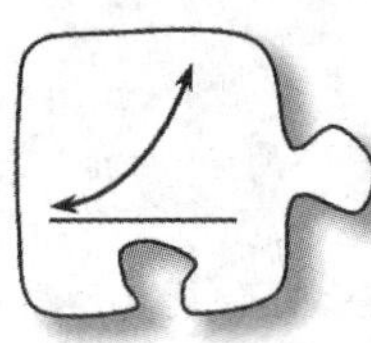

Section B.1 In Section B.1, you will investigate a family of exponential functions. You will recognize exponential growth when given situations, tables, graphs, or equations, and you will make connections between these representations. You will also extend your knowledge of exponents and their properties as you solve exponential equations. You will be introduced to step functions. At the end of the section, you will apply exponential functions to real-life situations involving growth and decay.

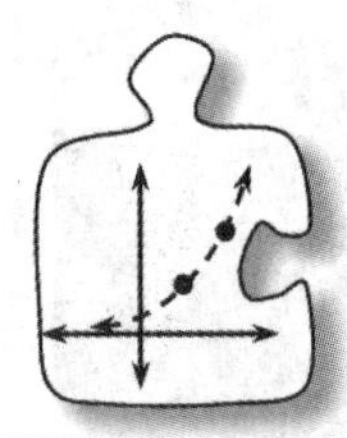

Section B.2 In Section B.2, you will find exponential equations that fit given data. In doing so, you will learn about fractional exponents.

B.1.1 What do exponential graphs look like?

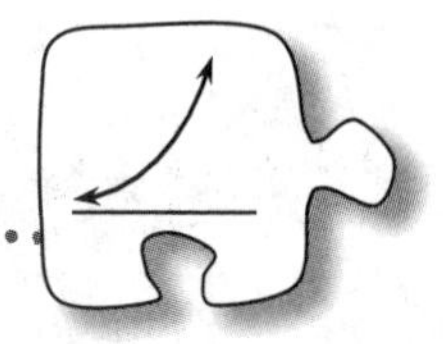

Investigating $y = b^x$

In this lesson you will investigate the characteristics of the family of functions $y = b^x$. As a team, you will generate data for various functions in this family, form questions about your data, and answer each of these questions using multiple representations. Your team will show what you have learned on a stand-alone poster.

B-1. BEGINNING TO INVESTIGATE EXPONENTIALS

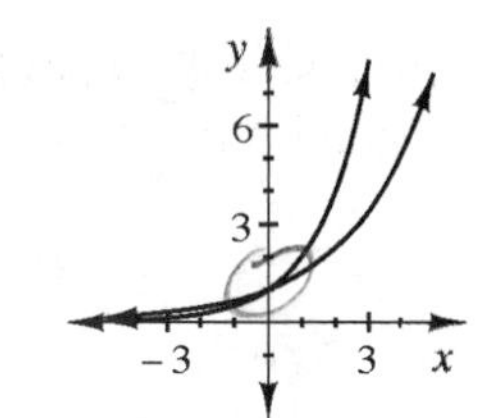

In Appendix A, you graphed several exponential functions. Some graphs, like those that modeled the rabbit populations in problem A-4, were *increasing* exponential functions and looked similar to the two exponential functions graphed at right.

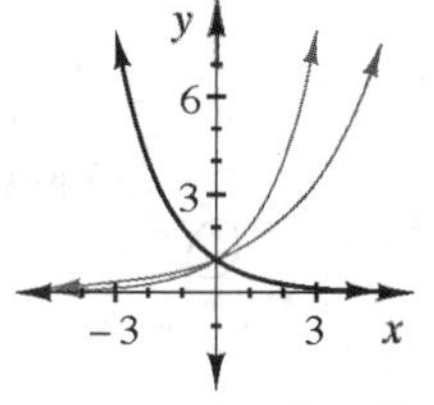

Other graphs, such as the rebound-height graphs from the bouncing ball activity (problem A-20), represented *decreasing* exponential functions and looked similar to the third curve, shown in bold at right.

You already know that equations of the form $y = mx + b$ represent the family of lines, and you know what effect changing the parameters m and b have on the graph. Today you will begin to learn more about the exponential function family. In their simplest form, the equations of exponential functions look like $y = b^x$.

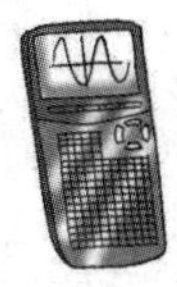

By experimenting with different values of b, find three equations in $y = b^x$ form that have graphs appearing to match the two graphs shown above. Confirm your results using your graphing calculator and be ready to share your results with the class.

B-2. INVESTIGATING $y = b^x$, Part One

What types of graphs exist for equations of the form $y = b^x$?

Your Task: With your team, try different values of b to try to find as many different looking graphs as possible. (Stick to small values of b, for example, less than 10. Keep the window on your calculator set from –10 to 10 in both the x and y direction.)

Decide as a team what different values of b to try so that you find as many different looking graphs as possible. Be sure to keep track of what you have tried with a sketch of the resulting graph so that you may refer to it later. Use the questions listed below to help get you started.

Discussion Points

What special values of b should we consider?

Are there any other values of b we should try?

How many different types of graphs can we find?

How do we know we have found all possible graphs?

B-3. The graph of the function $y = \left(\frac{1}{2}\right)^x$ is shown at right.

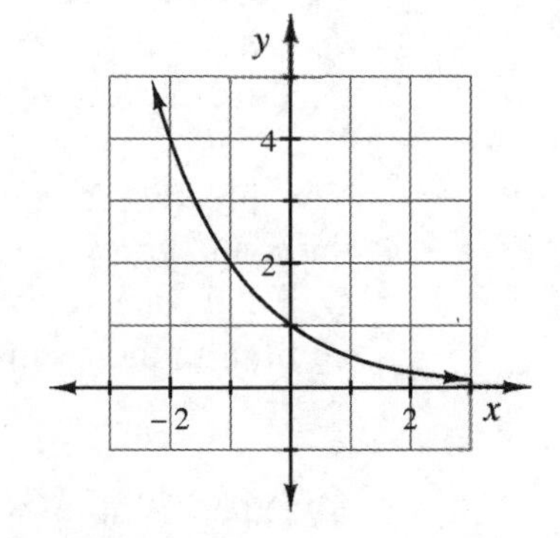

a. Describe what happens to y as x gets bigger and bigger. For example, what is y when $x = 20$? $x = 100$? $x = 1000$? $x =$ (a much larger number)?

b. Does the graph of $y = \left(\frac{1}{2}\right)^x$ have an x-intercept? Explain how you know.

c. When x is very large, the graph of $y = \left(\frac{1}{2}\right)^x$ approaches the x-axis. That is, as x gets larger and larger (farther to the right along the curve), the closer the curve gets to the x-axis. In this situation, the x-axis is called an asymptote of $y = \left(\frac{1}{2}\right)^x$. You can remind yourself about asymptotes by rereading the Math Notes box in Lesson 1.2.2.

Does $y = \left(\frac{1}{2}\right)^x$ have a vertical asymptote? In other words, is there a vertical line that the graph above approaches? Why or why not?

B-4. INVESTIGATING $y = b^x$, Part Two

Now that you, with your class, have found all of the possible graphs for $y = b^x$, your teacher will assign your team one or two of the types of graphs to investigate further. Completely describe the graphs. Use the Discussion Point questions below to guide your investigation of this graph. Look for ways to justify your summary statements using more than one representation (equation, table, graph).

As a team, organize your graphs and summary statements into a stand-alone poster that clearly communicates what you learned about your set of graphs. Be sure to include all of your observations along with examples to demonstrate them. Anyone should be able to answer the questions below after examining your poster. Use colors, arrows, labels, and other tools to help explain your ideas.

Discussion Points

How can we describe the shape of the graph?

What happens when x gets larger? What happens when x gets smaller?

How does changing the value of b change the graph?
Which aspects of the graph do not change?

Are there any special points? Can they be explained with the equation?

Does the graph have any symmetry? If so, where?

B-5. Exponential functions have some interesting characteristics. Consider functions of the form $y = b^x$ as you discuss the questions below.

a. Exponential functions such as $y = b^x$ are defined only for $b > 0$. Why do you think this is? That is, why would you not want to use negative values of b?

b. Can you consider $y = 1^x$ or $y = 0^x$ to be exponential functions? Why or why not? How are they different from other exponential function?

B-6. LEARNING LOG

Look over your work from this lesson. What questions did you ask yourself as you were making observations and statements? How does changing the value of b affect a graph? What questions do you still have after this investigation? Write a Learning Log entry describing what mathematical ideas you developed during this lesson. Title this entry "Investigating $y = b^x$" and label it with today's date.

B-7. A grocery store is offering a sale on bread and soup. Khalil buys four cans of soup and three loaves of bread for \$11.67. Ronda buys eight cans of soup and one loaf of bread for \$12.89.

a. Write equations for both Khalil's and Ronda's purchases.

b. Solve the system to find the price of one can of soup and the price of one loaf of bread.

B-8. If two expressions are equivalent, they can form an equation that is considered to be *always true*. For example, since $3(x-5)$ is equivalent to $3x-15$, then the equation $3(x-5)=3x-15$ is always true, that is, true for any value of x.

If two expressions are equal only for certain values of the variable, they can form an equation that is considered to be *sometimes true*. For example, $x+2$ is equal to $3x-8$ only when $x=5$, so the equation $x+2=3x-8$ is said to be sometimes true.

If two expressions are not equal for any value of the variable, they can form an equation that is considered to be *never true*. For example, $x-5$ is not equal to $x+1$ for *any* value of x, so the equation $x-5=x+1$ is said to be never true.

Is the equation $(x+3)^2=x^2+9$ always, sometimes or never true? Justify your reasoning completely.

B-9. Consider the sequence that begins 40, 20, 10, 5, …

a. Based on the information given, can this sequence be arithmetic? Can it be geometric? Why?

b. Assume this is a geometric sequence. On graph paper, plot the sequence on a graph up to $n=6$.

c. Will the values of the sequence ever become zero or negative? Explain.

B-10. If a ball is dropped from 160 cm and rebounds to 120 cm on the first bounce, how high will the ball be:

a. On the 2nd bounce?

b. On the 5th bounce?

c. On the nth bounce?

B-11. Simplify or multiply each of the following expressions as appropriate.

a. $(3x^2yz^4)^2$

b. $\left(\frac{r^2s}{rs^3t}\right)^3$

c. $(3m+7)(2m-1)$

d. $(x-3)^2$

B-12. Write and solve an equation for the problem below.

If 150 empty water bottles weigh 4.5 pounds, what would you expect 90 empty water bottles to weigh?

B-13. Sketch the shape of the graph of the function $y = b^x$ given each of the following values of b.

a. b is a number larger than 1.

b. b is a number between 0 and 1.

c. b is equal to 1.

B-14. For parts (a) and (b), find a recursive equation in a_n form for each sequence. (For a reminder about a_n form see the Math Notes box in Lesson A.3.2.) For parts (c) and (d) find an explicit equation for each sequence.

a. $108, 120, 132, \ldots$

b. $\frac{2}{5}, \frac{4}{5}, \frac{8}{5}, \ldots$

c. $3741, 3702, 3663, \ldots$

d. $117, 23.4, 4.68, \ldots$

B-15. Write the multiplier for each increase or decrease described below.

a. A 25% increase

b. A decrease of 18%

c. An increase of 39%

d. A decrease of 94%

B-16. Eeeeew! Hannah's volleyball team left their egg salad sandwiches sitting in their lockers over the weekend. When they got back on Monday they were moldy. "Perfect!" said Hannah. "I can use these sandwiches for my biology project. I'll study how quickly mold grows."

Using a transparent grid, Hannah estimated that about 12% of the surface of one sandwich had mold on it. She threw the sandwich out. For the rest of the week, Hannah came back when she had time. Each time she measured somebody else's sandwich and threw it out. She collected the following data:

Day 1 (Monday)	Day 2 (Tuesday)	Day 2 (Tuesday)	Day 4 (Thursday)	Day 4 (Thursday)	Day 4 (Thursday)	Day 5 (Friday)
12%	15%	13%	26%	27%	24%	38%

a. Create a scatterplot and sketch it. Is a linear model reasonable?

b. Based on the story, what kind of equation do you think will best fit the situation?

B-17. In 1999, Charlie received the family heirloom marble collection consisting of 1239 marbles. Charlie's great-grandfather had started the original marble collection in 1905. Each year, Charlie's great-grandfather had added the same number of marbles to his collection. When he passed them on to his son, he insisted that each future generation add the same number of marbles per year to the collection. When Charlie's father received the collection in 1966, there were 810 marbles.

a. By the time Charlie inherited the collection, how many years had it been in existence?

b. How many marbles are added to the collection each year?

c. Use the information you found in part (b) to figure out how many marbles were in the original collection when Charlie's great-grandfather started it.

d. Generalize this situation by writing a function describing the growth of the marble collection for each year (n) since Charlie's great-grandfather started it.

e. How old will the marble collection be when Charlie (or one of his children) has more than 2000 marbles? In what year will this occur?

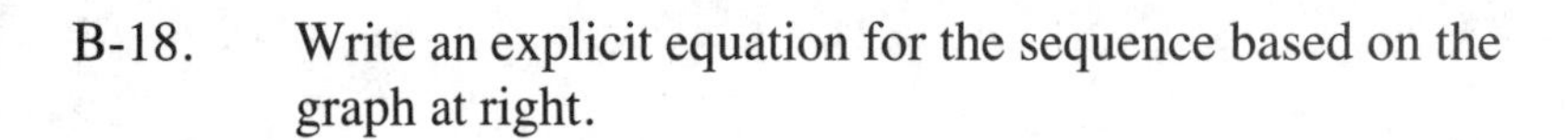

B-18. Write an explicit equation for the sequence based on the graph at right.

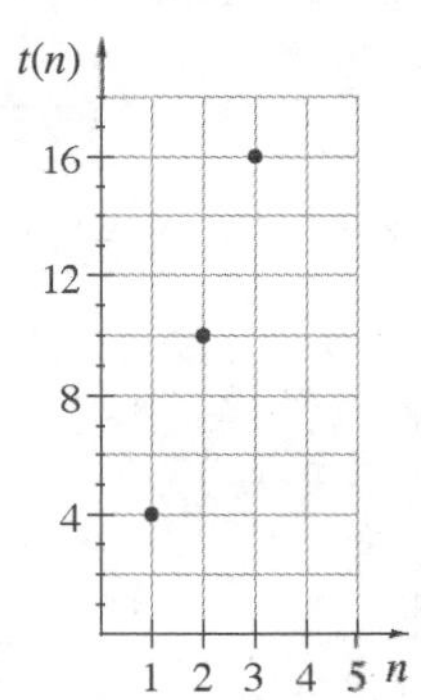

B.1.2 What is the connection?

Multiple Representations of Exponential Functions

In Lesson 1.2.3 you looked at multiple representations (such as a table, graph, equation, or situation) of linear functions. In this chapter you will use multiple representations to learn more about the multiplier and starting point of exponential functions.

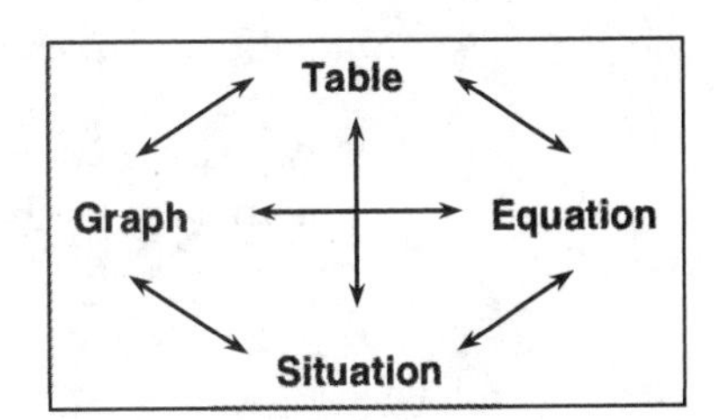

B-19. Let's look at some of the connections between the multiple representations of an exponential function.

a. Arnold dropped a ball during the bouncing ball activity and recorded its height in a table. Part of his table is shown at right. What was the rebound ratio of his ball? At what height did he drop the ball? Write an equation that represents his data. Explain your equation.

Bounce Number	Height (cm)
0	
1	
2	84.5
3	67.6
4	54.1

b. A major technology company, ExpoGrow, is growing incredibly fast. The latest prospectus (a report on the company) said that so far, the number of employees, y, could be found with the equation $y = 3(4)^x$, where x represents the number of years since the company was founded. How many people founded the company? How can the growth of this company be described?

c. A computer virus is affecting the technology center in such a way that each day, a certain portion of virus-free computers is infected. The number of virus-free computers is recorded in the table at right. How many computers are in the technology center? What portion of virus-free computers is infected each day? How many computers will remain virus-free at the end of the third day? Justify your answer.

Day	Uninfected Computers
0	27
1	18
2	12

d. As part of a major scandal, it was discovered that several statements in the prospectus for ExpoGrow in part (b) were false. If the company actually had five founders and doubles in size each year, what equation should it have printed in its report?

B-20. Most of the exponential equations you have used in this chapter have been in the form $y = ab^x$.

a. What does a represent in this equation? What does b represent?

b. How can you identify a by looking at a table? How can you find it in a situation? Give an example for each representation.

c. How can you determine b in each representation? Use arrows or colors to add your ideas about b to the examples you created in part (b).

B-21. MULTIPLE-REPRESENTATIONS WEB

What connections are you sure you can use in an exponential functions web? For example, if you have an exponential equation, such as $y = 20(3)^x$, can you complete a table? If so, draw an arrow from the equation and point at the table, as shown at right.

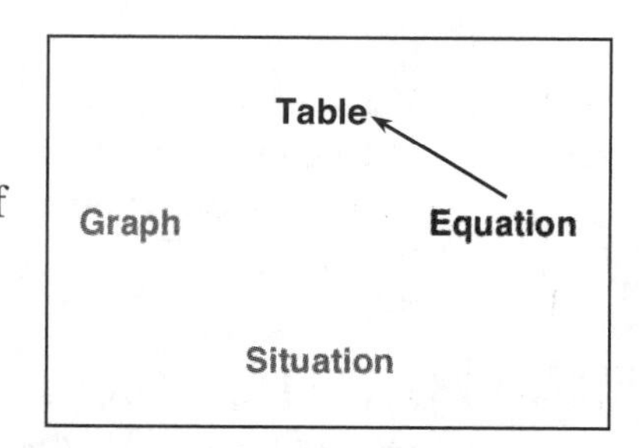

Copy the web, without any arrows, into your Learning Log. Discuss with your team the connections you have used so far in this chapter. Draw arrows to show which representations you can connect already. Which connections have you not used yet but you are confident that you could? Which connections do you still need to explore?

Can you think of examples from earlier in this lesson, or in Appendix A, to support your conclusions? Write down the problem numbers next to your arrows.

Title this entry "Multiple Representations Web for Exponential Functions" and label it with today's date. Be ready to share your findings with the rest of the class.

B-22. EQUATION → GRAPH

How can you sketch the graph of an exponential function directly from its equation without making a table first? Discuss this with your team. Then make a reasonable sketch of the graph of $y = 7(2)^x$ on your paper.

B-23. Each table below represents an exponential function of the form $y = ab^x$. Copy and complete each table on your paper and find the corresponding equation.

a.

x	y
0	1.8
1	5.76
2	18.432
3	
4	

b.

x	y
0	5
1	
2	245
3	
4	

B-24. Brianna is working on her homework. Her assignment is to come up with four representations for an exponential function of her choosing. She decides it is easiest to start by writing an equation, so she chooses $y = 1200\left(\frac{1}{2}\right)^x$. Help Brianna create the other three components of the web.

B-25. Sketch the graphs of $y = x^2$, $y = 2x^2$, and $y = \frac{1}{2}x^2$ on the same set of axes. Describe the similarities and differences among the graphs.

B-26. Write an equation or system of equations to solve this problem.

Morgan started the year with \$615 in the bank and is saving \$25 per week. Kendall started with \$975 and is spending \$15 per week. When will they both have the same amount of money in the bank?

B-27. Examine each sequence below. State whether it is arithmetic, geometric, or neither. For the sequences that are arithmetic, find the formula for $t(n)$. For the sequences that are geometric, find the sequence generator for $t(n)$.

a. $1, 4, 7, 10, 13, \ldots$

b. $0, 5, 12, 21, 32, \ldots$

c. $2, 4, 8, 16, 32, \ldots$

d. $5, 12, 19, 26, \ldots$

e. $x, x+1, x+2, x+3, \ldots$

f. $3, 12, 48, 192, \ldots$

B-28. Write an explicit equation for the sequence based on the graph at right.

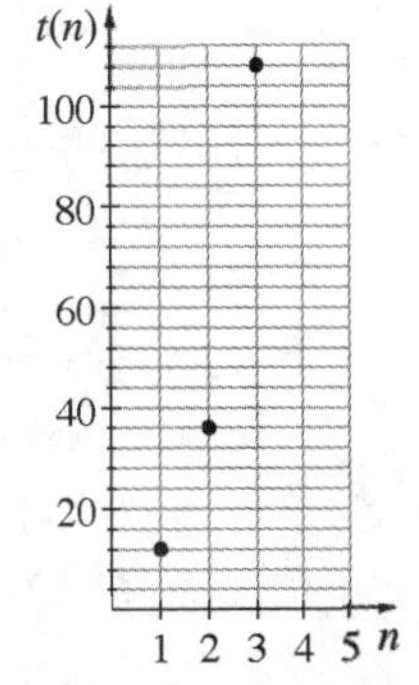

B.1.3 How does it grow?

More Applications of Exponential Growth

You may have heard the expression, "Money does not grow on trees." However, money does, in a sense, grow in a savings account. In today's lesson you will apply your understanding of exponential functions to solve problems involving money and interest. As you work, use the questions below to help focus your team's discussions.

How does it start?

How does it grow? What is the multiplier?

How is the rate written as a percent? As a decimal?

B-29. SAVING FOR COLLEGE

Suppose you have $1000 to invest and know of two investment options. You can invest in bonds (which pay 8% *simple* interest) or put your money in a credit union account (which pays 8% *compound* interest). Will the option you choose make a difference in the amount of money you earn? Examine these two situations below.

Bonds with Simple Interest:

a. If you invest in bonds, your $1000 would grow as shown in the table at right. How does money grow with simple interest?

b. By what percent would your balance have increased by the 4th year? Show how you know.

VALUE OF BONDS

Number of Years	Amount of Money (in dollars)
0	1000.00 (initial value)
1	1080.00
2	1160.00
3	1240.00
4	

Accounts with Compound Interest:

c. Instead, if you invest your $1000 in the credit union at 8% compound interest that is compounded once a year, its value would grow as shown in the table at right. Why is there $1166.40 in your account in the second year? Explain how the compound interest is calculated. How is it growing?

VALUE OF CREDIT UNION ACCOUNT

Number of Years	Amount of Money (in dollars)
0	1000.00 (initial value)
1	1080.00
2	1166.40
3	1259.71
4	

Problem continue on next page →

B-29. *Problem continued from previous page.*

d. What will be the balance of the credit union account at the 4th year? By what percent would this account balance increase at four years? Show how you know.

e. Which type of account – a bond with simple interest or a credit union account with compound interest – grows most quickly?

B-30. Assume that the interest is added at the beginning of a new year. Make one graph that shows how each type of investment (simple and compound) starts with $1000 and grows over 8 years. Discuss these questions in your team as you graph:

Discussion Points

Can we make the graph clearer with color?

What happens to the money in between the years?

How can we represent the "between" amount on a graph?

B-31. In previous courses you may have used **models** as an estimate of real behavior. Creating a best-fit line for scattered data is one example of a model. Models give you a mathematical way to describe the data and to make predictions.

The simple and compound interest situations in problem B-30 were both step functions. Writing equations for step functions can be very complicated. However, you can model the step functions with other equations with which you are already familiar.

a. Think about the growth and the starting point for the simple and compound interest situations from this lesson. Model each of the two step functions with an equation. Let y represent the money in the account after x years.

b. Check that your equation represents the tables in problem B-29. If your models do not match the tables, correct your equation.

c. Use your model to predict how much your original $1000 investment would be worth at the end of 20 years in the credit union.

d. Why are the equations considered models, instead of representations of the real behavior? Is there an advantage to using the model to make predictions?

B-32. In this course, use continuous functions to model situations, unless indicated otherwise.

A third option for investing money is a money market account, which offers 8% annual interest *compounded quarterly* (four times per year). This means that the 8% is divided into four parts over the year, so the bank pays 2% every three months.

a. Model the value (every three months) of the $1000 investment in this money market account with an equation.
Let y represent the money in the account after x quarters.

b. Use the model to find the value of your $1000 investment at four years. How does this compare with your other investment options from problem B-29?

B-33. If you invested $1000 in the credit union from problem B-29 (interest compounded yearly at 8%), how much would you have at 20 years? If you wanted to earn this same amount of money with bonds with simple interest, what interest rate would the bonds need to earn? Show how you know.

MATH NOTES

METHODS AND MEANINGS

Compounding Interest

A bank can pay **simple interest**, in which case the amount in the bank grows linearly. For example, 3% simple interest compounded annually on an initial investment of \$2500 would grow in a sequence with a common difference: $0.03(2500) = \$75$. The equation and table follow:

$$t(n) = 2500 + 75n$$

Number of Years, n	0	1	2	3	...	10
Amount in Bank, $t(n)$	2500.00	2575.00	2650.00	2725.00		3250.00

If the bank **compounds interest**, the relationship is exponential. For example, 3% annual interest, *compounded annually*, would have a multiplier of 1.03 every year. The equation and table using the example above are:

$$t(n) = 2500 \cdot 1.03^n$$

Number of Years, n	0	1	2	3	...	10
Amount in Bank, $t(n)$	2500	2575.00	2652.25	2731.82		3359.79

If the bank *compounds monthly*, the 3% annual interest becomes $\frac{3\%/\text{year}}{12 \text{ months/year}} = 0.25\%$ per month, and the multiplier becomes 1.0025. The equation and table for the first ten years follows:

$$t(m) = 2500 \cdot 1.0025^m$$

Number of Months, m	0	12	24	36	...	120
Amount in Bank, $t(m)$	2500	2576.00	2654.39	2735.13		3373.38

B-34. Your banker shows you the graph at right to explain what you can earn if you invest with him. Does this graph represent simple or compound interest? How can you tell? Write an equation to represent how much money you would have as time passes. Make sure you write a "let" statement.

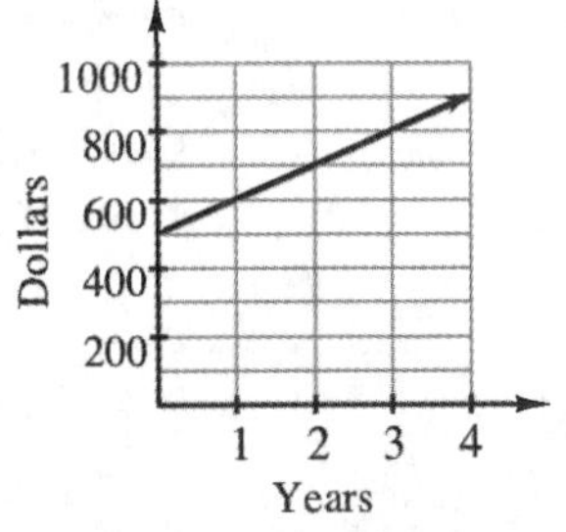

B-35. Each table below represents an exponential function in $y = ab^x$ form. Copy and complete each table on your paper and find a corresponding equation.

a.

x	y
–1	3
0	
1	75
2	
3	

b.

x	y
0	
1	
2	96.64
3	77.312
4	

B-36. Tickets for a concert have been in incredibly high demand, and as the date for the concert draws closer, the price of tickets increases exponentially. The cost of a pair of concert tickets was $150 yesterday, and today it is $162. As you complete parts (a) through (c) below, assume that each day's percent increase from the day before is the same.

a. What is the daily percent rate of increase? What is the multiplier?

b. What will be the cost of a pair of concert tickets one week from now?

c. What was the cost of a pair of tickets two weeks ago?

B-37. Dusty won $125,000 on the *Who Wants to Be a Zillionaire?* game show. He decides to place the money into an account that earns 6.25% interest compounded annually and plans not to use any of it until he retires.

a. Write an expression that represents how much money Dusty will have in t years.

b. How much money will be in the account when he retires in 23 years?

B-38. Solve the following systems of equations.

a. $3x - 2y = 14$
$-2x + 2y = -10$

b. $y = 5x + 3$
$-2x - 4y = 10$

c. Which system above is most efficiently solved by using the Substitution Method? Explain.

d. Which system above is most efficiently solved by using the Elimination Method? Explain.

B-39. If you flip a fair coin, what is the probability that it comes up "heads"? "Tails"?

B.1.4 What if it does not grow?

Exponential Decay

To learn more about how exponents affect growth, today you will study new situations in which the exponential function "decays" or decreases. This will lead to studying negative exponents.

B-40. THE PENNY LAB

What about situations that do not grow? In this activity, you will explore a situation that behaves exponentially, but whose results get smaller. This is an example of **exponential decay**.

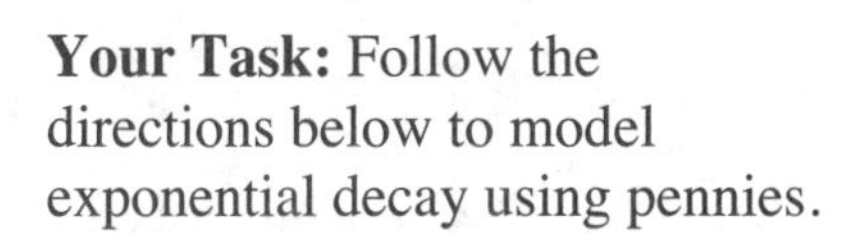

Your Task: Follow the directions below to model exponential decay using pennies.

Trial #0: Start with 100 pennies.

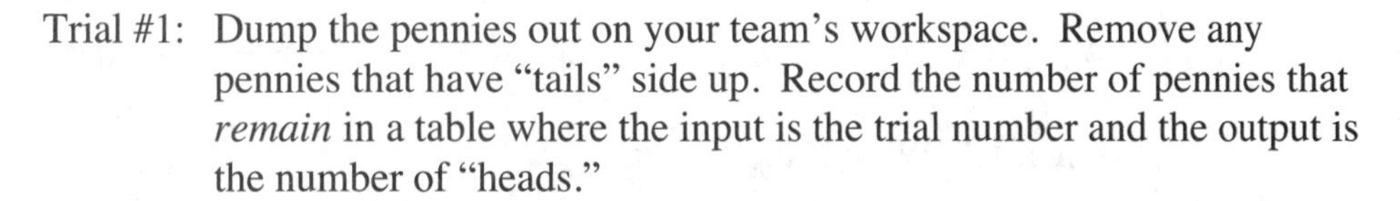

Trial #1: Dump the pennies out on your team's workspace. Remove any pennies that have "tails" side up. Record the number of pennies that *remain* in a table where the input is the trial number and the output is the number of "heads."

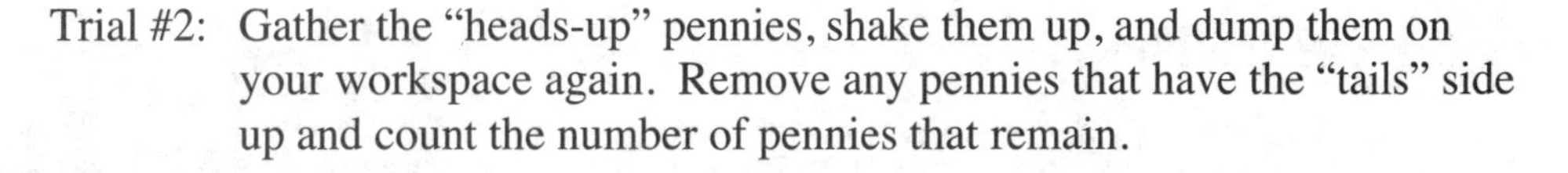

Trial #2: Gather the "heads-up" pennies, shake them up, and dump them on your workspace again. Remove any pennies that have the "tails" side up and count the number of pennies that remain.

Trial #x: Continue this process until the last penny is removed. Be sure to record all of your results in your table and then answer the questions below.

a. Is it possible that a team conducting this experiment might never remove their last penny? Explain.

b. Would the results of this experiment have been significantly different if you had removed the "heads" pennies each time?

c. If you had started with 200 pennies, how would this have affected the results?

B-41. Decide what your dependent and independent variables are for "The Penny Lab" data, clearly label them, and graph your data on your own graph paper. Then graph your data carefully on a team Lesson B.1.4 Resource Page transparency obtained from your teacher.

a. Stack your team's transparency with those from other teams on an overhead projector or document camera so that the axes are aligned. Then examine and describe the resulting scatterplot. Where does the graph cross the *y*-axis? Does the graph have any asymptotes? Should the graph be continuous or discrete?

b. Is this situation increasing or decreasing? What does this mean about the multiplier? Using what you know about the probability of flipping a fair coin, what would you expect or estimate the multiplier to be?

c. Write an equation for an exponential function that models the data. Make sure you also write a "let" statement for your variables.

d. What output does your function give for $x = 0$? What could this mean in relation to the situation?

e. Could there be an output value for $x = -1$? If so, what might it mean?

f. In the context of this situation, what should the domain of the model that you wrote in part (c) be? With the appropriate domain, what would a graph of your model look like?

g. What family of functions that you saw in previous chapters has graphs like the one you made in this problem? What are the first few values of this function? What is the equation?

B-42. HALF-LIFE

Carbon-14 dating is used to approximate the age of ancient discoveries and to learn more about things like dinosaur fossils. Scientists have studied the rate of decay of carbon-14 and have learned that no matter how much of this element they start with, only half of it will remain after about 5730 years (which is called its **half-life**).

All living things on this planet contain the same proportion of this carbon-14 relative to overall carbon in their bodies. Knowing how much carbon-14 to expect, scientists can then measure how much carbon-14 is left in ancient items to figure out how much time has passed since the object was living.

Problem continues on next page →

B-42. *Problem continued from previous page.*

a. If a living object is supposed to contain 100 grams of carbon-14, how much would be expected to remain after one half-life (5730 years)? After two half-lives (11,460 years)?

b. Draw a graph showing the expected amount, y, of carbon-14 (in grams) remaining after x half-lives.

c. Write an equation for a function that represents the amount of carbon-14 that will remain after x half-lives. Write a "let" statement.

d. What output does your function give for $x = 0$? Does this make sense? Justify why or why not.

e. What output would the function give for $x = -1$?

B-43. In addition to helping you learn about exponential decay, half-life can also provide insight into some special exponent properties.

a. For example, in part (d) of problem B-42, you determined that $100\left(\frac{1}{2}\right)^0 = 100$. So what must $\left(\frac{1}{2}\right)^0$ equal? What do you think 3^0 or $(-5)^0$ equals? How do your graphs from Lesson B.1.1 help you predict this? Use your calculator to check your predictions. Then write a conjecture about the value of x^0 (when $x \neq 0$).

b. What if $x = -1$? According to your graph, how much carbon-14 should there be when $x = -1$? Use this information to make sense of the value of $\left(\frac{1}{2}\right)^{-1}$. Confirm your conclusion with your calculator.

c. Now find the value of your equation when $x = -2$. Use this information to make sense of the value of $\left(\frac{1}{2}\right)^{-2}$. Then, as a team, write a conjecture about the value of x^{-2} when $x \neq 0$. Test your conjecture by predicting the value of 3^{-2} and $\left(\frac{2}{3}\right)^{-2}$. Be sure to test your predictions with your calculator.

B-44. Use a graphing calculator to compare the graphs of $y=\left(\frac{1}{2}\right)^x$ and $y=2^{-x}$.

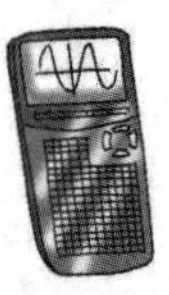

a. What do you notice? How does a negative exponent affect the base number?

b. Use this idea to rewrite each of the following expressions in a different form. If you and your team members disagree, check your results with the calculator.

i. $\left(\frac{1}{5}\right)^{-1}$ *ii.* 100^{-1} *iii.* $\left(\frac{5}{8}\right)^{-1}$ *iv.* $\left(\frac{1}{3}\right)^{-2}$

v. $\left(\frac{2}{3}\right)^{-3}$ *vi.* 6^{-3} *vii.* $\left(\frac{3}{2}\right)^{-1}$ *viii.* 2^{-5}

METHODS AND MEANINGS

MATH NOTES

Basic Laws of Exponents

In the expression x^3, x is the **base** and 3 is the **exponent**.

$$x^3 = x \cdot x \cdot x$$

The patterns that you have been using during this section of the book are called the **laws of exponents**. Here are the basic rules with examples:

Law	Examples	
$x^m x^n = x^{m+n}$ for all x	$x^3x^4 = x^{3+4} = x^7$	$2^5 \cdot 2^{-1} = 2^4$
$\frac{x^m}{x^n} = x^{m-n}$ for $x \neq 0$	$x^{10} \div x^4 = x^{10-4} = x^6$	$\frac{5^4}{5^7} = 5^{-3}$
$(x^m)^n = x^{mn}$ for all x	$(x^4)^3 = x^{4\cdot 3} = x^{12}$	$(10^5)^6 = 10^{30}$
$x^0 = 1$ for $x \neq 0$	$\frac{y^2}{y^2} = y^0 = 1$	$9^0 = 1$
$x^{-1} = \frac{1}{x}$ for $x \neq 0$	$\frac{1}{x^2} = (\frac{1}{x})^2 = (x^{-1})^2 = x^{-2}$	$3^{-1} = \frac{1}{3}$

B-45. The leadership class at Mt. Heron High School is organizing a shoe drive. A local business has agreed to donate boxes to collect the shoes in. If each box can hold 20 pairs of shoes, draw a step graph relating the number of shoes collected to the number of boxes needed for up to 200 pair of shoes.

B-46. Assume that a DVD loses 60% of its value every year it is in a video store. Suppose the initial value of the DVD was $80.

a. What multiplier would you use to calculate the video's new values?

b. What is the value of the DVD after one year? After four years?

c. Write a continuous function, $V(t)$, to model the value of a DVD after t years.

d. When does the video have no value?

e. Sketch a graph of this function. Be sure to scale and label the axes.

B-47. For each problem, write one or two equations to represent the situation and then solve. Be sure to define your variable(s) and clearly answer the question.

a. The Lees have three children. The oldest is twice as old as the youngest. The middle child is five years older than the youngest. If the sum of the ages is 57, how old is each child?

b. In Katy's garden there are 105 ladybugs. They are increasing at two ladybugs per month. There are currently 175 aphids and the number of aphids is decreasing at three aphids per month. When will the number of ladybugs and aphids in Katy's garden be the same?

B-48. Multiply and simplify each expression below.

a. $(x-3)^2$

b. $(2m+1)^2$

c. $x(x-3)(x+1)$

d. $(2y-1)(y^2+7)$

B-49. Consider the sequence $2, 8, 3y+5, \ldots$

a. Find the value of y if the sequence is arithmetic.

b. Find the value of y if the sequence is geometric.

B-50. After paying $20,000 for a car, you read that this model has decreased in value 15% per year over the last several years. If this trend continues, how much will the car be worth 5 years from now?

B-51. Jerry says, "I've got my money in a great account that compounds interest monthly. The equation $y = 388(1.008)^m$ represents how much money I have at the end of any month." What is Jerry's monthly interest rate? What is his annual interest rate? Write an equation to represent your total money if you invest $500 in an account with the same rate of return. Let m represent the number of months the money has been invested.

B-52. Solve each equation below for x. Check your solution.

a. $3x - 7(4 + 2x) = -x + 2$

b. $-5x + 2 - x + 1 = 0$

B-53. Solve each system of equations below.

a. $2x + y = -7y$
$y = x + 10$

b. $3x = -5y$
$6x - 7y = 17$

B-54. Find the equation of the line with x-intercept $(-4, 0)$ and y-intercept $(0, 9)$.

B-55. For each problem, write one or two equations to represent the situation and then solve. Be sure to define your variable(s) and clearly answer the question.

a. At the farmer's market Laura bought three pounds of heirloom tomatoes. If the tomatoes are priced at $8 for five pounds, what did Laura pay for her tomatoes?

b. Adult tickets for the school play cost $5 and student tickets cost $3. Thirty more student tickets were sold than adult tickets. If $1770 was collected, how many of each type of ticket were sold?

B-56. Determine which of the following equations are true for all values (always true). For those that are not, decide whether they are true for certain values (sometimes true) or not true for any values (never true). Justify your decisions clearly.

a. $(x - 5)^2 = x^2 + 25$

b. $(2x - 1)(x + 4) = 2x^2 + 7x - 4$

c. $\frac{2x^2y^3}{y^2} = 2x^2y$

d. $(3x - 2)(2x + 1) = 6x^2 - x - 5$

B.1.5 What are the connections?

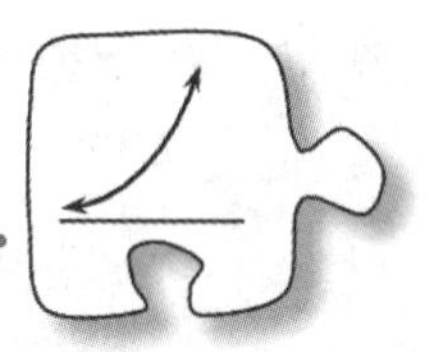

Graph → Equation

In Lesson B.1.2, you started a Multiple Representations Web for exponential functions. Today your team will develop methods for finding an equation from a graph. As you find ways to write equations based on a graph, you will build deeper understanding of exponential functions.

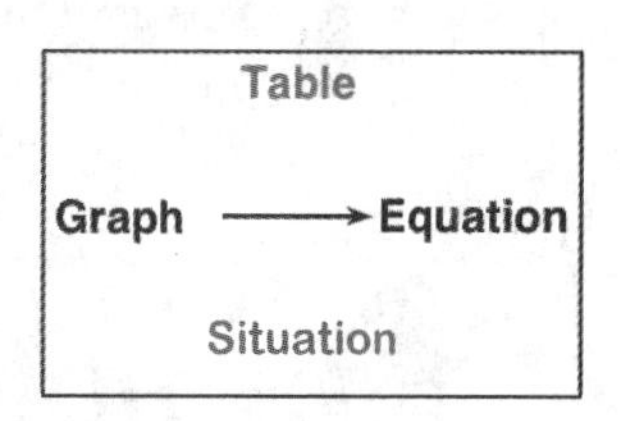

What information do we have?

Can we use other representations to help us think about our equation?

How can we be sure that our equation works?

B-57. GRAPH → EQUATION

Use the clues provided in each graph below to find a possible corresponding equation in $y = ab^x$ form. Assume that if the graph has an asymptote, it is located on the x-axis.

a.

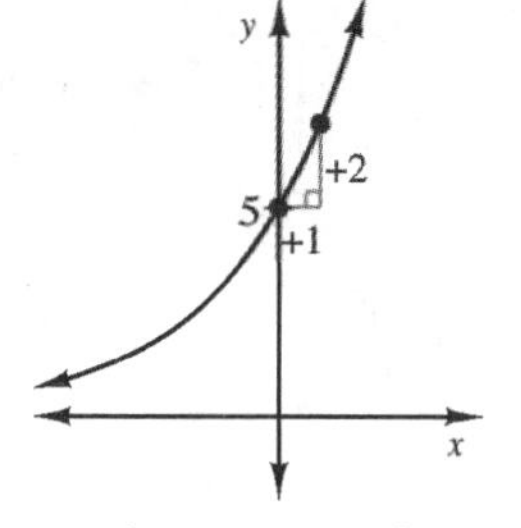

b.

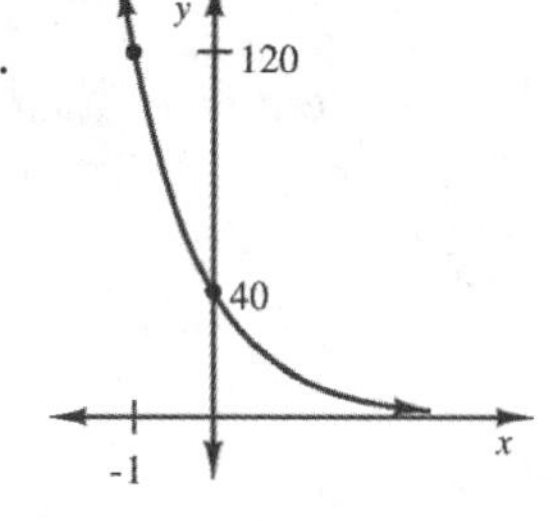

c.

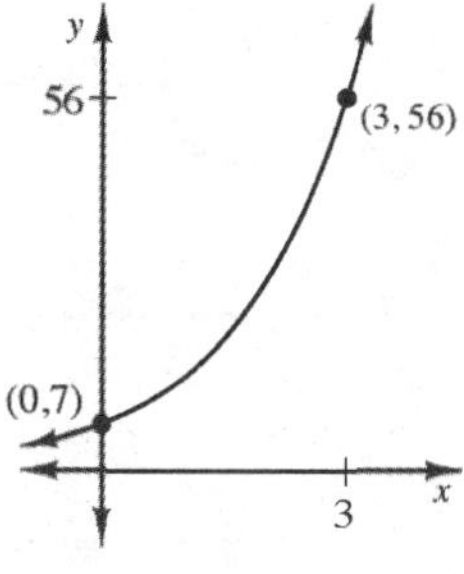

d.

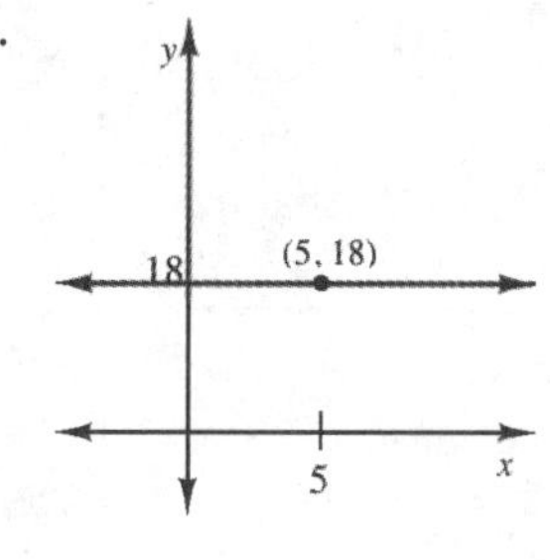

e.

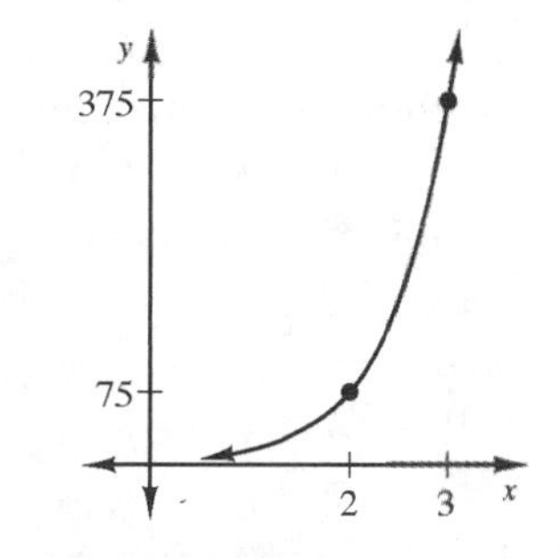

f.

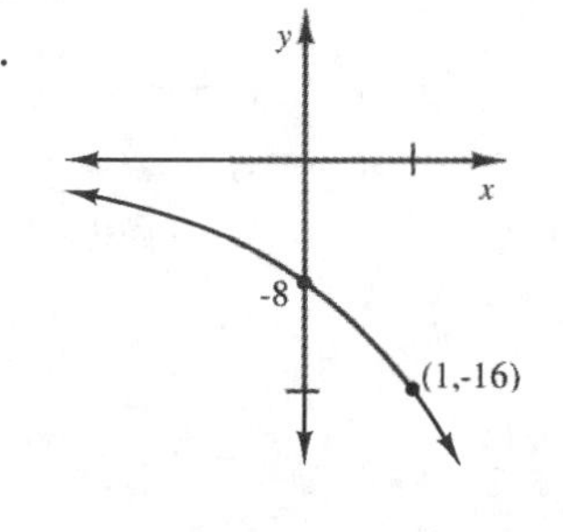

B-58. LEARNING LOG

Create a Learning Log entry in which you describe methods for creating an exponential equation given a graph. Be sure to include examples to illustrate your reasoning. Title this entry "Graph → Equation for Exponential Functions" and label it with today's date.

METHODS AND MEANINGS

MATH NOTES

Step Functions

A **step function** is a special kind of piecewise function (a function composed of parts of two or more functions). A step function has a graph that is a series of line segments that often looks like a set of steps. Step functions are used to model real-world situations where there are abrupt changes in the output of the function.

The endpoints of the segments on step functions are either open circles (indicating this point is not part of the segment) or filled-in circles (indicating this point is part of the segment).

The graph at right models a situation in which a tour bus company has busses that can each hold up to 20 passengers with 5 available busses.

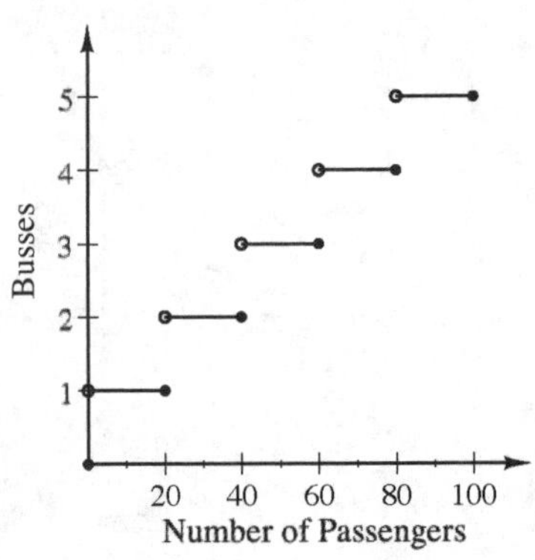

B-59. The drama club found that the best price for renting a fog machine was $38 for every three days, plus a one-time $60 delivery fee. Make a step graph that shows the cost of renting the fog machine for up to three weeks.

B-60. Use the clues in the graph at right to find a possible corresponding equation in $y = ab^x$ form. Assume the graph has an asymptote at the x-axis.

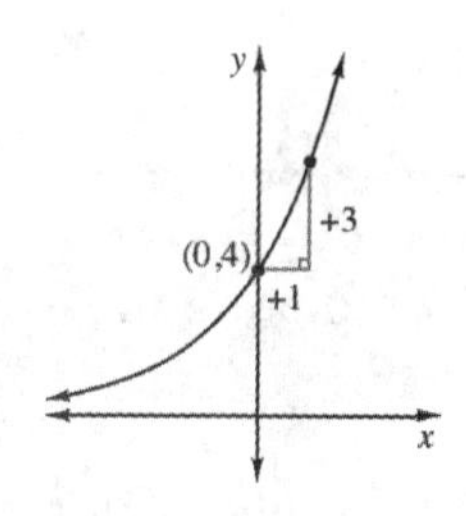

B-61. Kristin's grandparents started a savings account for her when she was born. They invested $500 in an account that pays 8% interest compounded annually.

a. Write an equation to model the amount of money in the account on Kristin's x^{th} birthday.

b. How much money is in the account on Kristin's 16th birthday?

c. What are the domain and range of the equation that you wrote in part (a)?

B-62. Graph $y = x^2 + 3$ and $y = (x+3)^2$. What are the similarities and differences between the graphs? How do these graphs compare to the graph of $y = x^2$?

B-63. Simplify.

a. $\sqrt[3]{-1000}$ b. $\sqrt[3]{\frac{1}{8}}$ c. $\sqrt[3]{-125}$ d. $\sqrt[4]{81}$

B-64. Solve each equation for the variable. Check your solutions, if possible.

a. $8a + a - 3 = 6a - 2a - 3$ b. $8(3m - 2) - 7m = 0$

c. $\frac{x}{2} + 1 = 6$ d. $|x - 3| + 5 = 11$

B.1.6 What is the connection?

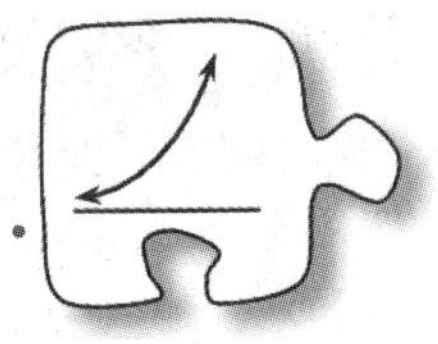

Completing the Multiple Representations Web

Review the Multiple Representations Web for exponential functions that you created in Lesson B.1.2. Are there any connections you have made since Lesson B.1.2 that you need to add to your web? What connections between representations do you still need to explore?

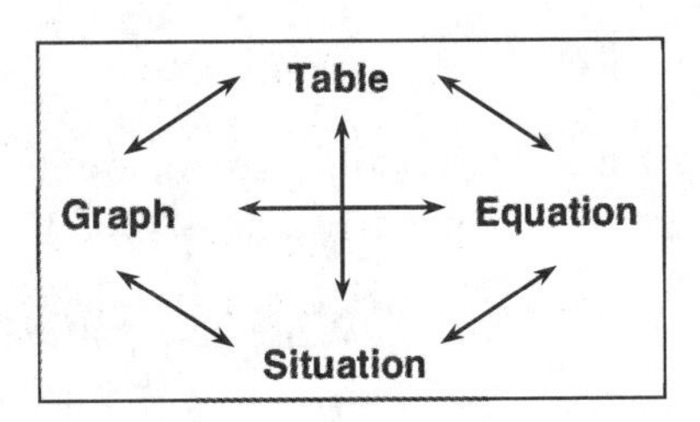

In today's lesson, design your own teamwork based on the connections that are incomplete in your web. Begin your teamwork today by planning which of the problems appear to your team to be the most challenging. The goal is for your team to complete the web by the end of this lesson.

B-65. WRITING A SITUATION

Each representation below represents a different set of data. For each part, brainstorm a situation that could fit the data. Provide enough information in your "problem" description so that someone else could generate the graph, table, or equation for the data. Be creative! Your team's situation may be selected for a future assessment!

a.

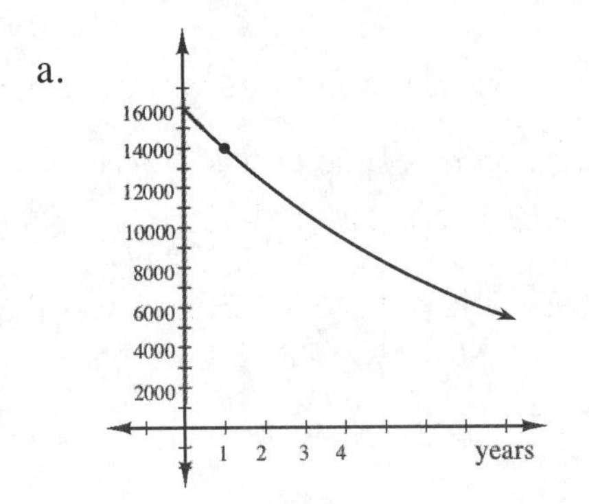

b. $B(t) = 180(1.22)^t$

c.

Year	Amount	
1980	226 million	x 1.02
1981	______	x 1.02
1982	______	
.		
.		
.		
1990	______	
____	______	
	1,000,000,000	

B-66. SITUATION → GRAPH

A virus has invaded Leticia's favorite mountain fishing lake. Currently there are an estimated 1800 trout in the lake, and the Fish and Game Department has determined that the rate of fish deaths will be one-third of the population per week if left untreated.

a. Sketch a graph showing how many fish are left in Leticia's favorite lake over several weeks.

b. Theoretically, will the trout ever completely disappear from the lake? Use the graph to justify your answer.

B-67. GRAPH → EQUATION

Suppose the annual fees for attending a public university were \$7000 in 2010 and the annual cost increase is shown in the graph at right. Note that x represents the number of years after 2010.

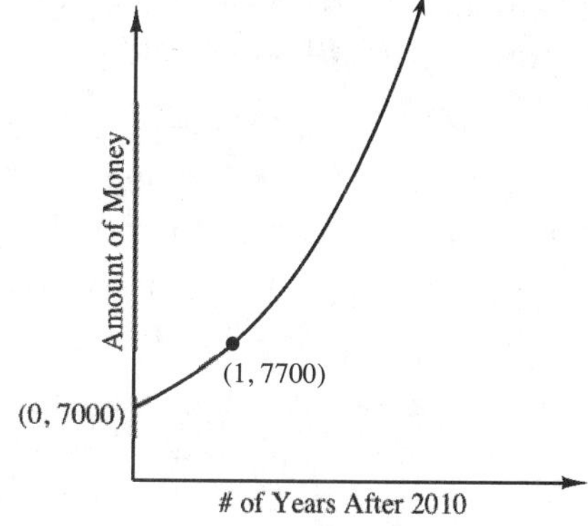

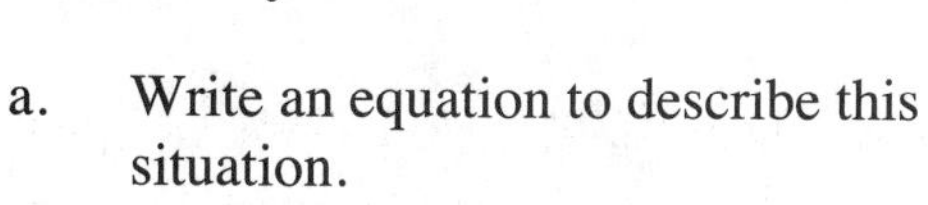

a. Write an equation to describe this situation.

b. Use this model to predict the cost of attending a public university in the first year you would be eligible to enroll.

c. What was the cost in 2000, assuming rate of increase was the same during the time period from 2000 to 2010?

d. Are you confident with your prediction in part (c)? Explain.

e. In 2012 the annual cost was actually \$8244. How accurate was the model? What actually happened?

B-68. EQUATION → GRAPH

For each equation below, make a reasonable sketch of the graph without making a table first. Discuss your strategy with your team before you begin.

a. $y = 5(3)^x$

b. $y = 10\left(\frac{1}{2}\right)^x$

c. $y = \frac{1}{10}(5)^x$

B-69. SITUATION → ?

Use each of the situations below to complete missing pieces of the web or to practice moving from a situation directly to a specific representation. For each part, decide which representation you will generate from the situation description based on where your team needs to work.

a. A 100-gram sample of a radioactive isotope decays at a rate of 6% every week. How big will the sample be one year from now?

b. The math club is fast becoming one of the most popular clubs on campus because of the fabulous activities it sponsors annually for Pi Day on March 14. Each year, the club's enrollment increases by 30%. If the club has 45 members this year, how many members should it expect to have 5 years from now?

c. Barbara made a bad investment. Rather than earning interest, her money is decreasing in value by 11% each week! After just one week, she is down to just $142.40. How much money did she start with? If she does not withdraw her money, how long will it be before she has less than half of what she originally invested?

d. Larry loves music. He bought $285 worth of MP3 files on his credit card, and now he cannot afford to pay off his debt. If the credit-card company charges him 18% annual interest compounded monthly, how does Larry's debt grow as time passes? How much would he owe at the end of the year if he had a "no payments for 12 months" feature for his credit card?

B-70. LEARNING LOG

Consider all of the things you have learned so far in this chapter. If you were creating a presentation for families for Open House Night and wanted to teach them the main ideas about exponential functions, what would they be? Write a Learning Log entry describing the main ideas and why they are important. Title this entry "Important Ideas about Exponential Functions" and include today's date.

B-71. The U.S. Census Bureau takes a census every 10 years. The population in 2000 was estimated at 281.4 million people. A model created at the time predicted that the population grew at about 2% per year.

a. If the Census Bureau had conducted a count in 2005, how many people would it have expected to count?

b. How many people would the Census Bureau have expected to count in the 2010 census?

c. The actual 2010 census put the population at 309 million people. What is the residual? What does it mean?

B-72. Find values of *a* and *b* that make each system of equations true (i.e., solve each system). Be sure to show your work or explain your thinking clearly.

a. $6 = a \cdot b^0$
$24 = a \cdot b^2$

b. $32 = a \cdot b^2$
$128 = a \cdot b^3$

B-73. Jack and Jill were working on simplifying the expression at right, but they were having some trouble. Then Jill had an idea.

$$\frac{3x^2y^{-3}}{x^{-1}y^2}$$

"Can't we separate the parts?" she said. *"That way, it might be easier to tell what we can simplify."* She rewrote the expression as shown at right.

$$3 \cdot x^2 \cdot \frac{1}{x^{-1}} \cdot y^{-3} \cdot \frac{1}{y^2}$$

"Okay," said Jack. *"Now we can rewrite each of the parts with negative exponents and simplify."*

a. Help Jack and Jill finish simplifying their expression.

b. Use their idea to rewrite and simplify $\frac{m^2pq^{-1}}{4m^{-2}pq^3}$.

B-74. A particular sequence can be represented by $t(n) = 2(3)^n$.

a. What are $t(0)$, $t(1)$, $t(2)$, and $t(3)$?

b. Graph this sequence. What is the domain?

c. On the same set of axes, graph the function $f(x) = 2(3)^x$.

d. How are the two graphs similar? How are they different?

B-75. Solve the system of equations at right algebraically.

$$2x - 3y = 12$$
$$y + x = -9$$

B-76. The cows at the Evaleen Dairy produce enough milk to fill a 4800-gallon tanker truck each day. The milk is then hauled to a processing plant where it is put into smaller storage containers and then used to fill gallon jugs that are delivered to local stores. The storage containers each hold 600 gallons of milk. Make a graph that shows the amount of milk in the tanker truck as each storage tank is filled.

B.2.1 How can I find the equation?

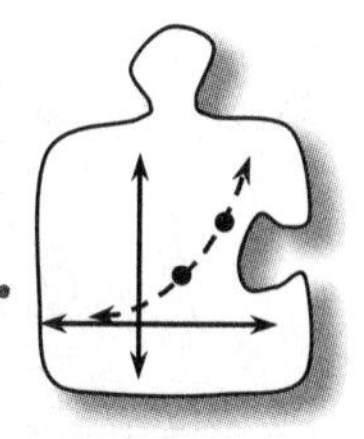

Curve Fitting and Fractional Exponents

In the next few lessons, you will use your knowledge of linear equations to help develop algebraic strategies for finding exponential functions. You will also learn more about working with roots and exponents.

B-77. Find the equation of the line in $y = mx + b$ form with slope 3 that passes through the point (5, 19). Take careful note of how you find m and b.

B-78. Can you use an idea similar to the one you used in problem B-77 to find an exponential equation in $y = ab^x$ form?

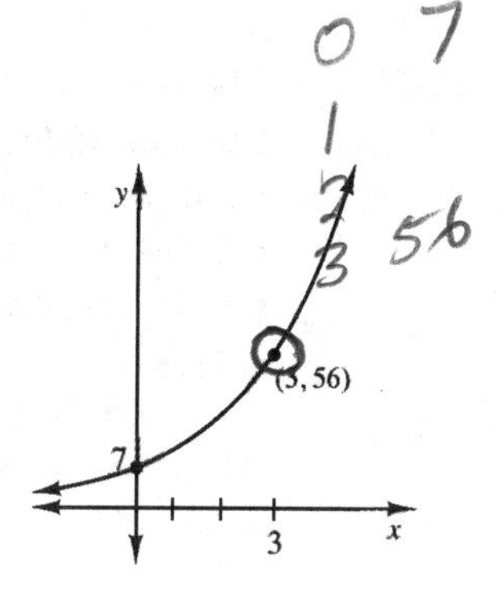

a. While trying to find the equation for the graph in part (c) of problem B-57 (shown again at right), Errol stated, *"I think 'a' must be 7 because the y-intercept is at (0, 7)."* Do you agree? Justify your answer.

b. *"But we still don't know what 'b' is,"* Errol noticed. His teammate, Sandy, had an idea. *"I think that* $56 = 7(b)^3$*."* How did she get this equation? Is it valid? Explain.

c. If you have not done so already, solve $56 = 7(b)^3$ for b. Explain how you solved this equation.

d. Use a and b to write the equation for this graph. Does it agree with the equation you found in part (c) of problem B-57?

B-79. Use Errol's and Sandy's method from problem B-78 to find the equation of an exponential function with an asymptote at $y = 0$ that passes through the points (0, 5) and (3, 320).

B-80. NEW NOTATION FOR ROOTS

a. Addison's teacher challenged his team to find a way to write $\sqrt[3]{17}$ with exponents. Addison started by writing this equation: $17^x = \sqrt[3]{17}$. Her team needed to find what x was equal to. Do you have any guesses about what the exponent might be? Discuss this with your team.

b. Addison said, *"But we also know that* $(\sqrt[3]{17})^3 = 17$, *and we want to write* $\sqrt[3]{17}$ *with an exponent instead, like* 17^x. *So why don't we combine this information and write* $(17^x)^3 = 17$*?"* Addison asked.

Addison continued, "*Oh, so* $(17^x)^3 = 17^{3x}$*?*" Is she correct? Is it true that $(17^x)^3 = 17^{3x}$? Be ready to share your reasoning with the class.

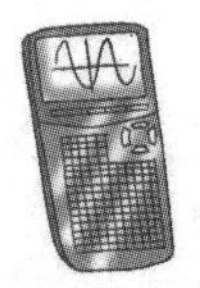

c. Addison wrote: $17^{3x} = 17^1$. Complete Addison's work to find the value of x in this equation. What does this tell you about another way to write $\sqrt[3]{17}$? Check your result by finding decimal approximations with your calculator.

d. Use similar logic to find exponential expressions for $\sqrt{5}$ and $\sqrt[5]{11}$. Show your reasoning. Then use your graphing calculator to find their decimal equivalents, rounded to the nearest 0.001.

B-81. REWRITING EXPRESSIONS

The property $(k^m)^n = k^{mn}$ can help you rewrite expressions with roots and fractional exponents, as it helped you in part (d) of problem B-80.

For example, since $16^{3/2} = (16^3)^{1/2}$, $16^{3/2}$ can be rewritten as $\sqrt{16^3}$. However, since $16^{3/2} = (16^{1/2})^3$, $16^{3/2}$ can also be rewritten as $(\sqrt{16})^3$ or 4^3.

With your team, find ways to rewrite the expressions below *two different ways*. Be ready to justify your answers.

a. $10^{2/3}$

b. $(\sqrt[3]{9})^4$

c. $\sqrt[5]{x^3}$

d. $(\sqrt{2})^5$

e. $5^{7/2}$

f. $y^{3/3}$

B-82. Fractional exponents can give surprising results when used with negative bases. Answer the following questions using what you now know rewriting fractional exponents and your mental math skills. Avoid using your calculator.

a. Show or explain why $(-27)^{1/2}$ has no real solution but $(-27)^{1/3} = -3$.

b. Given that $(-27)^{1/3} = -3$, is $(-27)^{2/3}$ positive or negative, or does it have no real solution? What about $(-27)^{1/4}$? And $(-27)^{1/5}$? Justify your answers.

c. Mischa was working with her team on the idea of negative bases, but she got confused. Consider her thinking below.

i. *"Wait,"* she said. *"Isn't it true that* $(-100)^{1/2}$ *has no real solution?"* What does Mischa mean? Is she right?

ii. *"But,"* she continued, *"I can figure out that* $(-100)^{2/4} = 10$.*"* Check her calculation. Is she correct?

iii. *"That doesn't make any sense, since* $\frac{2}{4}$ *can be reduced to* $\frac{1}{2}$*!"* What do you think?

B-83. Recall that when you investigated $y = b^x$ in problem B-2, the graphing calculator produced graphs like the one at right for negative values of b when you used the "zoom decimal" option. Use what you have learned about the meaning of fractional exponents to explain why $y = (-2)^x$ is impossible to graph accurately.

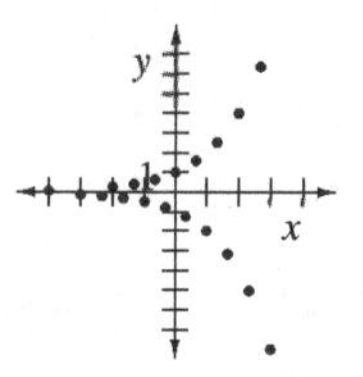

B-84. LEARNING LOG

You have now worked with exponents that have been zero, exponents that have been negative numbers, and exponents that have been fractions. In your Learning Log, explain everything you know about these kinds of exponents. Show equivalent ways to write expressions with zero, negative, and fractional exponents. What does each kind of exponent mean? Explain using both words and examples. Title this entry "Zero, Negative, and Fractional Exponents" and label it with today's date.

B-85. Find a possible exponential function in $y = a \cdot b^x$ form that represents each situation described below.

a. Has an initial value of 2 and passes through the point (3, 128).

b. Passes through the points (0, 4) and (2, 1).

B-86. Solve the following systems of equations. In other words, find values of a and b that make each system true. Be sure to show your work or explain your thinking clearly.

a. $3 = a \cdot b^0$
$75 = a \cdot b^2$

b. $18 = a \cdot b^2$
$54 = a \cdot b^3$

B-87. Evaluate each expression below.

a. $\sqrt[3]{-64}$ b. $\sqrt[5]{32}$ c. $\sqrt[3]{-8}$ d. $\sqrt[4]{10000}$

B-88. Rewrite $16^{3/4}$ in as many different ways as you can.

B-89. Find the equation of the line passing through the points (7, 16) and (2, –4). Then state the slope and x- and y-intercepts. Explain how you found them.

B.2.2 How can I find the equation?

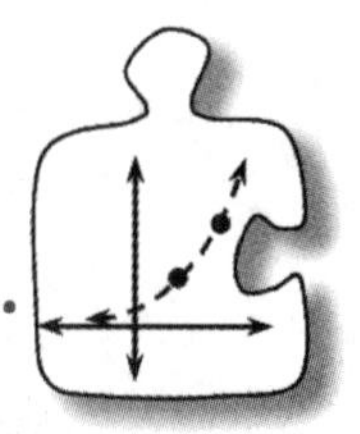

More Curve Fitting

In this lesson, you will continue your work from Lesson B.2.1 as you develop a new method to find linear and exponential equations given two points.

B-90. Mitchell was working on his algebra homework, when suddenly he had an idea about finding linear equations. He was trying to find the equation of the line that passes through the points (5, 15) and (3, 7). *"Look!"* he exclaimed. *"We know that the line can be written in the form* $y = mx + b$*, and we also know that the points (5, 15) and (3, 7) have to make the equation true. So we can substitute in these two points to create a system of equations. When we solve that, we'll know the values of m and b, and we'll have our equation!"*

a. What is Mitchell talking about? Use his method to find the equation of the line through the points (5, 15) and (3, 7).

b. Will Mitchell's method work to find the equation of a line through any two points? Justify your answer.

B-91. Use Mitchell's method from problem B-90 to find the equation of the line that passes through the points (2, 3) and (5, –6).

B-92. Can Mitchell's method from problem B-90 be used to find the *exponential* function that passes through the points $(2, 16)$ and $(6, 256)$? Consider this as you answer the questions below.

a. What is the general form for an exponential function that has an asymptote at $y = 0$?

b. Use the two points that you know to create a system of equations.

c. Solve both equations for a. Then set the equations equal to each other to solve your system of equations for b. Next, find a, and write the equation that goes through the two points.

B-93. Find an exponential function that passes through each pair of points.

a. $(-1,-2)$ and $(3,-162)$

b. $(2, 1.75)$ and $(-2, 28)$

METHODS AND MEANINGS

Negative and Fractional Exponents

For all x not equal to zero:

$x^0 = 1$ Examples: $2^0 = 1$, $(-3)^0 = 1$, $\left(\frac{1}{4}\right)^0 = 1$

For positive values of x:

$x^{-n} = \frac{1}{x^n}$ Examples: $x^{-3} = \frac{1}{x^3}$, $y^{-4} = \frac{1}{y^4}$, $4^{-2} = \frac{1}{4^2} = \frac{1}{16}$

$\frac{1}{x^{-n}} = x^n$ Examples: $\frac{1}{x^{-5}} = x^5$, $\frac{1}{x^{-2}} = x^2$, $\frac{1}{3^{-2}} = 3^2 = 9$

$x^{a/b} = (x^a)^{1/b} = \sqrt[b]{x^a}$ or $x^{a/b} = (x^{1/b})^a = (\sqrt[b]{x})^a$

Examples: $5^{1/2} = \sqrt{5}$, $3^{2/3} = \sqrt[3]{3^2} = \sqrt[3]{9}$,

$16^{3/4} = (16^{1/4})^3 = (\sqrt[4]{16})^3 = 2^3 = 8$

B-94. Find an exponential function that passes through each pair of points.

a. $(1, 7.5)$ and $(3, 16.875)$

b. $(-1, 1.25)$ and $(3, 0.032)$

B-95. Consider the pattern at right.

$\frac{1}{2^3} = \frac{1}{8}$

$\frac{1}{2^2} = \frac{1}{4}$

$\frac{1}{2^1} = \frac{1}{2}$

$\frac{1}{2^0} = 1$

a. Continue the pattern to find $\frac{1}{2^{-1}}$, $\frac{1}{2^{-2}}$, $\frac{1}{2^{-3}}$, and $\frac{1}{2^{-4}}$.

b. What is the value of $\frac{1}{2^{-n}}$?

c. Write a conjecture about how to rewrite $\frac{1}{a^{-n}}$ without a negative exponent.

B-96. Find the domain and range for each of the relations graphed below.

a.

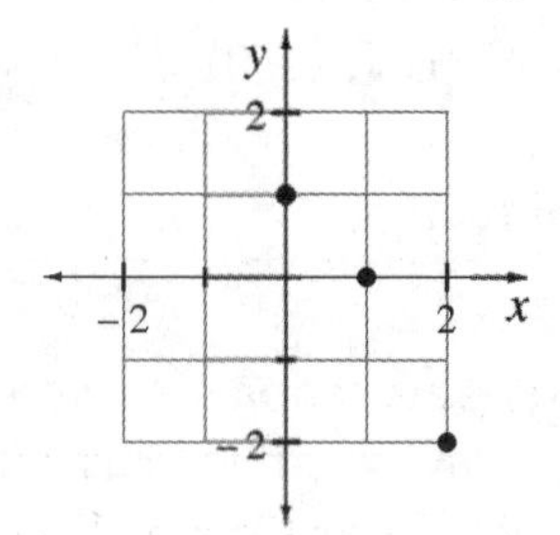

b.

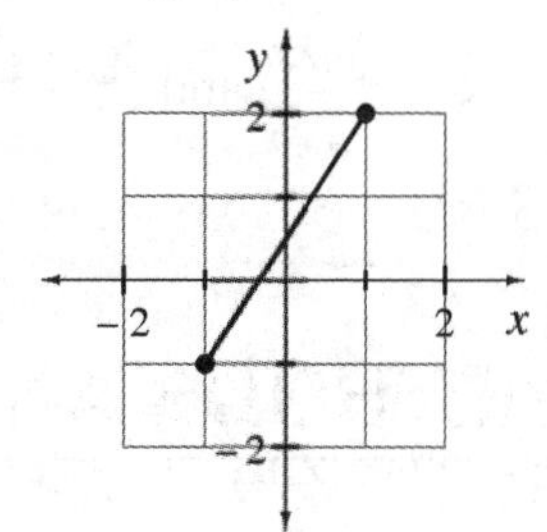

c.

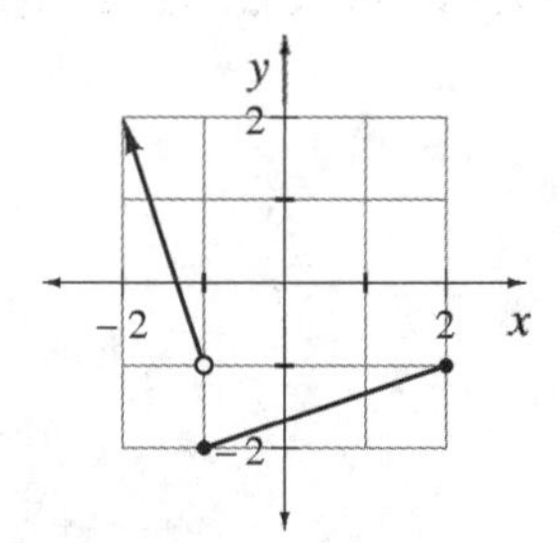

d.

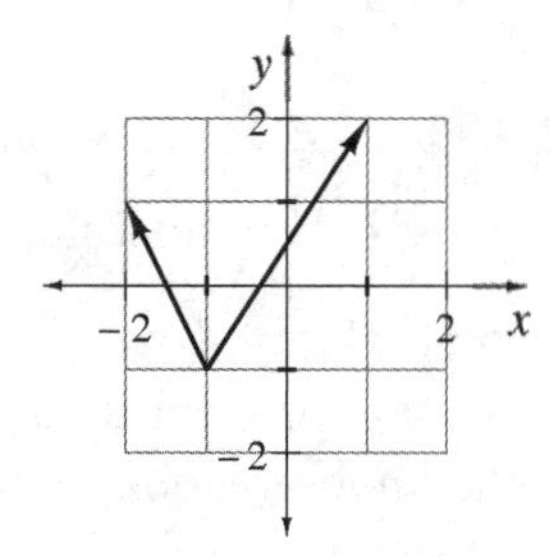

B-97. If $f(x) = 3(2)^x$, find the value of the expressions in parts (a) through (c) below. Then complete parts (d) through (f).

a. $f(-1)$

b. $f(0)$

c. $f(1)$

d. What value of x gives $f(x) = 12$?

e. Where does the graph of this function cross the x-axis? The y-axis?

f. If $g(x) = \frac{1}{3x}$, find $f(x) \cdot g(x)$.

B-98. Show two steps to simplify each of the following expressions, and then calculate the value of each expression.

a. $64^{2/3}$

b. $25^{5/2}$

c. $81^{7/4}$

B-99. What is the multiplier for the sequence shown in the graph at right?

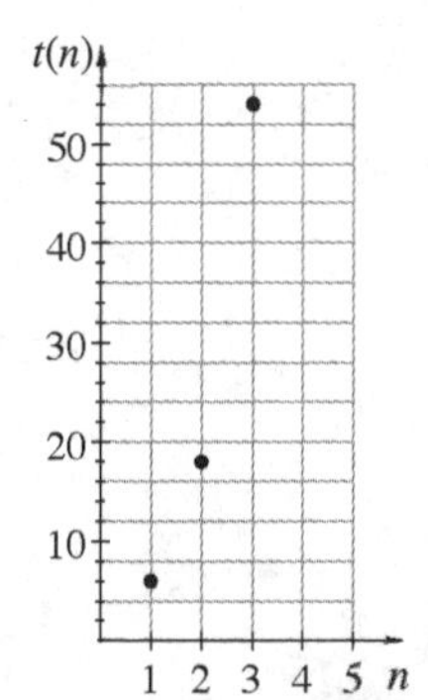

B.2.3 How can I use exponential functions?

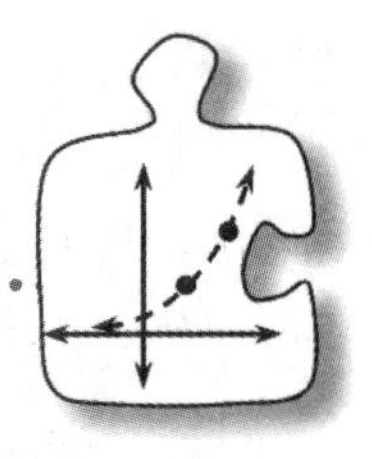

Solving a System of Exponential Functions Graphically

In this lesson, you will apply your skills with exponential functions to a system of equations as you explore the value of cars in an investigation called "Fast Cars."

B-100. FAST CARS

The moment you drive a new car off the dealer's lot, the car is worth less than what you paid for it. This phenomenon is called *depreciation*, which means you will sell the car for less than the price that you paid for it. Some cars depreciate more than others (that is, they depreciate at different rates), but most cars depreciate over time. On the other hand, some older cars actually increase in value. This is called *appreciation*. Let's suppose that in 2012, Jeralyn had a choice between buying a 2010 Fonda Concord EX for $27,000, which depreciates at 6% per year; a 2010 Padillac Escalate for $39,000, which depreciates at 22.5% per year; or a 1967 Fyord Rustang for $15,000 that is appreciating at 10% per year.

Your Task: Investigate the value of each of the three cars over time.

- Generate multiple representations of the value of each car over time.
- For each of the new cars, determine how much value they lost (in dollars) from the time they were new in 2010 until 2012.
- Decide which car Jeralyn should buy and defend your choice in as many ways as you can.

Discussion Points

What is the multiplier?

How can we represent this situation in a table? A graph? An equation?

What should we consider when deciding which car to buy?

Further Guidance

B-101. Investigate the changing values of each of the cars by addressing the questions below.

a. What is the multiplier for the Concord? For the Escalate? For the Rustang?

b. Make a table like the one below and calculate the value for each car for each year shown.

Year	Concord	Escalate	Rustang
0	$27,000	$39,000	$15,000
1	$25,380	$30,225	
2			
3			
4			
5			
...			
10			
...			
n			

c. On your own graph paper, graph the data for all three cars on the same set of axes. Are the graphs linear? How are they similar? How are they different? You may want to use a different color for each car.

d. Write a function to represent the value of each car.

e. What were the values of the Concord and the Escalate when they were new? How much value (in dollars) did each car lose from 2010 to 2012?

f. Using the graph, which of the three cars is worth the most after one year? After 3 years? After 10 years? In how many years will the values of the Concord and Escalate be the same?

g. Pick one of the three cars and explain why Jeralyn should buy it. Has this problem changed your view of buying cars?

Further Guidance section ends here.

B-102. As you saw in "The Penny Lab," half-life applies to situations other than radioactive decay. In fact, the idea can be applied to anything that is depreciating or decaying exponentially.

a. Using the values in problem B-100, Fast Cars, estimate the half-life of the value of the Concord and the Escalate.

b. According to the mathematical model, when will each car have no value?

B-103. In 2009, a brand new SUV cost \$35,000 to drive off the lot. In 2012 that same SUV was valued at \$22,500. Write an exponential equation to represent this information. Then find the rate of depreciation for the SUV.

MATH NOTES

Equations for Sequences

Arithmetic Sequences

The equation for an arithmetic sequence is: $t(n) = mn + b$ or $a_n = mn + a_0$ where n is the term number, m is the sequence generator (the common difference), and b or a_0 is the zeroth term. Compare these equations to a continuous linear function $f(x) = mx + b$ where m is the growth (slope) and b is the starting value (y-intercept).

For example, the arithmetic sequence 4, 7, 10, 13, ... could be represented by $t(n) = 3n + 1$ or by $a_n = 3n + 1$. (Note that "4" is the first term of this sequence, so "1" is the zeroth term.)

Another way to write the equation of an arithmetic sequence is by using the first term in the equation, as in $a_n = m(n-1) + a_1$, where a_1 is the first term. The sequence in the example could be represented by $a_n = 3(n-1) + 4$.

You could even write an equation using any other term in the sequence. The equation using the fourth term in the example would be $a_n = 3(n-4) + 13$.

Geometric Sequences

The equation for a geometric sequence is: $t(n) = ab^n$ or $a_n = a_0 \cdot b^n$ where n is the term number, b is the sequence generator (the multiplier or common ratio), and a or a_0 is the zeroth term. Compare these equations to a continuous exponential function $f(x) = ab^x$, where b is the growth (multiplier) and a is the starting value (y-intercept).

For example, the geometric sequence 6, 18, 54, ... could be represented by $t(n) = 2 \cdot 3^n$ or by $a_n = 2 \cdot 3^n$.

You can write a first term form of the equation for a geometric sequence as well: $a_n = a_1 \cdot b^{n-1}$. For the example, first term form would be $a_n = 6 \cdot 3^{n-1}$.

B-104. Find the equation of an exponential function that passes through the points $(2, 48)$ and $(5, 750)$.

B-105. After noon, the number of people in Mal-Wart grows steadily until 6:00 p.m. If the equation $y = 228 + 58x$ represents the number of people in the store x hours after noon:

a. How many people were in the store at noon?

b. At what rate is the number of shoppers growing?

c. When were there 402 shoppers in the store?

B-106. Wade and Dwayne were working together writing an equation for the sequence 12, 36, 108, 324, ... Wade wrote $t(n) = 4 \cdot 3^n$, and Dwayne wrote $t(n) = 12 \cdot 3^{n-1}$.

a. Make a table for the first four terms of each of their sequences. What do you notice?

b. How do you think Dwayne explained his method of writing the equation to Wade?

c. For the sequence 10.3, 11.5, 12.7, ..., Wade wrote $t(n) = 9.1 + 1.2n$ while Dwayne wrote $t(n) = 10.3 + 1.2(n-1)$. Make a table for the first four terms of each of their sequences. Are both forms of the equation correct?

d. Dwayne calls his equations the **"first term" form**. Why do you think he calls them "first term" form? Why does Dwayne subtract one in both situations?

B-107. Write an explicit equation for the sequence graphed at right.

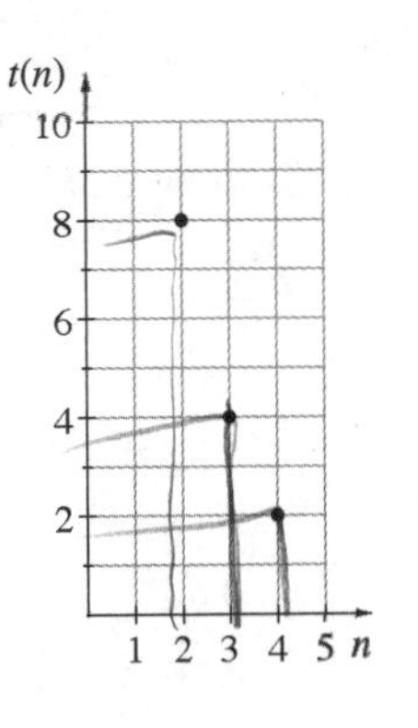

B-108. Write an explicit equation for the sequence graphed at right.

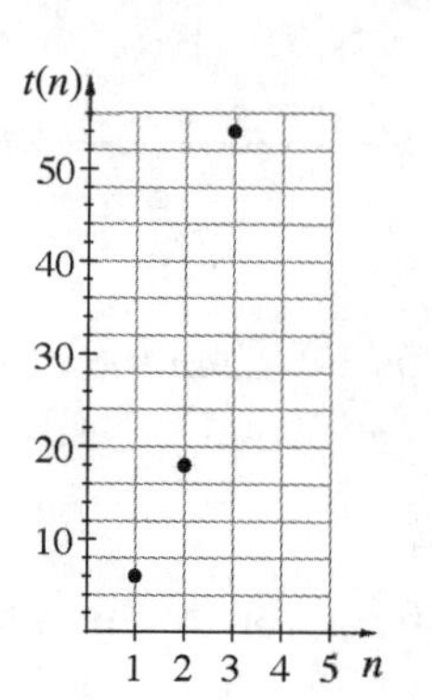

B-109. Solve each system of equations.

a. $y = 3x + 11$
$x + y = 3$

b. $y = 2x + 3$
$x - y = -4$

c. $x + 2y = 16$
$x + y = 2$

d. $2x + 3y = 10$
$3x - 4y = -2$

$x = 5 + 3y/2$

$3(5 + 3y/2) - 4y$

$15 + 9y/6 - 4y = -2$

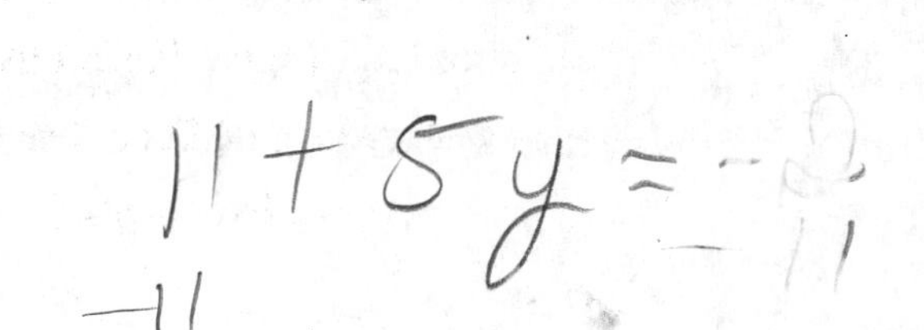

Appendix B Closure What have I learned?

Reflection and Synthesis

The activities below offer you a chance to reflect about what you have learned during this chapter. As you work, look for concepts that you feel very comfortable with, ideas that you would like to learn more about, and topics you need more help with. Look for connections between ideas as well as connections with material you learned previously.

① TEAM BRAINSTORM

What have you studied in this chapter? What ideas were important in what you learned? With your team, brainstorm a list. Be as detailed as you can. To help get you started, a list of Learning Log entries and Math Notes boxes are below.

What topics, ideas, and words that you learned *before* this chapter are connected to the new ideas in this chapter? Again, be as detailed as you can.

How long can you make your list? Challenge yourselves. Be prepared to share your team's ideas with the class.

Learning Log Entries

- Lesson B.1.1 – Investigating $y = b^x$
- Lesson B.1.2 – Multiple Representations Web for Exponential Functions
- Lesson B.1.5 – Graph → Equation for Exponential Functions
- Lesson B.1.6 – Important Ideas about Exponential Functions
- Lesson B.2.1 – Zero, Negative, and Fractional Exponents

Math Notes

- Lesson B.1.3 – Compounding Interest
- Lesson B.1.4 – Basic Laws of Exponents
- Lesson B.1.5 – Step Functions
- Lesson B.2.2 – Negative and Fractional Exponents
- Lesson B.2.3 – Equations for Sequences

② MAKING CONNECTIONS

Below is a list of the vocabulary used in this chapter. Make sure that you are familiar with all of these words and know what they mean. Refer to the glossary or index for any words that you do not yet understand.

appreciation	asymptote	compound interest
depreciation	exponential function	fractional exponents
half-life	initial value	model
multiplier	parameter	roots
simple interest	step function	

Make a concept map showing all of the connections you can find among the key words and ideas listed above. To show a connection between two words, draw a line between them and explain the connection. A word can be connected to any other word as long as you can justify the connection.

While you are making your map, your team may think of related words or ideas that are not listed above. Be sure to include these ideas on your concept map.

③ PORTFOLIO: EVIDENCE OF MATHEMATICAL PROFICIENCY

If you took a photograph of your poster from Lesson B.1.1, include it in your portfolio. Your photo provides evidence of your growing understanding of exponential functions.

Showcase your early understanding of x-intercepts by answering the following questions:

How many different kinds of graphs can you create that have:

a. *No x-intercepts?*

b. *One x-intercept?*

c. *Two x-intercepts?*

d. *Three or more x-intercepts?*

For each type of graph, show a sketch, label the key points, and give its equation. Make sure that each graph you give as an example represents a different family, and describe the family in words or with a general equation. Show how to calculate the x-intercepts of each of your sample graphs.

Your teacher may give you the Appendix B Closure Resource Page: "Multiple Representations of Exponential Functions Graphic Organizer." Complete it to showcase your current understanding of the multiple representations of an exponential function.

④ WHAT HAVE I LEARNED?

Most of the problems in this section represent typical problems found in this chapter. They serve as a gauge for you. You can use them to determine which types of problems you can do well and which types of problems require further study and practice. Even if your teacher does not assign this section, it is a good idea to try these problems and find out for yourself what you know and what you still need to work on.

Solve each problem as completely as you can. The table at the end of the closure section has answers to these problems. It also tells you where you can find additional help and practice with problems like these.

CL B-110. Find an exponential function in $y = ab^x$ form that satisfies each of the following sets of conditions.

a. Has a y-intercept of $(0, 2)$ and a multiplier of 0.8.

b. Passes through the points $(0, 3.5)$ and $(2, 31.5)$.

CL B-111. Sam wants to create an arithmetic sequence and a geometric sequence, both of which have $t(1) = 8$ and $t(7) = 512$. Is this possible? If it is, help Sam create his sequences. If not, justify why not.

CL B-112. Write each expression below as an equivalent expression without negative exponents.

a. 3^{-2} b. m^{-4} c. $(\frac{1}{2})^{-3}$ d. $(\frac{3}{5x})^{-1}$

CL B-113. Write each expression below in radical form and compute the value without using a calculator.

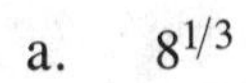

a. $8^{1/3}$ b. $16^{3/4}$ c. $125^{4/3}$

CL B-114. Best Price Parking charges \$2 for the first hour of parking and \$0.50 for each additional hour. Create a step function graph that represents this information.

CL B-115. A share of ABC stock was worth \$60 in 2005 and only worth \$45 in 2010.

a. Find the multiplier and the percent decrease.

b. Write an exponential function that models the value of the stock starting from 2005.

c. Assuming that the decline in value continues at the same rate, use your answer to (b) to predict the value in 2020.

CL B-116. Write an equation or system of equations to solve this problem.

An adult ticket to the amusement park costs \$24.95 and a child's ticket costs \$15.95. A group of 10 people paid \$186.50 to enter the park. How many were adults?

CL B-117. Solve each system of equations.

a. $2x - y = 9$
$y = x - 7$

b. $-4x + y = 5$
$2x = -y - 13$

CL B-118. Write a recursive equation for the sequence graphed at right.

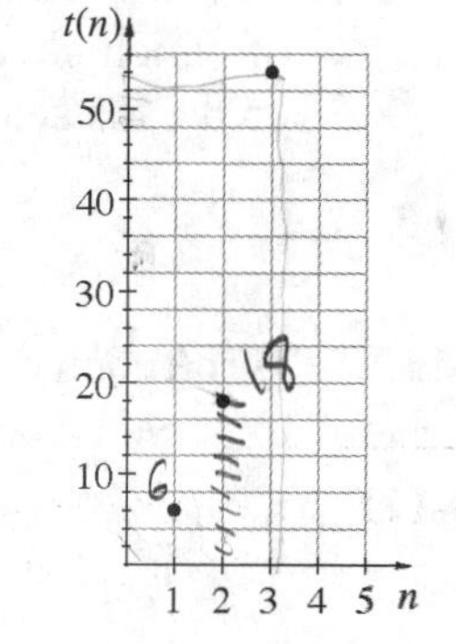

CL B-119. Write an equation for the line that passes through the points $(-5, 4)$ and $(3, -2)$.

CL B-120. Check your answers using the table at the end of this section. Which problems do you feel confident about? Which problems were hard? Have you worked on problems like these in previous math classes? Use the table to make a list of topics you need help on, and a list of topics you need to practice more.

Answers and Support for Closure Activity #4:
What Have I Learned?

Note: MN = Math Note, LL = Learning Log

Problem	Solutions	Need Help?	More Practice
CL B-110.	a. $y = 2(0.8)^x$ b. $y = 3.5(3)^x$	Lessons B.2.1 and B.2.2	Problems B-23, B-35, B-60, B-85, B-94, and B-104
CL B-111.	Arithmetic: $t(n) = 84n - 76$ Geometric: $t(n) = 4(2)^n$	Section A.2 MN: A.3.2 and B.2.3	Problems CL A-120, B-14, B-27, and B-106
CL B-112.	a. $\frac{1}{9}$ b. $\frac{1}{m^4}$ c. 8 d. $\frac{5x}{3}$	MN: B.1.4 and B.2.2	Problem CL A-123, B-11, B-75, and B-97
CL B-113.	a. $\sqrt[3]{8} = 2$ b. $(\sqrt[4]{16})^3 = 8$ c. $(\sqrt[3]{125})^4 = 625$	Lesson B.2.1 MN: B.2.2 LL: B.2.1	Problems B-87, B-88, and B-98
CL B-114.	Cost ($) 1 2 3 4 1 2 3 4 Time (hours)	MN: B.1.5	Problems B-45 and B-59
CL B-115.	a. annual multiplier ≈ 0.944 $\approx 5.6\%$ decrease b. $f(x) = 60(0.944)^x$ c. $f(15) = 25.28$	Section B.1 LL: B.1.6	Problem B-15, B-36, B-46, B-71, and B-103

Problem	Solutions	Need Help?	More Practice
CL B-116.	If $a = \#$ of adults, $c = \#$ of children $a + c = 10$ $24.95a + 15.95c = 186.50$ $a = 3$ adults	Explanations and practice of topics from previous courses are available in the *Core Connections Algebra Parent Guide with Extra Practice,* available free at www.cpm.org.	Problems B-7 and B-26
CL B-117.	a. $(2, -5)$ b. $(-3, -7)$	Topic from previous course	Problems CL A-121, B-38, B-53, B-75, and B-109
CL B-118.	$a_1 = 2$, $a_{n+1} = 3 \cdot a_n$	Topic from previous course	Problems B-99 and B-108
CL B-119.	$y = -\frac{3}{4}x + \frac{1}{4}$	Topic from previous course	Problems CL A-124 and B-89

Core Connections Algebra 2
Checkpoint Materials

Note to Students (and their Teachers)

Students master different skills at different speeds. No two students learn exactly the same way at the same time. At some point you will be expected to perform certain skills accurately. Most of the Checkpoint problems incorporate skills that you should have developed in previous courses. If you have not mastered these skills yet it does not mean that you will not be successful in this class. However, you may need to do some work outside of class to get caught up on them.

Starting in Chapter 2 and finishing in Chapter 12, there are 18 problems designed as Checkpoint problems. Each one is marked with an icon like the one above. After you do each of the Checkpoint problems, check your answers by referring to this section. If your answers are incorrect, you may need some extra practice to develop that skill. The practice sets are keyed to each of the Checkpoint problems in the textbook. Each has the topic clearly labeled, followed by the answers to the corresponding Checkpoint problem and then some completed examples. Next, the complete solution to the Checkpoint problem from the text is given, and there are more problems for you to practice with answers included.

Remember, looking is not the same as doing! You will never become good at any sport by just watching it, and in the same way, reading through the worked examples and understanding the steps is not the same as being able to do the problems yourself. How many of the extra practice problems do you need to try? That is really up to you. Remember that your goal is to be able to do similar problems on your own confidently and accurately. This is your responsibility. You should not expect your teacher to spend time in class going over the solutions to the Checkpoint problem sets. If you are not confident after reading the examples and trying the problems, you should get help outside of class time or talk to your teacher about working with a tutor.

Checkpoint Topics

2A. Finding the Distance Between Two Points and the Equation of a Line

2B. Solving Linear Systems in Two Variables

3A. Rewriting Expressions with Integral and Rational Exponents

3B. Using Function Notation and Identifying Domain and Range

4A. Writing Equations for Arithmetic and Geometric Sequences

4B. Solving For One Variable in an Equation with Two or More Variables

5A. Multiplying Polynomials

5B. Factoring Quadratics

Checkpoint 2A

Problem 2-53

Finding the Distance Between Two Points and the Equation of a Line

Answers to problem 2-53: a: $\sqrt{45} = 3\sqrt{5} \approx 6.71$; $y = \frac{1}{2}x + 5$, b: 5; $x = 3$,
c: $\sqrt{725} \approx 26.93$; $y = -\frac{5}{2}x + \frac{5}{2}$, d: 4; $y = -2$

The distance between two points is found by using the Pythagorean Theorem. The most commonly used equation of a line is $y = mx + b$ where m represents the slope of the line and b represents the y-intercept of the line. One strategy for both types of problems is to create a generic right triangle determined by the given points. The lengths of the legs of the triangle are used in the Pythagorean Theorem to find the distance. They are also used in the slope ratio to write an equation of the line. This strategy is not necessary for vertical or horizontal pairs of points, however.

Example: For the points $(-1,-2)$ and $(11,2)$, find the distance between them and determine an equation of the line through them

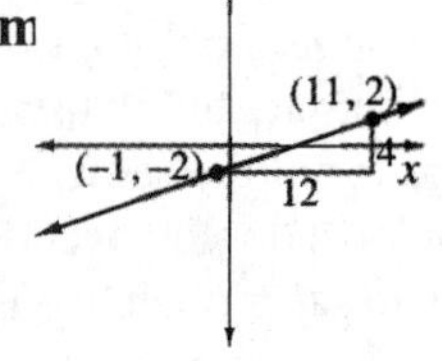

Solution: Using a generic right triangle, the legs of the triangle are 12 and 4. The distance between the points is the length of the hypotenuse.

$$d^2 = 12^2 + 4^2 = 160 \Rightarrow d = \sqrt{160} = 4\sqrt{10} \approx 12.65$$

The slope of the line, $m = \frac{\text{vertical change}}{\text{horizontal change}} = \frac{4}{12} = \frac{1}{3}$. Substituting this into the equation of a line, $y = mx + b$, gives $y = \frac{1}{3}x + b$. Next substitute any point that is on the line for x and y and solve for b. Using $(11,2)$, $2 = \frac{1}{3} \cdot 11 + b$, $2 = \frac{11}{3} + b$, $b = -\frac{5}{3}$.

The equation is $y = \frac{1}{3}x - \frac{5}{3}$.

Some people prefer to use formulas that represent the generic right triangle.

$$\text{slope} = \frac{y_2 - y_1}{x_2 - x_1} = \frac{2-(-2)}{11-(-1)} = \frac{4}{12} = \frac{1}{3}$$

$$\text{distance} = \sqrt{(x_2 - x_1)^2 + (y_2 - y_1)^2} = \sqrt{(11-(-1))^2 + (2-(-2))^2} = \sqrt{12^2 + 4^2} = \sqrt{160}$$

Notice that $x_2 - x_1$ and $y_2 - y_1$ represent the lengths of the horizontal and vertical legs respectively.

Now we can go back and solve the original problems.

a. $d^2 = 6^2 + 3^2 \Rightarrow d^2 = 45 \Rightarrow d = \sqrt{45} = 3\sqrt{5} \approx 6.71$

$m = \frac{3}{6} = \frac{1}{2} \Rightarrow y = \frac{1}{2}x + b$

Using the point $(4, 7) \Rightarrow 7 = \frac{1}{2} \cdot 4 + b \Rightarrow b = 5$.

The equation is $y = \frac{1}{2}x + 5$.

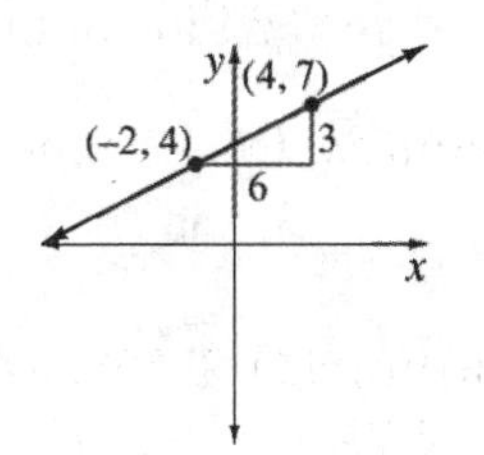

b. Since this is a vertical line, the distance is simply the difference of the y values. $d = 4 - (-1) = 5$.

Vertical lines have an *undefined* slope and the equation of the line is of the form $x = k \Rightarrow x = 3$.

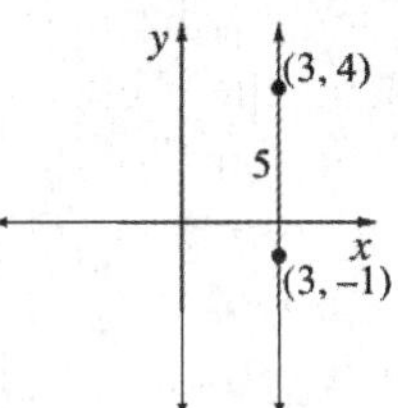

c. $d^2 = (-25)^2 + 10^2 \Rightarrow d^2 = 725 \Rightarrow d = \sqrt{725} \approx 26.93$

$m = \frac{-25}{10} = -\frac{5}{2} \Rightarrow y = -\frac{5}{2}x + b$

Using the point $(3, -5) \Rightarrow -5 = -\frac{5}{2} \cdot 3 + b \Rightarrow b = -5 + \frac{15}{2} = \frac{5}{2}$

The equation is $y = -\frac{5}{2}x + \frac{5}{2}$

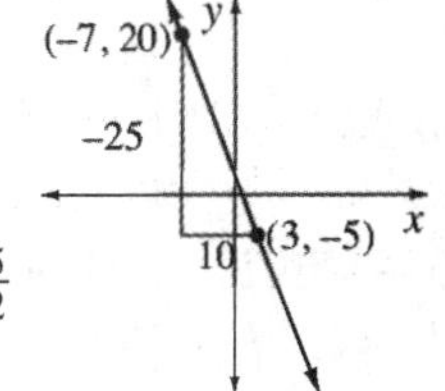

d. Since this is a horizontal line, the distance is simply the difference of the x values. $d = 5 - 1 = 4$.

Horizontal lines have a slope of 0 and the equation of the line is of the form $y = k \Rightarrow y = -2$.

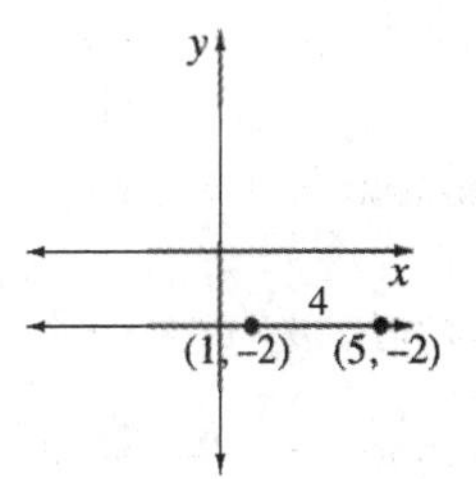

Here are some more to try. For each pair of points, compute the distance between them and then find an equation of the line through them.

1. $(2,3)$ and $(1,2)$
2. $(-3,-5)$ and $(-1,0)$
3. $(4,2)$ and $(8,-1)$
4. $(1,3)$ and $(5,7)$
5. $(0,4)$ and $(-1,-5)$
6. $(-3,2)$ and $(2,-3)$
7. $(4,2)$ and $(-1,-2)$
8. $(3,1)$ and $(-2,-4)$
9. $(4,1)$ and $(4,10)$
10. $(10,2)$ and $(2,22)$
11. $(-10,3)$ and $(-2,-5)$
12. $(-3,5)$ and $(12,5)$
13. $(-4,10)$ and $(-6,15)$
14. $(-6,-3)$ and $(2,10)$

Answers:

1. $\sqrt{2} \approx 1.41$; $y = x + 1$
2. $\sqrt{29} \approx 5.39$; $y = \frac{5}{2}x + \frac{5}{2}$
3. 5; $y = -\frac{3}{4}x + 5$
4. $\sqrt{32} = 4\sqrt{2} \approx 5.66$; $y = x + 2$
5. $\sqrt{82} \approx 9.06$; $y = 9x + 4$
6. $\sqrt{50} = 5\sqrt{2} \approx 7.07$; $y = -x - 1$
7. $\sqrt{41} \approx 6.40$; $y = \frac{4}{5}x - \frac{6}{5}$
8. $\sqrt{50} = 5\sqrt{2} \approx 7.07$; $y = x - 2$
9. 9; $x = 4$
10. $\sqrt{464} \approx 21.54$; $y = -\frac{5}{2}x + 27$
11. $\sqrt{128} = 8\sqrt{2} \approx 11.31$; $y = -x - 7$
12. 15; $y = 5$
13. $\sqrt{29} \approx 5.39$; $y = -\frac{5}{2}x$
14. $\sqrt{233} \approx 15.26$; $y = \frac{13}{8}x + \frac{27}{4}$

Checkpoint 2B

Problem 2-152

Solving Linear Systems in Two Variables

Answers to problem 2-152: (3, 2)

You can solve systems of equations using a variety of methods. For linear systems, you can graph the equations, use the Substitution Method, or use the Elimination Method. Each method works best with certain forms of equations. Following are some examples. Although the method that is easiest for one person may not be easiest for another, the most common methods are shown below.

Example 1: Solve the system of equations $x = 4y - 7$ and $3x - 2y = 1$.

Solution: For this, we will use the Substitution Method. Since the first equation tells us that *x* is equal to $4y - 7$, we can substitute $4y - 7$ for *x* in the second equation. This allows us to solve for *y*, as shown at right.

$$3(4y-7)-2y=1$$
$$12y-21-2y=1$$
$$10y-21=1$$
$$10y=22$$
$$y=\frac{22}{10}=2.2$$

Then substitute $y = 2.2$ into either original equation and solve for *x*: Choosing the first equation, we get $x = 4(2.2) - 7 = 8.8 - 7 = 1.8$. To verify the solution completely check this answer in the second equation by substituting. $3(1.8) - 2(2.2) = 5.4 - 4.4 = 1$

Answer: The solution to the system is $x = 1.8$ and $y = 2.2$ or $(1.8, 2.2)$.

Example 2: Solve the system of equations $y = \frac{3}{4}x - 1$ and $y = -\frac{1}{3}x - 1$.

Solution: Generally graphing the equations is not the most efficient way to solve a system of linear equations. In this case, however, both equations are written in *y* = form so we can see that they have the same *y*-intercept. Since lines can cross only at one point, no points or infinite points, and these lines have different slopes (they are not parallel or coincident), the *y*-intercept must be the only point of intersection and thus the solution to the system. We did not actually graph here, but we used the principles of graphs to solve the system. Substitution would work nicely as well.

Answer: $(0, -1)$

Example 3: Solve the system $x+2y=16$ and $x-y=2$.

Solution: For this, we will use the Elimination Method. We can subtract the second equation from the first and then solve for y, as shown at right.

$$\begin{array}{r} x+2y=16 \\ -(x-y=2) \\ \hline 0+3y=14 \\ 3y=14 \\ y=\frac{14}{3} \end{array}$$

We then substitute $y=\frac{14}{3}$ into either original equation and solve for x. Choosing the second equation, we get $x-\frac{14}{3}=2$, so $x=2+\frac{14}{3}=\frac{20}{3}$. Checking our solution can be done by substituting both values into the first equation.

Answer: The solution to the system is $(\frac{20}{3},\frac{14}{3})$.

Example 4: Solve the system $x+3y=4$ and $3x-y=2$.

Solution: For this, we will use the Elimination Method, only we will need to do some multiplication first. If we multiply the second equation by 3 and add the result to the first equation, we can eliminate y and solve for x, as shown at right.

$$\begin{array}{r} x+3y=4 \\ +\ 9x-3y=6 \\ \hline 10x\quad\ \ =10 \\ x=1 \end{array}$$

We can then find y by substituting $x=1$ into either of the original equations. Choosing the second, we get $3(1)-y=2$, which solves to yield $y=1$. Again, checking the solution can be done by substituting both values into the first equation.

Answer: The solution to this system is $(1,1)$.

Now we can return to the original problem.

Solve the following system of linear equations in two variables.

$$5x - 4y = 7$$
$$2y + 6x = 22$$

For this system, you can use either the Substitution or the Elimination Method, but each choice will require a little bit of work to get started.

Substitution Method:

Before we can substitute, we need to isolate one of the variables. In other words, we need to solve one of the equations for either x or for y. If we solve the second equation for y, it becomes $y = 11 - 3x$. Now we substitute $11 - 3x$ for y in the first equation and solve for x, as shown at right.

$$\begin{aligned} 5x - 4(11 - 3x) &= 7 \\ 5x - 44 + 12x &= 7 \\ 17x - 44 &= 7 \\ 17x &= 51 \\ x &= 3 \end{aligned}$$

Then we can substitute the value for x into one of the original equations to find y. Thus we find that $2y + 6(3) = 22 \Rightarrow 2y = 22 - 18 = 4 \Rightarrow y = \frac{4}{2} = 2$.

Elimination Method:

$$\begin{aligned} 5x - 4y &= 7 \\ 6x + 2y &= 22 \end{aligned}$$

Before we can eliminate a variable, we need to rearrange the second equation so that the variables line up, as shown at right. Now we see that we can multiply the second equation by 2 and add the two equations to eliminate y and solve for x, as shown below right.

$$\begin{aligned} 5x - 4y &= 7 \\ +\ 12x + 4y &= 44 \\ \hline 17x \qquad &= 51 \\ x &= 3 \end{aligned}$$

We can then substitute $x = 3$ into the first equation to get $5(3) - 4y = 7$. Simplifying and solving, we get $-4y = -8$ and thus $y = 2$.

Answer: $(3, 2)$

Here are some more to try. Find the solution to these systems of linear equations. Use the method of your choice.

1. $y = 3x - 1$
   $2x - 3y = 10$

2. $x = -0.5y + 4$
   $8x + 3y = 31$

3. $2y = 4x + 10$
   $6x + 2y = 10$

4. $3x - 5y = -14$
   $x + 5y = 22$

5. $4x + 5y = 11$
   $2x + 6y = 16$

6. $x + 2y = 5$
   $x + y = 5$

7. $2x - 3 = y$
   $x - y = -4$

8. $y + 2 = x$
   $3x - 3y = x + 14$

9. $2x + y = 7$
   $x + 5y = 12$

10. $y = \frac{3}{5}x - 2$
    $y = \frac{x}{10} + 1$

11. $2x + y = -2x + 5$
    $3x + 2y = 2x + 3y$

12. $4x - 3y = -10$
    $x = \frac{1}{4}y - 1$

13. $4y = 2x$
    $2x + y = \frac{x}{2} + 1$

14. $3x - 2y = 8$
    $4y = 6x - 5$

15. $4y = 2x - 4$
    $3x + 5y = -3$

16. $\frac{x}{3} + \frac{4y}{3} = 300$
    $3x - 4y = 300$

Answers:

1. $(-1, -4)$
2. $(\frac{7}{2}, 1)$
3. $(0, 5)$
4. $(2, 4)$
5. $(-1, 3)$
6. $(5, 0)$
7. $(7, 11)$
8. $(-8, -10)$
9. $(\frac{23}{9}, \frac{17}{9})$
10. $(6, 1.6)$
11. $(1, 1)$
12. $(-\frac{1}{4}, 3)$
13. $(\frac{1}{2}, \frac{1}{4})$
14. no solution
15. $(\frac{4}{11}, -\frac{9}{11})$
16. $(300, 150)$

Checkpoint 3A

Problem 3-67

Expressions with Integral and Rational Exponents

Answers to problem 3-67: a: $x^{1/5}$, b: x^{-3}, c: $\sqrt[3]{x^2}$, d: $x^{-1/2}$, e: $\frac{1}{xy^8}$, f: $\frac{1}{m^3}$, g: $xy^3\sqrt{x}$, h: $\frac{1}{81x^6y^{12}}$

The following properties are useful for rewriting expressions with integral (positive or negative whole numbers) or rational (fractional) exponents.

$x^0 = 1$ Examples: $2^0 = 1$, $(-3)^0 = 1$, $(\frac{1}{4})^0 = 1$ (Note that 0^0 is undefined.)

$x^{-n} = \frac{1}{x^n}$ Examples: $x^{-12} = \frac{1}{x^{12}}$, $y^{-4} = \frac{1}{y^4}$, $4^{-2} = \frac{1}{4^2} = \frac{1}{16}$

$\frac{1}{x^{-n}} = x^n$ Examples: $\frac{1}{x^{-5}} = x^5$, $\frac{1}{x^{-2}} = x^2$, $\frac{1}{3^{-2}} = 3^2 = 9$

$x^{a/b} = (x^a)^{1/b} = (\sqrt[b]{x})^a$ Examples: $5^{1/2} = \sqrt{5}$

or : $16^{3/4} = (\sqrt[4]{16})^3 = 2^3 = 8$

$x^{a/b} = (x^{1/b})^a = (\sqrt[b]{x})^a$ $4^{2/3} = \sqrt[3]{4^2} = \sqrt[3]{16} = 2\sqrt[3]{2}$

$x^a x^b = x^{(a+b)}$ Examples: $x^7x^2 = x^9$, $y^{-4}y = y^{-3}$, $2^3 2^2 = 2^5 = 32$

$(x^a)^b = x^{ab}$ Examples: $(x^2)^3 = x^6$, $(a^6b^4)^{1/2} = a^3b^2$, $(3^3)^3 = 3^9 = 19683$

Now we can go back and solve the original problems.

a. Using the fourth property above, $\sqrt[5]{x} = x^{1/5}$.

b. Using the second property above, $\frac{1}{x^3} = x^{-3}$.

c. Using the fourth property above, $x^{2/3} = \sqrt[3]{x^2}$.

d. Using the second and fourth properties above, $\frac{1}{\sqrt{x}} = \frac{1}{x^{1/2}} = x^{-1/2}$.

e. Using the second property above, $x^{-1}y^{-8} = \frac{1}{xy^8}$.

f. Using the second and sixth properties above, $(m^2)^{-3/2} = m^{-3} = \frac{1}{m^3}$.

g. Using the fourth, fifth, and sixth properties above, $(x^3y^6)^{1/2} = x^{3/2}y^3 = x^1x^{1/2}y^3 = xy^3\sqrt{x}$.

h. Using the second and sixth properties above, $(9x^3y^6)^{-2} = 9^{-2}x^{-6}y^{-12} = \frac{1}{81x^6y^{12}}$.

Here are some exercises to try. For problems 1 through 12, rewrite each expression. For problems 13 through 24, simplify each expression. You should not need a calculator for any of these problems.

1. x^{-5}	2. m^0	3. 4^{-1}
4. $\sqrt[3]{y}$	5. $\frac{1}{c^4}$	6. $\frac{1}{b^{-2}}$
7. $12^{1/12}$	8. $z^{-3/4}$	9. $\frac{1}{(\sqrt[6]{7})^5}$
10. 0^0	11. $9^{1/2}$	12. $\sqrt[5]{a^3}$
13. $(f^3)\sqrt[3]{f^3}$	14. $(\frac{1}{27})^{-1/3}$	15. $(v^2 g^{3/4})^8$
16. $(\frac{1}{q^6})^7$	17. $d^{-9}d^{-4}$	18. $(3xw^4)^{-2}$
19. $(u^3 r^{-4})^{-2}$	20. $n^3(n^2)^5$	21. $4(\sqrt{4})^4$
22. $6(k^{1/2}t^5)^2$	23. $p^{15}p^{-15}$	24. $h^8 s^{12}(\sqrt[8]{h})(s^{1/4})$

Answers:

1. $\frac{1}{x^5}$	2. 1	3. $\frac{1}{4}$
4. $y^{1/3}$	5. c^{-4}	6. b^2
7. $\sqrt[12]{12}$	8. $\frac{1}{z^{3/4}}$	9. $7^{-1/6}$
10. undefined	11. 3	12. $a^{3/5}$
13. f^4	14. 3	15. $v^{16}g^6$
16. q^{-42}	17. $d^{-13} = \frac{1}{d^{13}}$	18. $\frac{1}{9x^2 w^{12}}$
19. $\frac{r^8}{u^6}$	20. n^{13}	21. 64
22. $6kt^{10}$	23. 1	24. hs^3

Checkpoint 3B

Problem 3-116

Using Function Notation and Identifying Domain and Range

Answers to problem 3-116: Domain: all x; Range: $y \geq 0$

a. $g(-5)=8$ b. $g(a+1)=2a^2+16a+32$

c. $x=1$ or $x=-7$ d. $x=-3$

An equation is called a function if there exists *no more than one* output for each input. If an equation has two or more outputs for a single input value, it is not a function. The set of possible inputs of a function is called the domain, while the set of all possible outputs of a function is called the range.

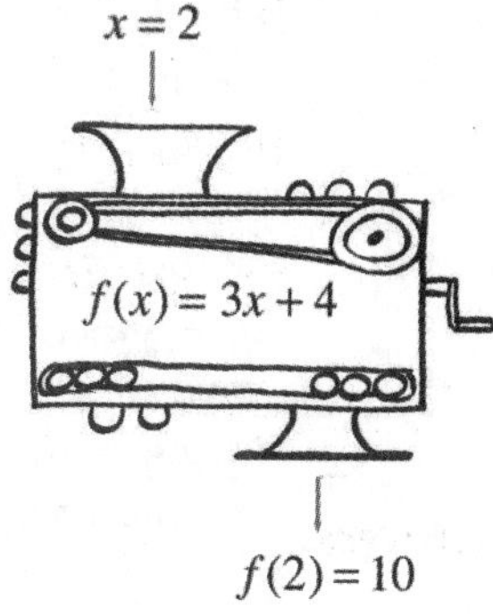

Functions are often given names, most commonly "*f*," "*g*," or "*h*." The notation $f(x)$ represents the output of a function, named *f*, when *x* is the input. It is pronounced "*f* of *x*." The notation $g(2)$, pronounced "*g* of 2," represents the output of function *g* when $x=2$.

Similarly, the function $y=3x+4$ and $f(x)=3x+4$ represent the *same function*. Notice that the notation is interchangeable, that is $y=f(x)$. In some textbooks, $3x+4$ is called the **rule** of the function. The graph of $f(x)=3x+4$ is a line extending forever in both the *x* (horizontal) and the *y* (vertical) directions, so the domain and range of $f(x)=3x+4$ are all real numbers.

Examples 1 through 3: For each function below, give the domain and range. Then calculate $f(2)$ and solve $f(x)=3$.

Example 1: $f(x)=|x-1|-2$

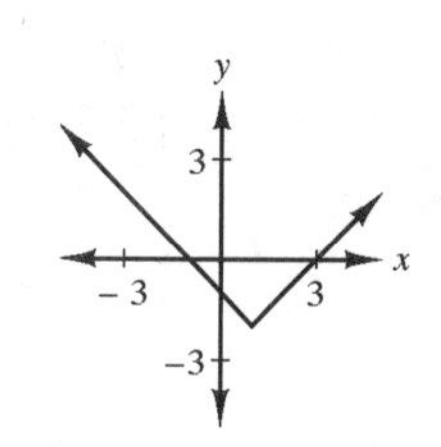

Solution: We start by graphing the function, as shown at right. Since we can use any real number for *x* in this equation, the domain is all real numbers. The smallest possible result for y is –2, so the range is $y \geq -2$. By looking at the graph or substituting $x=2$ into the equation, $f(2)=|2-1|-2=-1$. To solve $f(x)=3$, find the points where the horizontal line $y=3$ intersects the graph or solve the equation $3=|x-1|-2$, which yields $x=-4$ or $x=6$.

Example 2: $f(x)$ is given by the graph below.

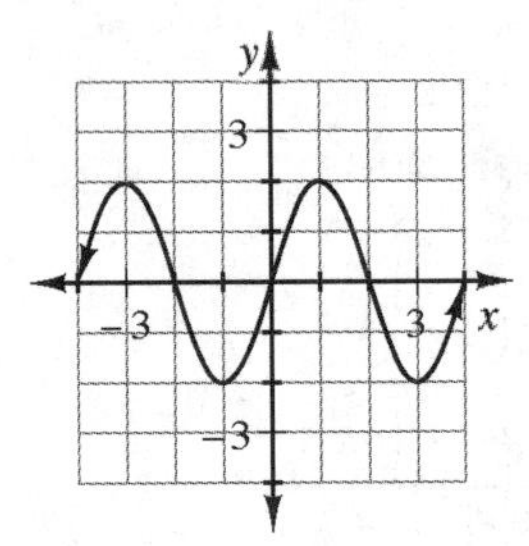

The arrows indicate that the graph continues indefinitely right and left and we see no disruption in the smooth function, so the domain is all real numbers. All of the y-values fall between -2 and 2, so the range is $-2 \le y \le 2$. We can see from the graph that when $x = 2$, the value of the function appears to be 0, or $f(2) \approx 0$. Since $-2 \le y \le 2$, the value of the function never gets as high as 3, so $f(x) = 3$ has no solution.

Example 3: $f(x) = \sqrt{x+3}$

Solution: Again, we start by making a graph of the function, which is shown at right. Since the square root of a negative number does not exist, we can only use x-values of -3 or larger. Thus, the domain is $x \ge -3$. We can see from the graph and the equation that the smallest possible y-value is zero, so the range is $y \ge 0$. Looking at the graph gives an approximate answer when $x = 2$ of $y \approx 2.25$. Or, by substituting $x = 2$ into the equation, we get $f(2) = \sqrt{2+3} = \sqrt{5}$. To solve $f(x) = 3$, find the point where $y = 3$ intersects the graph or solve $3 = \sqrt{x+3}$, which gives $x = 6$.

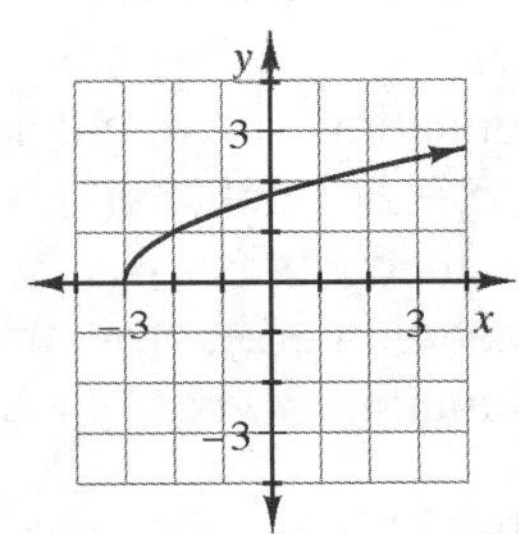

Now we can go back and solve the original problem.

The graph is a parabola opening upward with vertex $(-3,0)$, as shown at right. Thus, the domain is all real numbers and the range is $y \ge 0$.

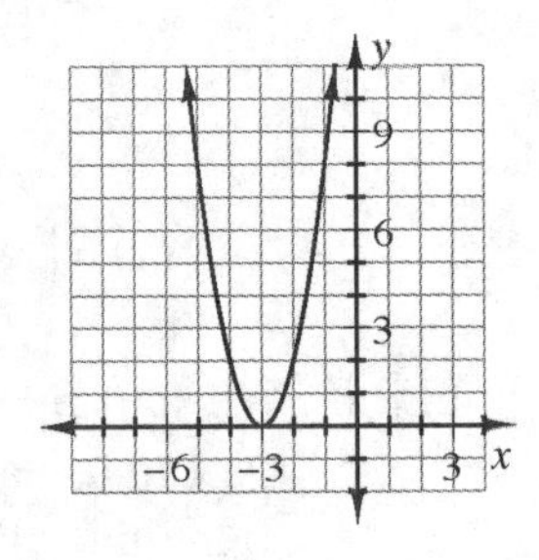

$g(-5) = -2(-5+3) = 2(-2)^2 = 8$

$$g(a+1) = 2(a+1+3)^2 = 2(a+4)^2$$
$$= 2(a^2 + 8a + 16) = 2a^2 + 16a + 32$$

If $g(x) = 32$, then $32 = 2(x+3)^2$. Dividing both sides by 2, we get $16 = (x+3)^2$. Taking the square root of both sides gives $\pm 4 = x + 3$, which leads to the values $x = 1$ or -7.

If $g(x) = 0$, then $0 = 2(x+3)^2$. Diving both sides by two or applying the Zero Product Property gives $0 = (x+3)^2$ and then $0 = x + 3$. Thus $x = -3$.

Here are some more to try.

For each graph in problems 1–3, describe the domain and range.

1. 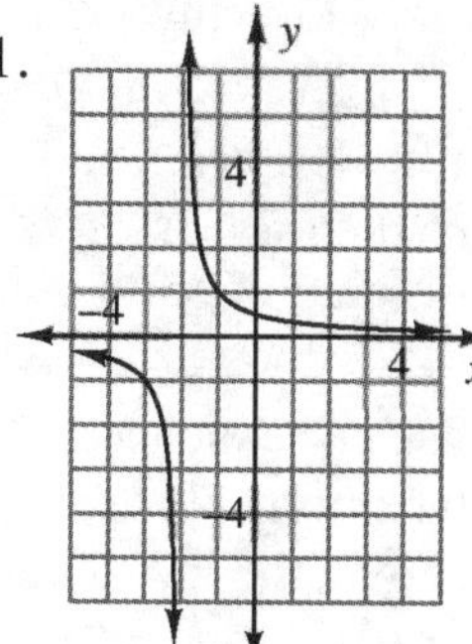

2. 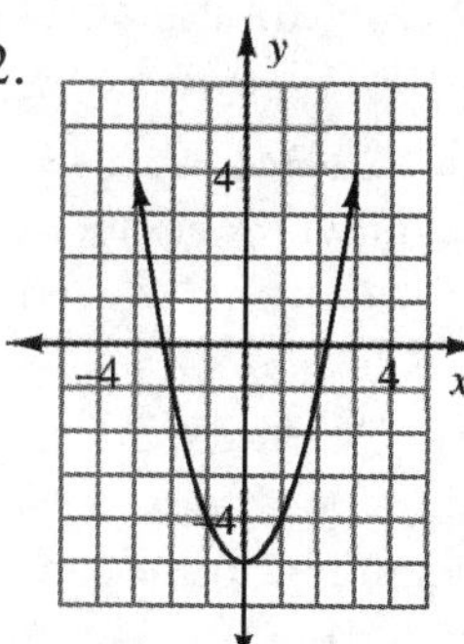

3. 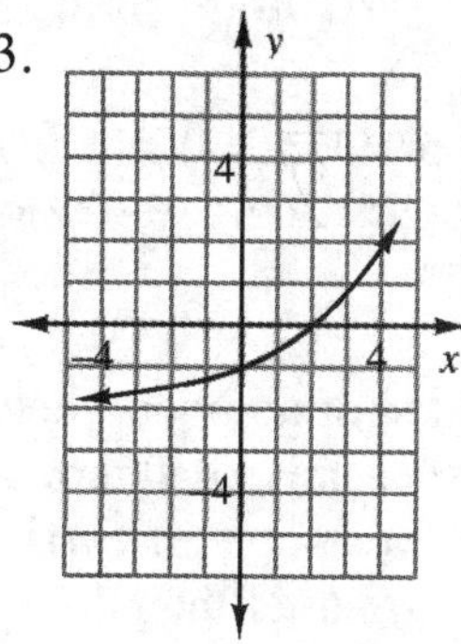

4. If $f(x) = 3 - x^2$, calculate $f(5)$ and $f(3a)$.

5. If $g(x) = 5 - 3x^2$, calculate $g(-2)$ and $g(a+2)$.

6. If $f(x) = \frac{x+3}{2x-5}$, calculate $f(2)$ and $f(2.5)$.

7. If $f(x) = x^2 + 5x + 6$, solve $f(x) = 0$.

8. If $g(x) = 3(x-5)^2$, solve $g(x) = 27$.

9. If $f(x) = (x+2)^2$, solve $f(x) = 27$.

Answers:

1. Domain: $x \neq -2$, Range: $y \neq 0$

2. Domain: all real numbers, Range: $y \geq -5$

3. Domain: all real numbers, Range: $y > -2$

4. $f(5) = -22$, $f(3a) = 3 - 9a^2$

5. $g(-2) = -7$, $g(a+2) = -3a^2 - 12a - 7$

6. $f(2) = -5$, not possible

7. $x = -2$ or $x = -3$

8. $x = 8$ or $x = 2$

9. $x = -2 \pm \sqrt{27}$

Checkpoint 4A

Problem 4-42

Writing Equations for Arithmetic and Geometric Sequences

Answers to problem 4-42: a: E $t(n)=-2+3n$; R $t(0)=-2, t(n+1)=t(n)+3$, b: E $t(n)=6(\frac{1}{2})^n$; R $t(0)=6, t(n+1)=\frac{1}{2}t(n)$, c: $t(n)=10-7n$, d: $t(n)=5(1.2)^n$, e: $t(4)=1620$

An ordered list of numbers such as: 4, 9, 16, 25, 36, ... creates a sequence. The numbers in the sequence are called terms. One way to identify and label terms is to use function notation. For example, if $t(n)$ is the name of the sequence above, the initial value is 4 and the second term after the initial value is 16. This is written $t(0)=4$ and $t(2)=16$. Some books use subscripts instead of function notation. In this case $t_0=4$ and $t_2=16$. The initial value is *not* part of the sequence. It is only a reference point and is useful in writing a rule for the sequence. When writing a sequence, start by writing the first term after the initial value, $t(1)$ or t_1.

Arithmetic sequences have a common difference between the terms. The rule for the values in an arithmetic sequences can be found by $t(n)=a+dn$ where a = the initial value, d = the common difference and n = the number of terms after the initial value.

Geometric sequences have a common ratio between the terms. The rule for the values in a geometric sequence may be found by $t(n)=ar^n$ where a = the initial value, r = the common ratio and n = the number of terms after the initial value.

Example 1: Find a rule for the sequence: –2, 4, 10, 16, ...

Solution: There is a common difference between the terms $(d=6)$ so it is an arithmetic sequence. Work backward to find the initial value: $a=-2-6=-8$.
Now use the general rule: $t(n)=a+dn=-8+6n$.

Example 2: Find a rule for the sequence: 81, 27, 9, 3, ...

Solution: There is a common ratio between the terms $(r=\frac{1}{3})$ so it is a geometric sequence. Work backward to find the initial value: $a=81\div\frac{1}{3}=243$.
Now use the general rule: $t(n)=ar^n=243(\frac{1}{3})^n$.

A rule such as $t(n)=5-7n$ is called an explicit rule because any term can be found by substituting the appropriate value for n into the rule. To find the 10th term after the initial value, $t(10)$, substitute 10 for n. $t(10)=5-7(10)=-65$.

A second way to find the terms in a sequence is by using a recursive formula. A recursive formula tells first term or the initial value and how to get from one term to the next.

Example 3: (using subscript notation)
Write the first five terms of the sequence determined by: $b_1 = 8,\ b_{n+1} = b_n \cdot \frac{1}{2}$

Solution: $b_1 = 8$ tells you the first term and $b_{n+1} = b_n \cdot \frac{1}{2}$ tells you to multiply by $\frac{1}{2}$ to get from one term to the next.

$b_1 = 8$ $\quad b_2 = b_1 \cdot \frac{1}{2} = 8 \cdot \frac{1}{2} = 4$ $\quad b_3 = b_2 \cdot \frac{1}{2} = 4 \cdot \frac{1}{2} = 2$

$b_4 = b_3 \cdot \frac{1}{2} = 2 \cdot \frac{1}{2} = 1$ $\quad b_5 = b_4 \cdot \frac{1}{2} = 1 \cdot \frac{1}{2} = \frac{1}{2}$

The sequence is: $8, 4, 2, 1, \frac{1}{2}, \ldots$

Now we can go back and solve the original problems.

a. It is an arithmetic sequence $(d = 3)$. Working backward the initial value is $1 - 3 = -2$. Using the general formula the explicit rule: $t(n) = a + dn = -2 + 3d$. A possible recursive rule is $t(1) = 1,\ t(n+1) = t(n) + 3$.

b. It is a geometric sequence $(r = \frac{1}{2})$. Working backward the initial value is $3 \div \frac{1}{2} = 6$. Using the general formula for the explicit rule: $t(n) = ar^n = 6(\frac{1}{2})^n$. A possible recursive rule is $t(0) = 6,\ t(n+1) = \frac{1}{2}t(n)$.

c. $t(2)$ is halfway between $t(1)$ and $t(3)$ so $t(2) = 10$. This means $d = -7$ and the initial value is 24. Using the general formula the explicit rule: $t(n) = a + dn = 24 - 7d$.

d. The common ratio $r = \frac{8.64}{7.2} = 1.2$ so $t(1) = \frac{7.2}{1.2} = 6,\ t(0) = \frac{6}{1.2} = 5$. Using an initial value of 5 and a common ratio of 1.2 in the general formula for the explicit rule: $t(n) = ar^n = 5(1.2)^n$.

e. The common difference is the difference in the values divided by the number of terms. $d = \frac{t(12)-t(7)}{12-7} = \frac{116-1056}{5} = -188$. Working backward three terms: $t(4) = 1056 - 3(-188) = 1620$.

Here are some more to try.

Write the first 6 terms of each sequence.

1. $t(n) = 5n + 2$
2. $t(n) = 6(-\frac{1}{2})^n$
3. $t(n) = -15 + \frac{1}{2}n$
4. $t_n = -3 \cdot 3^{n-1}$
5. $t(1) = 3,\ t(n+1) = t(n) - 5$
6. $t_1 = \frac{1}{3},\ t_{n+1} = \frac{1}{3}t_n$

For each sequence, write an explicit and recursive rule.

7. $10, 50, 250, 1250, \ldots$
8. $4, 8, 12, 16, \ldots$
9. $-2, 5, 12, 19, \ldots$
10. $16, 4, 1, \frac{1}{4}, \ldots$
11. $-12, 6, -3, \frac{3}{2}, \ldots$
12. $\frac{5}{6}, \frac{2}{3}, \frac{1}{2}, \frac{1}{3}, \ldots$

For each sequence, write an explicit rule.

13. A geometric sequence

n	$t(n)$
0	
1	15
2	45
3	
4	

14. An arithmetic sequence

n	$t(n)$
0	27
1	15
2	
3	
4	

15. An arithmetic sequence

n	$t(n)$
1	
2	$3\frac{1}{3}$
3	
4	
5	$4\frac{1}{3}$

16. A geometric sequence

n	$t(n)$
1	
2	
3	–24
4	48
5	

Solve each problem.

17. An arithmetic sequence has $t(3) = 52$ and $t(10) = 108$. Find a rule for $t(n)$ and find $t(100)$.

18. An arithmetic sequence has $t(1) = -17$, $t(2) = -14$ and $t(n) = 145$. What is the value of n?

19. An arithmetic sequence has $t(61) = 810$ and $t(94) = 1239$. Find a rule for $t(n)$.

20. A geometric sequence has $t(4) = 12$ and $t(7) = 324$. Find the common ratio and a rule for $t(n)$.

Answers:

1. $7, 12, 17, 22, 27, 32$
2. $-3, \frac{3}{2}, -\frac{3}{4}, \frac{3}{8}, -\frac{3}{16}, \frac{3}{32}$
3. $-14\frac{1}{2}, -14, -13\frac{1}{2}, -13, -12\frac{1}{2}, -12$
4. $-3, -9, -27, -81, -243, -729$
5. $3, -2, -7, -12, -17, -22$
6. $\frac{1}{3}, \frac{1}{9}, \frac{1}{27}, \frac{1}{81}, \frac{1}{243}, \frac{1}{729}$

Rules for problems 7 through 20 may vary.

7. $t(n) = 2 \cdot 5^n$; $t(0) = 2$, $t(n+1) = 5t(n)$
8. $t(n) = 4n$; $t(0) = 0$, $t(n+1) = t(n) + 4$
9. $t(n) = -9 + 7n$; $t(0) = -9$, $t(n+1) = t(n) + 7$
10. $t(n) = 64(\frac{1}{4})^n$; $t(0) = 64$, $t(n+1) = \frac{1}{4}t(n)$
11. $t(n) = 24(-\frac{1}{2})^n$; $t(0) = 24$, $t(n+1) = -\frac{1}{2}t(n)$
12. $t(n) = 1 - \frac{1}{6}n$; $t(0) = 1$, $t(n+1) = t(n) - \frac{1}{6}$
13. $t(n) = 5 \cdot 3^n$
14. $t(n) = 27 - 12n$
15. $t(n) = 2\frac{2}{3} + \frac{1}{3}n$
16. $t(n) = 3(-2)^n$
17. $t(n) = 28 + 8n$; $t(100) = 828$
18. $n = 55$
19. $t(n) = 17 + 13n$
20. $t(n) = \frac{4}{27}(3)^n$

Checkpoint 4B

Problem 4-87

Solving for One Variable in an Equation with Two or More Variables

Answers to problem 4-87: a: $y=\frac{1}{3}x-4$, b: $y=\frac{6}{5}x-\frac{1}{5}$, c: $y=(x+1)^2+4$, d: $y=x^2+4x$

When we want to solve for one variable in an equation with two or more variables it usually helps to start by simplifying, such as removing parentheses and fractions. Next isolate the desired variable in the same way as you solve an equation with only one variable. Here are two examples.

Example 1: Solve $\frac{x-3y}{4}+2(x+1)=7$ for y.

Solution: First multiply all terms by 4 to remove the fraction and then simplify, as shown at right. Then, to isolate y, we subtract $9x$ from both sides to get $-3y=-9x+20$. Dividing both sides by –3 results in $y=3x-\frac{20}{3}$.

$$(4)\frac{x-3y}{4}+4(2)(x+1)=4(7)$$
$$x-3y+8x+8=28$$
$$9x-3y=20$$

Answer: $y=3x-\frac{20}{3}$

Example 2: Solve $x+2\sqrt{y+1}=3x+4$ for y.

Solution: First, we isolate the radical by subtracting x from both sides to get $2\sqrt{1+y}=2x+4$ and then dividing both sides by 2 to get $\sqrt{1+y}=x+2$. Then, we remove the radical by squaring both sides, as shown at right. Lastly, we isolate y by subtracting 1 from both sides of the equation.

$$(\sqrt{y+1})^2=(x+2)^2$$
$$y+1=(x+2)(x+2)$$
$$y+1=x^2+4x+4$$

Answer: $y=x^2+4x+3$

Now we can go back and solve the original problems.

a.

$$x - 3(y+2) = 6$$
$$x - 3y - 6 = 6$$
$$x - 3y = 12$$
$$-3y = -x + 12$$
$$y = \frac{-x+12}{-3} \text{ or } y = \frac{1}{3}x - 4$$

b.

$$\frac{6x-1}{y} - 3 = 2$$
$$\frac{6x-1}{y} = 5$$
$$(y)\frac{6x-1}{y} = 5(y)$$
$$6x - 1 = 5y$$
$$y = \frac{6x-1}{5} \text{ or } y = \frac{6}{5}x - \frac{1}{5}$$

c.

$$\sqrt{y-4} = x+1$$
$$(\sqrt{y-4})^2 = (x+1)^2$$
$$y - 4 = (x+1)^2$$
$$y = (x+1)^2 + 4 \text{ or } x^2 + 2x + 5$$

d.

$$\sqrt{y+4} = x+2$$
$$(\sqrt{y+4})^2 = (x+2)^2$$
$$y + 4 = x^2 + 4x + 4$$
$$y = x^2 + 4x$$

Here are some more to try. Solve each equation for y.

1. $2x - 5y = 7$
2. $2(x+y) + 1 = x - 4$
3. $4(x-y) + 12 = 2x - 4$
4. $x = \frac{1}{5}y - 2$
5. $x = y^2 + 1$
6. $\frac{5x+2}{y} - 1 = 5$
7. $\sqrt{y+3} = x - 2$
8. $(y+2)^2 = x^2 + 9$
9. $\frac{x+2}{4} + \frac{4-y}{2} = 3$
10. $\sqrt{2y+1} = x + 3$
11. $x = \frac{2}{4-y}$
12. $x = \frac{y+1}{y-1}$

Answers:

1. $y = \frac{2}{5}x - \frac{7}{5}$
2. $y = -\frac{1}{2}x - \frac{5}{2}$
3. $y = \frac{1}{2}x + 4$
4. $y = 5x + 10$
5. $y = \pm\sqrt{x-1}$
6. $y = \frac{5}{6}x + \frac{1}{3}$
7. $y = x^2 - 4x + 1$
8. $y = \pm\sqrt{x^2+9} - 2$
9. $y = \frac{1}{2}x - 1$
10. $y = \frac{1}{2}x^2 + 3x + 4$ or $y = \frac{1}{2}(x+4)(x+2)$
11. $y = \frac{4x-2}{x}$ or $y = 4 - \frac{2}{x}$
12. $y = \frac{x+1}{x-1}$

Checkpoint 5A

Problem 5-49

Multiplying Polynomials

Answers to problem 5-49:

a. $2x^3 + 2x^2 - 3x - 3$ b. $x^3 - x^2 + x + 3$

c. $2x^2 + 12x + 18$ d. $4x^3 - 8x^2 - 3x + 9$

The product of polynomials can be found by using the Distributive Property. Using generic rectangles or, in the case of multiplying two binomials, the FOIL Method can help you to keep track of the terms to be sure that you are multiplying correctly.

Example: Multiply $(3x-2)(4x+5)$.

Solution 1: When multiplying binomials, such as $(3x-2)(4x+5)$, you can use a generic rectangle. You consider the terms of your original binomials as the dimensions (length and width) of the rectangle. To find the area of each piece, you multiply the terms that represent the length and width of that piece. To get your final answer, you add the areas of each of the interior pieces and simplify by combining like terms. This process is shown in the diagram below.

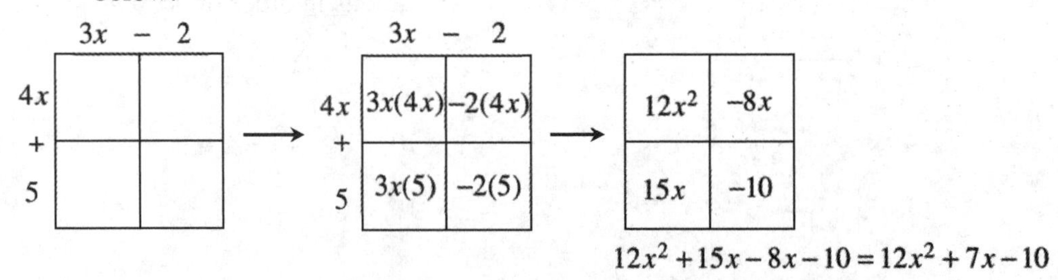

$12x^2 + 15x - 8x - 10 = 12x^2 + 7x - 10$

Solution 2: You might view multiplying binomials with generic rectangles as a form of double distribution. The $4x$ is distributed across the first row of the generic rectangle. Then the 5 is distributed across the second row of the generic rectangle. Some people write it this way:

$$(3x-2)(4x+5) = (3x-2)4x + (3x-2)5 = 12x^2 - 8x + 15x - 10 = 12x^2 + 7x - 10$$

Solution 3: Another approach to multiplying binomials is to the FOIL Method. This method uses the mnemonic "FOIL," which is an acronym for First, Outside, Inside, Last, to help you remember which terms to multiply.

F. Multiply the FIRST terms of each binomial. $(3x)(4x)=12x^2$
O. Multiply the OUTSIDE terms. $(3x)(5)=15x$
I. Multiply the INSIDE terms. $(-2)(4x)=-8x$
L. Multiply the LAST terms of each binomial . $(-2)(5)=-10$

Finally combine like terms to get $12x^2+15x-8x-10=12x^2+7x-10$.

Answer: $12x^2+7x-10$

Now we can go back and solve the original problems.

a: $(x+1)(2x^2-3)$

Solution: We can use the FOIL Method here. Multiplying the *first* terms, we get $(x)(2x^2)=2x^3$. Multiplying the *outside* terms, we get $(x)(-3)=-3x$. Multiplying the *inside* terms, we get $(1)(2x^2)=2x^2$. Multiplying the *last* terms, we get $(1)(-3)=-3$. Adding these results, we get $2x^3-3x+2x^2-3$. Generally, answers are expressed in with terms in order of decreasing powers of x, so we rearrange terms for the answer.

Answer: $2x^3+2x^2-3x-3$

b: $(x+1)(x-2x^2+3)$

Solution: This is a good problem for a generic rectangle, as shown at right. After calculating the area of each individual cell, we find our expression by adding them together to get $x^3-2x^2+x^2+3x-2x+3$. Then we combine like terms to get a simplified answer.

	x^2	$-2x$	$+3$
x	x^3	$-2x^2$	$3x$
$+1$	x^2	$-2x$	3

Answer: x^3-x^2+x+3

c: $2(x+3)^2$

Solution: Here we write out the factors and use the Distributive Property, as shown in the solution at right.

$$\begin{aligned}&2(x+3)(x+3)\\&=(2x+6)(x+3)\\&=(2x+6)(x)+(2x+6)(3)\\&=2x^2+6x+6x+18\\&=2x^2+12x+18\end{aligned}$$

Answer: $2x^2+12x+18$

d: $(x+1)(2x-3)^2$

Solution: Write out the factors. Multiply two of the factors together and then multiply that result by the third factor. This process is shown at right.

$$\begin{aligned}&(x+1)(2x-3)(2x-3)\\&=(2x^2-x-3)(2x-3)\\&=4x^3-6x^2-2x^2+3x-6x+9\\&=4x^3-8x^2-3x+9\end{aligned}$$

Answer: $4x^3-8x^2-3x+9$

Here are some more to try. Multiply and simplify.

1. $(2x+3)(x-7)$
2. $(4x-2)(3x+5)$
3. $(x-2)(x^2+3x+5)$
4. $(x+8)(x-12)$
5. $4(3x-5)^2$
6. $(2x+y)(2x-y)$
7. $(2x+3)^2$
8. $(5x-8)(2x+7)$
9. $(x+3)(x^2-4x+7)$
10. $(x+7)(x-11)$
11. $-8x^2(5x^2+7)$
12. $(2x+y)(x+1)^2$

Answers:

1. $2x^2-11x-21$
2. $12x^2+14x-10$
3. x^3+x^2-x-10
4. $x^2-4x-96$
5. $36x^2-120x+100$
6. $4x^2-y^2$
7. $4x^2+12x+9$
8. $10x^2+19x-56$
9. $x^3-x^2-5x+21$
10. $x^2-4x-77$
11. $-40x^4-56x^2$
12. $2x^3+4x^2+2x+x^2y+2xy+y$

Checkpoint 5B

Problem 5-100

Factoring Quadratics

Answers to problem 5-100:

a. $(2x+1)(2x-1)$ b. $(2x+1)^2$

c. $(2y+1)(y+2)$ d. $(3m+1)(m-2)$

Factoring quadratics means changing the expression into a product of factors or to find the dimensions of the generic rectangle that represents the quadratic. You can use Diamond Problems with generic rectangles or just guess and check with FOIL Method or the Distributive Property to factor.

Here are some examples using Diamond Problems and generic rectangles:

Example 1: Factor $x^2 + 6x + 8$.

Solution: Multiply the x^2-term by the constant term and place the result in the top of the diamond. This will be the product of the two sides of the diamond. Then place the x-term at the bottom of the diamond. This will be the sum of the sides. Then find two terms that multiply to give the top term in the diamond and add to give the bottom term in the diamond, in this case $2x$ and $6x$. This tells us how the x-term is split in the generic rectangle. Once we have the area of the generic rectangle we can find the dimensions by looking for common factors among rows and columns. Study the example below.

Diamond: top $8x^2$, sides ? and ?, bottom $6x$ → Diamond: top $8x^2$, sides $2x$ and $4x$, bottom $6x$ →

x^2	$4x$
$2x$	8

→

	x	$+\ 4$
x	x^2	$4x$
$+\ 2$	$2x$	8

→ $(x+2)(x+4)$

Example 2: Factor $5x^2 - 13x + 6$.

Diamond: top $30x^2$, sides $-3x$ and $-10x$, bottom $-13x$ →

$5x^2$	$-10x$
$-3x$	6

→

	x	$-\ 2$
$5x$	$5x^2$	$-10x$
-3	$-3x$	6

→ $(5x-3)(x-2)$

Now we can go back and solve the original problems.

a.

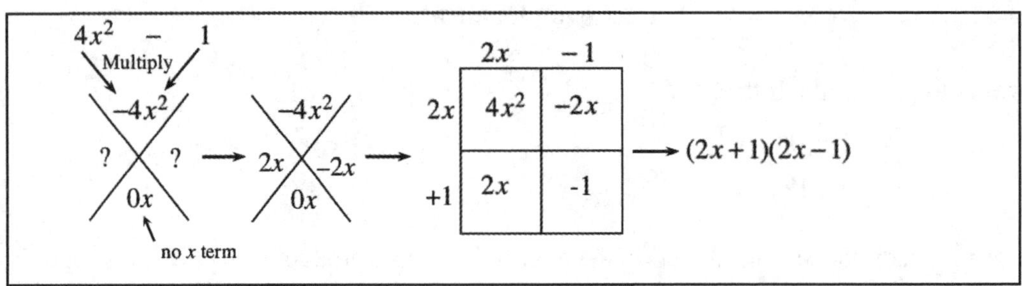

b.

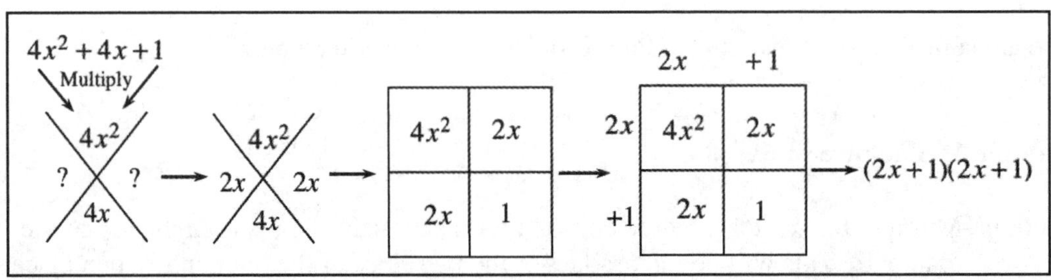

c.

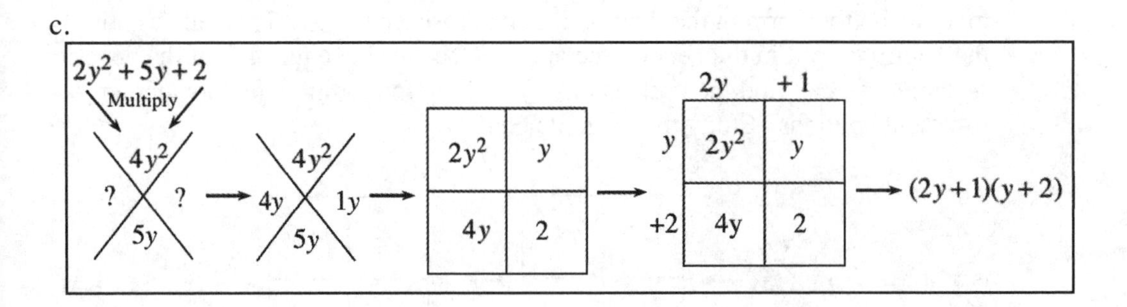

d.

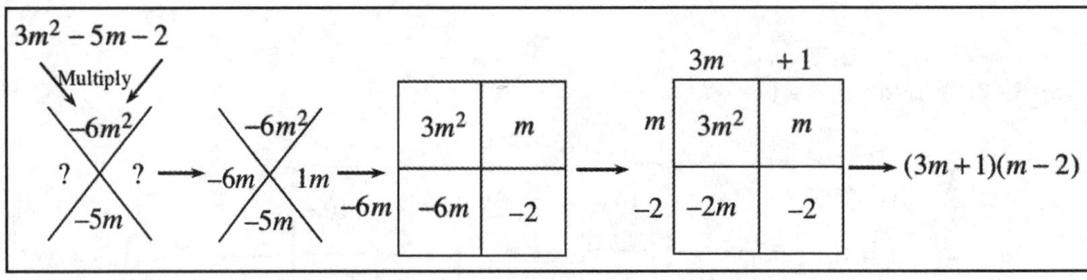

Here are some more to try. Factor each expression.

1. $2x^2 + 7x - 4$
2. $7x^2 + 13x - 2$
3. $3x^2 + 11x + 10$
4. $x^2 + 5x - 24$
5. $2x^2 + 5x - 7$
6. $3x^2 - 13x + 4$
7. $64x^2 + 16x + 1$
8. $5x^2 + 12x - 9$
9. $8x^2 + 24x + 10$
10. $6x^3 + 31x^2 + 5x$

Answers:

1. $(x+4)(2x-1)$
2. $(7x-1)(x+2)$
3. $(3x+5)(x+2)$
4. $(x+8)(x-3)$
5. $(2x+7)(x-1)$
6. $(3x-1)(x-4)$
7. $(8x+1)^2$
8. $(5x-3)(x+3)$
9. $2(4x^2+12x+5) = 2(2x+1)(2x+5)$
10. $x(6x^2+31x+5) = x(6x+1)(x+5)$

Glossary

3-dimensional coordinate system In three dimensions the z-axis is perpendicular to the x-y plane at $(0, 0)$. Points in 3-dimensions are represented with coordinates (x, y, z). The first octant where x,-y, and-z are positive is shown at right with the point $(2, 3, 1)$.

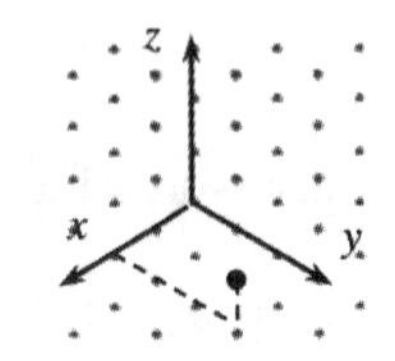

30°-60°-90 triangle A special right triangle with acute angle measures of 30° and 60°. The side lengths are always in the ratio of $1:\sqrt{3}:2$.

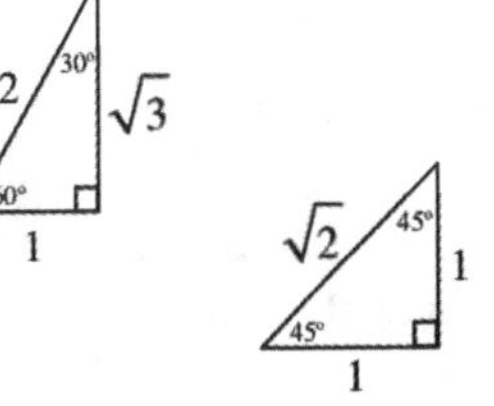

45°-45°-90 triangle A special right triangle with acute angle measures of 45°. The side lengths are always in the ratio of $1:1:\sqrt{2}$.

absolute value The absolute value of a number is the distance of the number from zero. Since the absolute value represents a distance without regard to direction, it is always a positive real number. For example, $|-7| = 7$, and $|7| = 7$. The absolute value of a complex number is its distance from zero in the complex plane. For a complex number $a + bi$, $|a + bi| = \sqrt{a^2 + b^2}$. For example, $|3 - 2i| = \sqrt{3^2 + (-2)^2} = \sqrt{13}$.

algebraic strategies Using algebraic strategies means to write an algebraic representation of the problem and then to rewrite those expressions to get equivalent, but more useful results that lead to a solution for the problem or that reveal more information to help solve it.

amplitude The amplitude of a cyclic graph is one-half the distance between the highest and lowest points. In the graph at right, a is the amplitude.

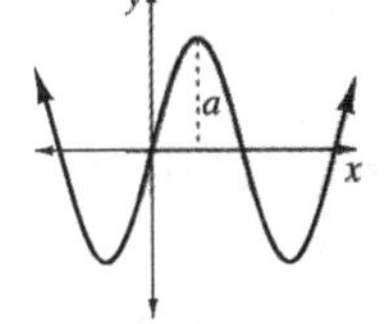

angle An angle is formed by two rays joined at a common endpoint (the vertex). In geometric figures, angles are usually formed by two segments with a common endpoint.

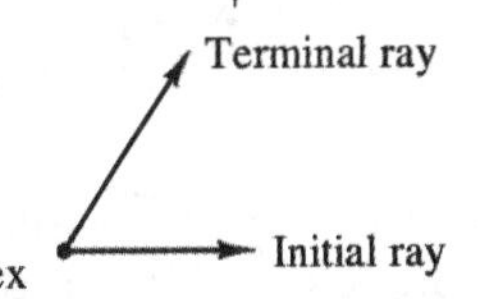

angles of rotation. Angles with one vertex at the origin and formed by counter-clockwise rotation from the positive x-axis, are referred to as angles of rotation in standard position. For an angle θ, in standard position, the positive x-axis is the initial ray and the terminal ray may point in any direction. The measure of such an angle may have any real value.

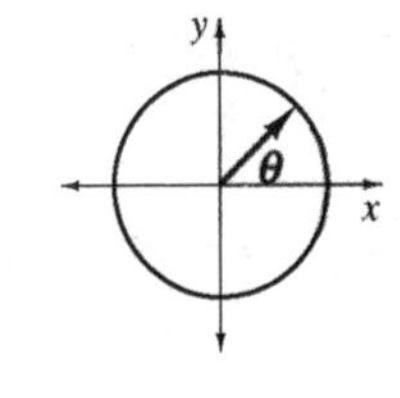

angle sum and difference identities Trigonometric identities that involve angle sums or differences. They are: $\sin(x \pm y) = \sin(x)\cos(y) \pm \cos(x)\sin(y)$ and $\cos(x \pm y) = \cos(x)\cos(y) \mp \sin(x)\sin(y)$.

annual Occurring once every year.

appreciation An increase in value.

arccosine of *x* See *cosine inverse* ($\cos^{-1} x$).

arcsine of *x* See *sine inverse* ($\sin^{-1} x$).

arctangent of *x* See *tangent inverse* ($\tan^{-1} x$).

area For a 2-dimensional region, the number of non-overlapping square units needed to cover the region

area model See *generic rectangle*. (p. 126)

argument Used with sigma notation for sequences to describe the nth term. In the expression, $\sum_{k=1}^{10}(2k+1)$ the expression $2k+1$ is the argument.

arithmetic sequence In an arithmetic sequence the difference between sequential terms is constant. Each term of an arithmetic sequence can be generated by adding the common difference to the previous term. For example in the sequence, 4, 7, 10, 13, …, the common difference is 3. (p. A34)

arithmetic series An arithmetic series is the sum of the terms of an arithmetic sequence. Given the arithmetic sequence $3, 7, 11, ..., 43$, the corresponding arithmetic series is $3+7+11+...+43$.

association A relationship between two (or more) variables. An association between numerical variables can be displayed on a scatterplot, and described by its form, direction, strength, and outliers. Possible association between two categorical variables can be studied in a relative frequency table. Also see *scatterplot*.

asymptote A line that a graph of a curve approaches as the *x*-values approach positive or negative infinity. An asymptote is often represented by a dashed line on a graph. For example, the graph at right has an asymptote at $y=-3$. (p. 37)

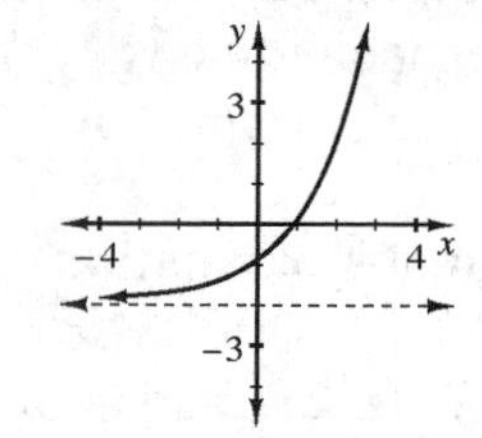

average See *mean*.

average rate of change The average rate of change of a function over an interval is the change in the value of the dependent quantity divided by the change in the independent quantity. It is the change in the *y*-value divided by the change in the *x*-value for two distinct points on the graph, which is the slope of the line through these two distinct points. (p. 137)

axes In a coordinate plane, the two perpendicular number lines that intersect at the origin (0, 0). The *x*-axis is horizontal and the *y*-axis is vertical. In 3-dimensions a third number line, the *z*-axis is perpendicular to the *x*-*y* plane at the origin (0, 0, 0). See *coordinate axes* and *3-dimensional coordinate system* for an illustration.

b When the equation of a line is expressed in $y = mx + b$ form, the parameter *b* gives the *y*-intercept of the line. For example, the *y*-intercept of the line $y = -\frac{1}{3}x + 7$ is (0, 7).

bar graph A bar graph is a set of rectangular bars that have height proportional to the number of data elements in each category. Usually the bars are separated from each other. It is a way of displaying one-variable data that can be put into categories (like what color you prefer, your gender, or the state you were born in). Also see *histogram*.

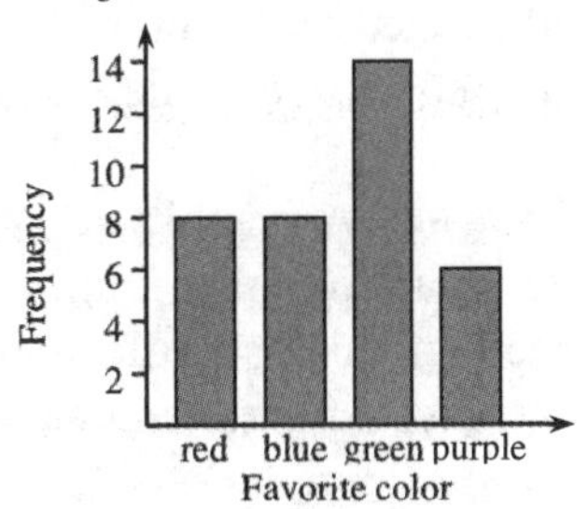

base When working with an exponential expression in the form a^b, *a* is called the base. For example, 2 is the base in 2^5. (5 is the exponent, and 32 is the value.) Also see *exponent*.

best-fit line See *line of best fit*.

bias A systematic inaccuracy in data due to a process that favors certain outcomes.

biased wording Words used in a survey question that intentionally or unintentionally influence results.

bin width An interval, or the width of a bar, on a histogram.

binomial An expression that is the sum or difference of exactly two terms, each of which is a monomial. For example, $-2x + 3y^2$ is a binomial. (p. 135)

The Binomial Theorem The formula for the expansion of $(x + y)^n$ is called the Binomial Theorem. $(x+y)^n = {}_nC_n x^n + {}_nC_{n-1} x^{n-1} y + {}_nC_{n-2} x^{n-2} y^2 + \ldots + {}_nC_1 x y^{n-1} + {}_nC_0 y^n$

For example, $(x + y)^3 = {}_3C_3 x^3 + {}_3C_2 x^2 y + {}_3C_1 x y^2 + {}_3C_0 y^3 = 1x^3 + 3x^2 y + 3xy^2 + 1y^3$

bound The highest or lowest value that a statistical prediction is within. Also see *margin of error* and *boundary line*.

boundary line or curve (1) A line or curve on a two-dimensional graph that divides the graph into two regions. A boundary line or curve is used when graphing inequalities with two variables. For example, the inequality $y < \frac{2}{3}x + 2$ is graphed at right. The dashed boundary line has equation $y = \frac{2}{3}x + 2$. A boundary line is also sometimes called a "dividing line." (2) A line drawn parallel to and above or below the least squares regression line at a distance equivalent to the largest residual. The line determines the upper or lower limit on the values that a prediction is likely to be. (p. 197)

$y < \frac{2}{3}x + 2$

boundary point The endpoint of a ray or segment on a number line where an inequality is true. For strict inequalities (that is, inequalities involving < or >), the point is not part of the solution. We find boundary points by solving the equality associated with our inequality. For example, the solution to the equation $2x+5=11$ is $x=3$, so the inequality $2x+5 \geq 11$ has a boundary point at 3. The solution to that inequality is illustrated on the number line at right. A boundary point is also sometimes called a "dividing point." (p. 186)

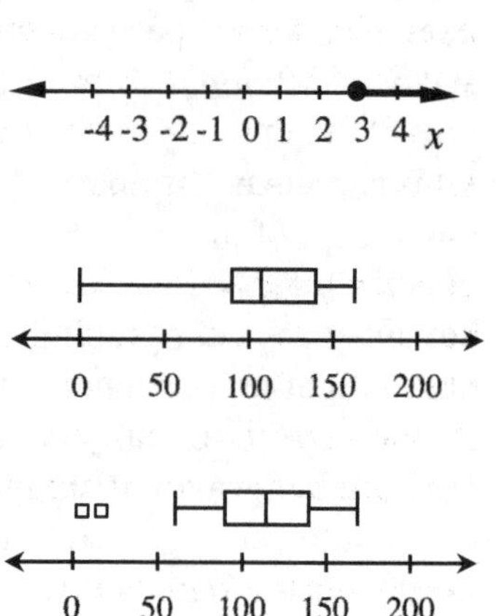

boxplot A graphic way of displaying the five number summary of a distribution of data: minimum, first quartile, median, third quartile, and maximum. A **modified boxplot** displays outliers separately from the boxplot. Also see *five number summary*.

census The process of measuring every member of the population.

center (of a data distribution) A number that represents the middle of a data set, or that represents a "typical" value of the set. Two ways to measure the center of a data set are the mean and the median. When dealing with measures of center, it is often useful to consider the distribution of the data. For symmetric distributions with no outliers, the mean or median can represent the middle, or "typical" value, of the data well. However, in the presence of outliers or non-symmetrical data distributions, the median may be a better measure. Also see *mean* and *median*.

circle In a plane, the set of all points equidistant from a single point. The general equation of a circle is $(x-h)^2+(y-k)^2=r^2$ where the point (h,k) is the center of the circle of radius r.

circle graph A way of displaying data that can be put into categories (like what color you prefer, your gender, or the state you were born in). A circle graph shows the proportion each category is of the whole.

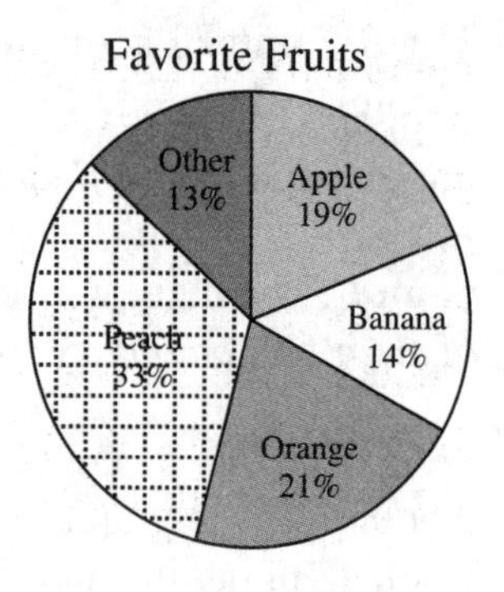

circular functions The periodic functions based on the unit circle, including $y=\sin x$, $y=\cos x$, and $y=\tan x$. See *sine function*, *cosine function*, and *tangent function*.

closed question A question that limits respondents to some set number of responses from which to choose.

closed set A set of numbers is said to be closed under an operation if the result of applying the operation to any two numbers in the set produces a number in the set. For example, the whole numbers are a closed set under addition, because if you add any two whole numbers the result is always a whole number. However, the whole numbers are not closed under division: if you divide any two whole numbers you do not always get a whole number. (p. 139)

closure properties A closure properties states that a particular set of numbers is a closed set under a specific operation. For example, the closure property of rational numbers states that the product or sum of two rational numbers is a rational number. For example, $\frac{1}{2}$ and $\frac{3}{4}$ are both rational numbers; $\frac{1}{2}+\frac{3}{4}$ is $\frac{5}{4}$; and $\frac{5}{4}$ is a rational number. Also, 2.2 and 0.75 are both rational numbers; $2.2 \cdot 0.75$ is 1.65; and 1.65 is a rational number.

coefficient When variable(s) are multiplied by a number, the number is called a coefficient of that term. The numbers that are multiplied by the variables in the terms of a polynomial are called the coefficients of the polynomial. For example, 3 is the coefficient of $3x^2$. (p. 135)

cofunction A trigonometric function whose value for the complement of an angle is equal to the value of a given trigonometric function of the angle itself. For example, the cofunction of sine is cosine and the cofunction of tangent is cotangent.

cofunction identities Trigonometric identities that relate sine and cosine, tangent and cotangent, and secant and cosecant. The value of a trigonometric function of an angle equals the value of the co-function of the complement of the angle.

coincide Two graphs coincide if they have all their points in common. For example, the graphs of $y=2x+4$ and $3y=6x+12$ coincide; both graphs are lines with a slope of 2 and a y-intercept of 4. When the graphs of two equations coincide, those equations share all the same solutions and have an infinite number of intersection points.

combination A combination is the number of ways we can select items from a larger set without regard to order. For instance, choosing a committee of 3 students from a group of 5 volunteers is a combination since the order in which committee members are selected does not matter. We write ${}_nC_r$ to represent the number of combinations of n things taken r at a time (or n choose r). For instance, the number of ways to select a committee of 3 students from a group of 5 is ${}_5C_3$. You can use Pascal's Triangle to find ${}_5C_3$ or use permutations and divided by the number of arrangements $\frac{{}_5P_3}{{}_3P_3}=\frac{5!}{3!2!}$. Formulas for combinations include: ${}_nC_r=\frac{{}_nP_r}{r!}=\frac{n!}{r!(n-r)!}$.

combination histogram and box plot A way to visually represent a distribution of data. The box plot is drawn with the same x-axis as the histogram.

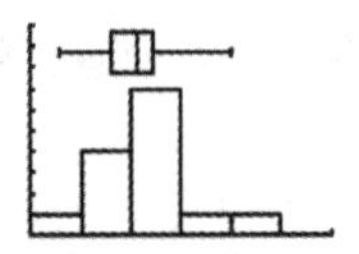

common difference The difference between consecutive terms of an arithmetic sequence or the *generator* of the sequence. When the common difference is positive the sequence increases; when it is negative the sequence decreases. In the sequence $3, 7, 11, \ldots, 43$, the common difference is 4. (p. A34)

common factor A common factor is a factor that is the same for two or more terms. For example, x^2 is a common factor of $3x^2$ and $-5x^2y$.

common logarithm The logarithm with base 10. If no base is given, the logarithm is understood to be base 10. (p. 239)

common ratio Common ratio is another name for the multiplier or *generator* of a geometric sequence. It is the number to multiply one term by to get the next one. In the sequence: 96, 48, 24, ... the common ratio is $\frac{1}{2}$. (p. A34)

complete graph A complete graph is one that includes everything that is important about the graph (such as intercepts and other key points, asymptotes, or limitations on the domain or range), and that makes the rest of the graph predictable based on what is shown. For example, a complete graph of the equation $y = \frac{1}{3}(x-2)^2(x+3)$ is shown at right. (p. 9)

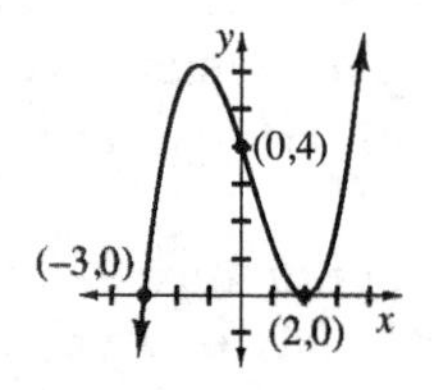

completing the square A standard procedure for rewriting a quadratic equation from standard form to graphing (or vertex) form is called completing the square. Completing the square is also used to solve quadratic equations in one variable. For example, the expression $x^2 - 6x + 4$ starts with the first two terms of $(x-3)^2$. To "complete the square" we need to add 9 to $x^2 - 6x$. Since the original expression only adds 4, completing the square would increase the expression by 5, so $(x-3)^2 - 5$ is an equivalent form that is useful for solving or graphing. (p. 75)

complex conjugates The complex number $a + bi$ has a complex conjugate $a - bi$. Similarly, the conjugate of $c - di$ is $c + di$. What is noteworthy about complex numbers conjugates is that both their product $(a+bi)(a-bi) = a^2 - b^2i^2 = a^2 + b^2$ and their sum $(a+bi)+(a-bi) = 2a$ are real numbers. If a complex number is a zero (or root) of a real polynomial function, then its complex conjugate is also a zero (or root).

complex numbers Numbers written in the form $a + bi$ where a and b are real numbers, are called complex numbers. Each complex number has a real part, a, and an imaginary part, bi. Note that real numbers are also complex numbers with $b = 0$, and imaginary numbers are complex numbers where $a = 0$.

complex plane A set of coordinate axes with all the real numbers on the horizontal axis (the real axis) and all the imaginary numbers on the vertical axis (the imaginary axis) defines the complex plane. Complex numbers are graphed in the complex plane using the same method we use to graph coordinate points. Thus, the complex number $1 + 3i$ is located at the point (1, 3) in the complex plane.

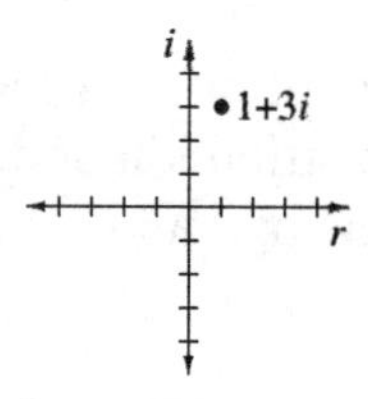

composite function A function that is created as the result of using the outputs of one function as the inputs of another can be seen as a composite function. For example the function $h(x)=|\log x|$ can be seen as the composite function $f(g(x))$ where $f(x)=|x|$ and $g(x)=\log x$. See *composition*. (p. 225)

composition When the output of one function is used as the input for a second function, a new function is created which is a composition of the two original functions. If the first function is $g(x)$ and the second is $f(x)$, the composition can be written as $f(g(x))$ or $f \circ g(x)$. Note that the order in which we perform the functions matters and $g(f(x))$ will usually be a different function.

compound interest Interest that is paid on both the principal and the previously accrued interest. (p. B15)

compress A term used informally to describe the relationship of a graph to its parent graph when the graph increases or decreases more slowly than the parent. For example, the solid parabola shown at right is a compressed version of its parent, shown as a dashed curve. (p. 66)

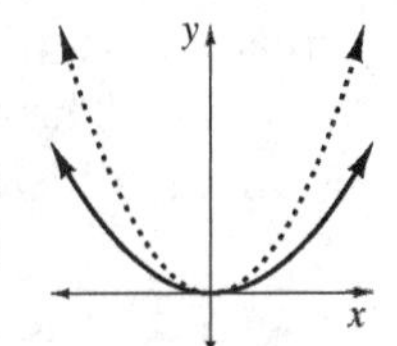

conjugate Every complex number $a+bi$ has a conjugate, $a-bi$, and both the sum and product of the conjugates are real. Similarly, an irrational number that can be written $a+\sqrt{b}$ where a and b are rational, has a conjugate, $a-\sqrt{b}$, and the product and sum of these conjugates are rational.

constant term A number that is not multiplied by a variable. In the expression $2x+3(5-2x)+8$, the number 8 is a constant term. The number 3 is not a constant term, because it is multiplied by a variable inside the parentheses.

constraint A limitation or restriction placed on a function or situation, either by the context of the situation or by the nature of the function.

continuous For this course, when the points on a graph are connected and it makes sense to connect them, we say the graph is continuous. Such a graph will have no holes or breaks in it. This term will be more completely defined in a later course. (p. A10)

continuously compounding interest For this course, continuously compounding interest can be thought of as interest that is computed and added to the balance of an account every instant.

control limit The upper and lower limits of a critical measurement that determines acceptable quality in a manufacturing process. See *statistical process control*.

convenience sampling A subgroup of the population for which it was easy to collect data. A convenience sample is not a random sample.

coordinate axes For two dimensions, two perpendicular number lines, the x- and y-axes, that intersect where both are zero and that provide the scale(s) for labeling each point in a plane with its horizontal and vertical distance and direction from the origin $(0, 0)$. In three dimensions, a third number line, the z-axis, is perpendicular to a plane and intersects it at origin $(0, 0, 0)$. The z-axis provides the scale for the height of a point above or below the plane. See *3-dimensional coordinate system*.

coordinates The numbers in an ordered pair (a, b) or triple (a, b, c) used to locate a point in the plane or in space in relation to a set of coordinate axes.

correlation coefficient, *r* A measure of how much or how little data is scattered around the least squares regression line. It is a measure of the strength of an association that has already been determined to be linear. The correlation coefficient takes on values between –1 and 1. The closer to 1 or –1 the correlation coefficient is, the less scattered the data is around the LSRL.

cosecant The cosecant is the reciprocal of the sine.

cosine In a right triangle (as shown at right) the ratio $\frac{\text{adjacent side}}{\text{hypotenuse}}$ is known as the cosine of the acute angle. At right, $\cos B = \frac{a}{c}$ since the side length a is adjacent to angle B. On a unit circle the cosine of an angle is the x-coordinate of the point the where the terminal ray of an angle in standard position intersects the unit circle.

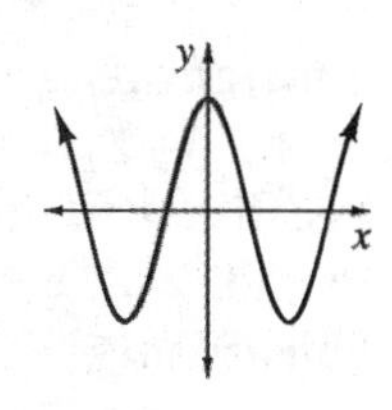

cosine function The cosine of angle θ, denoted $\cos\theta$, is the x-coordinate of the point on the unit circle reached by a rotation angle of θ radians in standard position. The general equation for the cosine function is $y = a\cos b(x-h)+k$. This function has amplitude a, period $\frac{2\pi}{b}$, horizontal shift h, and vertical shift k.

cosine inverse ($\cos^{-1} x$) Read as the inverse of cosine x, $\cos^{-1} x$ is the measure of the angle with cosine x. We can also write $y = \arccos x$. Note that the notation refers to the inverse of the cosine function, *not* $\frac{1}{\cos x}$. Because $y = \cos^{-1} x$ is equivalent to $x = \cos y$ and there are infinitely many angles y such that $\cos y = x$, the inverse *function* is restricted to select the *principal* value of y such that $0 \le y \le \pi$. The graph of the inverse cosine function is at right.

cotangent The cotangent is the reciprocal of the tangent. The graph of the cotangent function is at right.

counterexample An example showing that a statement has at least one exception; that is, a situation in which the statement is false. For example, the number 4 is a counterexample to the hypothesis that all even numbers are greater than 7.

cubic A cubic polynomial is a polynomial of the form $y = ax^3 + bx^2 + cx + d$. "Cube" refers to the third (3) power.

cube root In the equation $a = b^3$, the value b that is multiplied by itself three times to give the value a. For example, the cube root of 8 is 2 because $8 = 2 \cdot 2 \cdot 2 = 2^3$. This is written $\sqrt[3]{8} = 2$.

cycle One cycle of a graph of a trigonometric function is the shortest piece that represents all possible outputs. The length of one cycle is the distance along the x-axis needed to generate all possible output values or the distance around the unit circle needed to generate all possible outcomes.

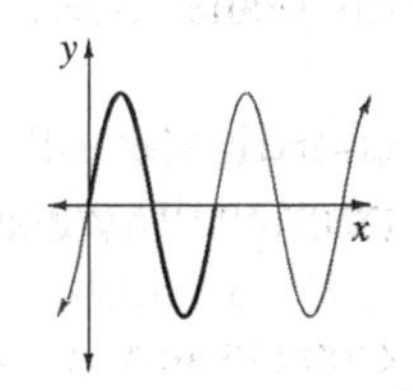

cyclic function The term cyclic function is sometimes used to describe trigonometric functions, but it also includes any function that sequentially repeats its outputs at regular intervals.

data distribution See *distribution*.

degree One degree is an angle measure that is $\frac{1}{360}$ of a full circle or $\frac{\pi}{180}$ radians.

degree of a polynomial The degree of a monomial is the sum of the exponents of its variables. For example, the degree of $3x^2y^5z$ is 8. For a polynomial the degree is the degree of the monomial term with the highest degree. Example: for the polynomial $2x^5y^2 - 4x^4z^6 + x^7z$ the degree is 10.

degree of a polynomial in one variable The highest power of the variable. The degree of a polynomial function also indicates the maximum number of factors of the polynomial and provides information for predicting the number of "turns" the graph can take.

dependent variable When one quantity depends for its value on one or more others, it is called the dependent variable. For example, we might relate the speed of a car to the amount of force you apply to the gas pedal. Here, the speed of the car is the dependent variable; it depends on how hard you push the pedal. The dependent variable appears as the output value in an $x \rightarrow y$ table, and is usually placed relative to the vertical axis of a graph. We often use the letter y and the vertical y-axis for the dependent variable. When working with functions or relations, the dependent variable represents the output value. In Statistics, the dependent variable is often called the response variable. Also see *independent variable*. (p. 6)

depreciation A decrease in value possibly because of normal wear and tear, age, decay, decrease in price. (p. B38)

description of a function A complete description of a function includes: a description of the shape of the graph, where it increasing and/or decreases, all the intercepts, domain and range, description of special points, and description of lines of symmetry.

difference of squares A polynomial that can be factored as the product of the sum and difference of two terms. The general pattern is $x^2 - y^2 = (x+y)(x-y)$. For example, the difference of squares $4x^2 - 9$ can be factored as $(2x+3)(2x-3)$. (p. 128)

difference of cubes A polynomial of the form $x^3 - y^3$. It can be factored as follows: $x^3 - y^3 = (x-y)(x^2 + xy + y^2)$. For example, the difference of cubes $8x^3 - 27$ can be factored as $(2x-3)(4x^2 + 6x + 9)$. (p. 427)

dilation A transformation which vertically compresses or stretches the graph of a function. For example, the graph of $g(x) = 2(x^2 + 3x - 5)$ is a dilation of the function $f(x) = x^2 + 3x - 5$ by a factor of 2.

dimensions The dimensions of a flat region or space tell how far it extends in each direction. For example, the dimensions of a rectangle might be 16 cm wide by 7 cm high.

direction (of an association) If one variable in a relationship increases as the other variable increases, the direction is said to be a positive association. If one variable decreases as the other variable increases, there is said to be a negative association. If there is no apparent pattern in the scatterplot, then the variables have no association. When describing a linear association, you can use the slope, and its numerical interpretation in context, to describe the direction of the association.

discrete graph A graph that consists entirely of separated points is called a discrete graph. For example, the graph shown at right is discrete. Also see *continuous*. (p. A10)

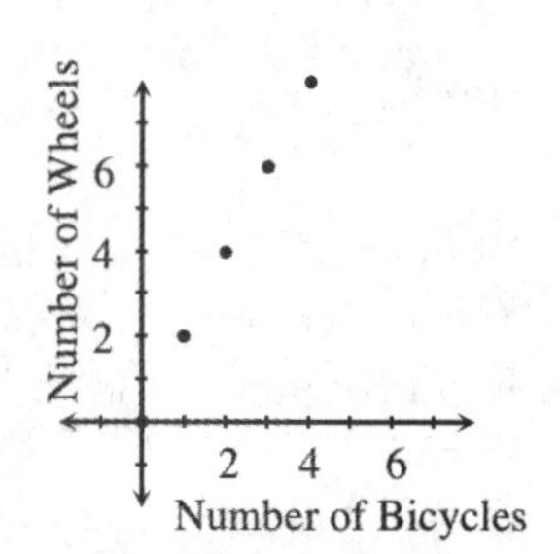

discriminant For quadratic equations in standard form $ax^2 + bx + c = 0$, the discriminant is $b^2 - 4ac$. If the discriminant is positive, the equation has two roots; if the discriminant is zero, the equation has one root; if the discriminant is negative, the equation has no real-number roots. For example, the discriminant of the quadratic equation $2x^2 - 4x - 5$ is $(-4)^2 - 4(2)(-5) = 56$, which indicates that that equation has two roots (solutions). (p. 396)

distance formula An application of the Pythagorean Theorem to find the distance between two points in a plane. The distance between any two points (x_1, y_1) and (x_2, y_2) is $\sqrt{(x_2 - x_1)^2 + (y_2 - y_1)^2}$. In the example at right the distance is $\sqrt{4^2 + 5^2}$. (p. 76)

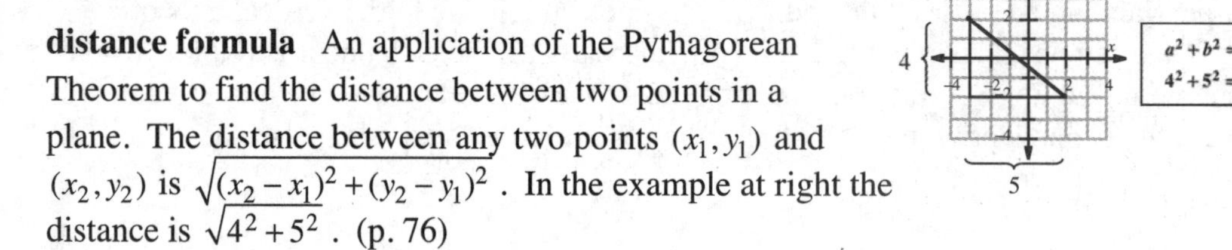

distribution The statistical distribution of a variable is a description (usually a list, table, or graph) of the number of times each possible outcome occurs. A distribution of data is often summarized using its center, shape, spread, and outliers, and can be displayed with a combination histogram and boxplot. (p. C13)

Distributive Property We use the Distributive Property to write a product of expressions as a sum of terms. The Distributive Property states that for any numbers or expressions a, b, and c, $a(b+c)=ab+ac$. For example, $2(x+4)=2\cdot x+2\cdot 4=2x+8$. We can demonstrate this with a generic rectangle.

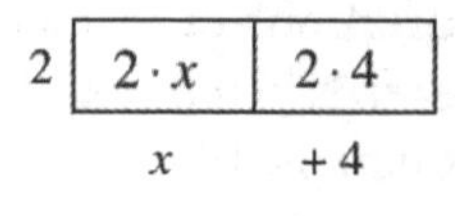

dividing line See *boundary line.*

dividing point See *boundary point.*

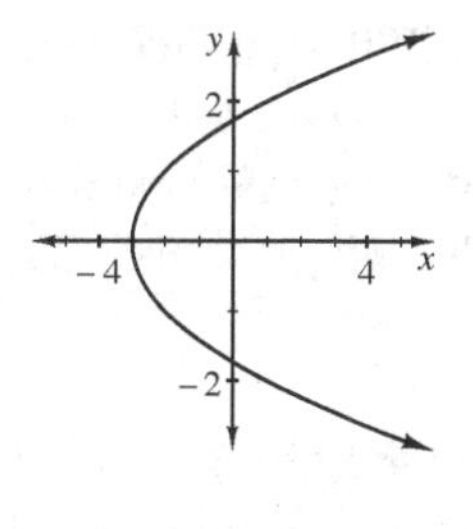

domain The set of all input values for a relation or function. For example, the domain of the function graphed at right is $x\geq-3$. For variables, the domain is the set of numbers the variable may represent. Also see *input*. (p. 6)

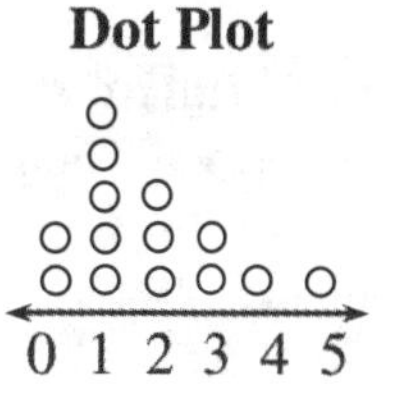

dot plot A way of displaying one-variable data that has an order and can be placed on a number line. Dot plots are generally used when the data is discrete (separate and distinct) and numerous pieces of data are of equal value.

double angle identities Trigonometric identities that involve doubling angle measures. They are: $\sin(2x)=2\sin(x)\cos(x)$ and $\cos(2x)=\cos^2(x)-\sin^2(x)$.

double-peaked See *shape (of a data display).*

double root A root of a function that occurs exactly twice. If an expression of the form $(x-a)^2$ is a factor of a polynomial, then the polynomial has a double root at $x=a$. The graph of the polynomial does not pass through the x-axis at $x=a$ but is tangent to the axis at $x=a$.

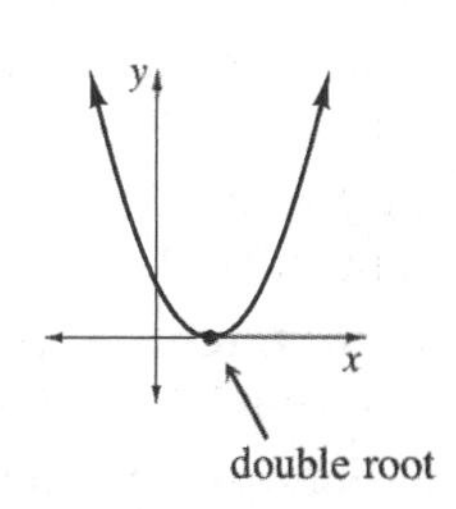

e In mathematics, the base of a natural logarithm. $e\approx 2.71828\ldots$

Elimination Method A method for solving a system of equations. The key step in using the Elimination Method is to add or subtract both sides of two equations to eliminate one of the variables. For example, the two equations in the system at right can be added together to get the simplified result $7x=14$. We can solve this equation to find x, then substitute the x-value back into either of the original equations to find the value of y.

$$5x+2y=10$$
$$2x-2y=4$$

Equal Values Method A method for solving a system of equations. To use the equal values method, take two expressions that are each equal to the same variable and set those expressions equal to each other. For example, in the system of equations at right, $-2x+5$ and $x-1$ each equal y. So we write $-2x+5=x-1$, then solve that equation to find x. Once we have x, we substitute that value back into either of the original equations to find the value of y.

$$y=-2x+5$$
$$y=x-1$$

equation A mathematical sentence in which two expressions appear on either side of an "equals" sign (=), stating that the two expressions are equivalent. For example, the equation $7x+4.2=-8$ states that the expression $7x+4.2$ has the value –8. In this course, an equation is often used to represent a rule relating two quantities. For example, a rule for finding the area y of a tile pattern with figure number x might be written $y=4x-3$.

equivalent Two expressions are equivalent if they have the same value. For example, $2+3$ is equivalent to $1+4$. Two equations are equivalent if they have all the same solutions. For example, $y=3x$ is equivalent to $2y=6x$. Equivalent equations have the same graph. (pp. 123, 133)

evaluate To evaluate an expression, substitute the value(s) given for the variable(s) and perform the operations according to the order of operations. For example, evaluating $2x+y-10$ when $x=4$ and $y=3$ gives the value 1.

even function A function where $f(-x)=f(x)$ for all values of x defined for the function. The graph of the function will be symmetric about the y-axis. (p. 108)

event One or more results of an experiment.

excluded value A value that is undefined for a given function and therefore excluded from the domain of the function. (p. 152)

expected value The expected value for an outcome is the product of the probability of the outcome and the value placed on that outcome. The expected value of an event is the sum of the expected values for its possible outcomes. For example, in a lottery where 7 numbers are drawn from 77 and you have to have chosen all seven to win, the probability that your ticket is the $1,000,000 winner is $\frac{1}{2404808340}$ and the expected value is $0.000416.

experiment A process that applies a treatment (change) to a group of subjects to determine if there is a measureable difference from another group. If an experiment properly implements randomization, controls (balances) the effects of lurking variables between the groups, and is replicated with many subjects, cause and effect can often be determined. (p. 461)

explicit equation (for a sequence) An equation for a term in a sequence that determines the value of any term $t(n)$ directly from n, without necessarily knowing any other terms in the sequence. Also see *recursive equation*. (p. A25)

exponent In an expression of the form a^b, b is called the exponent. For example, in the expression 2^5, 5 is called the exponent. (2 is the base, and 32 is the value.) The exponent indicates how many times to use the base as a multiplier. For example, in 2^5, 2 is used 5 times: $2^5=2\cdot2\cdot2\cdot2\cdot2=32$. For exponents of zero, the rule is: for any number $x\neq0$, $x^0=1$. For negative exponents, the rule is: for any number $x\neq0$, $x^{-n}=\frac{1}{x^n}$, and $\frac{1}{x^{-n}}=x^n$. Also see *laws of exponents*. (pp. B20, B36)

exponential function An exponential function in this course has an equation of the form $y = ab^x + c$, where a is the initial value, b is positive and is the multiplier, and $y = c$ is the equation of the horizontal asymptote. An example of an exponential function is graphed at right. (p. 57)

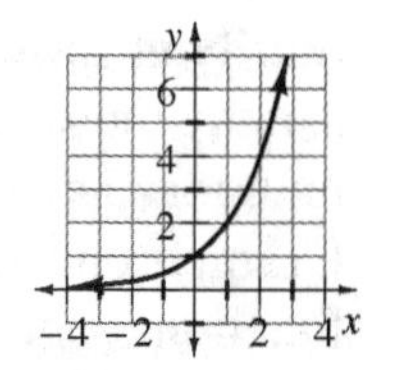

expression An expression is a combination of individual terms separated by plus or minus signs. Numerical expressions combine numbers and operation symbols; algebraic (variable) expressions include variables. For example, $4 + (5 - 3)$ is a numerical expression. In an algebraic expression, if each of the following terms, $6xy^2$, 24, and $\frac{y-3}{4+x}$, are combined, the result may be $6xy^2 + 24 - \frac{y-3}{4+x}$. An expression does not have an "equals" sign. (p. 135)

extraneous solution Sometimes in the process of solving equations, multiplying or squaring expressions involving a variable will lead to a numerical result that does not make the original equation true. This false result is called an extraneous solution. For example, in the process of solving the equation $\sqrt{x+3} = 9 - x$ both sides of the equation are squared to get $x + 3 = x^2 - 19x + 81$ which has solutions 6 and 13. 6 is a solution of the original equation, but 13 is extraneous, because $\sqrt{13+3} \neq 9 - 13$. (p. 173)

extrapolate A prediction made outside the range of the observed data. Often extrapolations are not very reliable predictions.

$f^{-1}(x)$ Read this as "*f* inverse of *x*," the inverse function for $f(x)$. (p. 219)

factor A factor is part of a product. A polynomial expression $p(x)$ is a factor of another polynomial expression $P(x)$ when there is a polynomial $q(x)$ such that $p(x)q(x) = P(x)$. In the equation $3x^2 - 9x + 6 = 3(x-2)(x-1)$, the expressions $(x-2)$, $(x-1)$, and 3 are factors.

Factor Theorem States that if a is a root of a polynomial then $x - a$ is a factor, and if $x - a$ is a factor then a is a root. For example, the polynomial $x^2 - 5x - 6 = (x-6)(x+1)$ and the roots are 6 and −1.

factored completely A polynomial is factored completely if none of the resulting factors can be factored further using integer coefficients. For example, $-2(x+3)(x-1)$ is the completely factored form of $-2x^2 - 4x + 6$.

factored form A quadratic equation in the form $a(x+b)(x+c) = 0$, where a is nonzero, is said to be in factored form. For example, $-7(x+2)(x-1.5) = 0$ is a quadratic equation in factored form.

factorial A shorthand notation for the product of a list of consecutive positive integers from the given number down to 1: $n! = n(n-1)(n-2)(n-3) \cdot \ldots \cdot 3 \cdot 2 \cdot 1$. For example, $5! = 5 \cdot 4 \cdot 3 \cdot 2 \cdot 1 = 120$.

family of functions A group of functions that have at least one common characteristic, usually the shape and the form of the equation. For example the quadratic family of functions have graphs that are parabolas, and equations of the form $y = ax^2 + bx + c$. Examples of other families are linear functions, exponential functions, and absolute value functions. (p. 98)

Fibonacci Sequence The sequence of numbers $1, 1, 2, 3, 5, 8, 13, \ldots$. Each term of the Fibonacci sequence (after the first two terms) is the sum of the two preceding terms. (p. A26)

first quartile (Q1) The median of the lower half of a set of data which has been written in numerical order.

first term form (of a sequence) An equation of a sequence written in first term form uses the first term of the sequence and its common difference or ratio. The first term form of an arithmetic sequence is $a_n = a_1 + d(n-1)$, where a_1 is the first term and d is the common difference. The first term form of a geometric sequence is $a_n = a_1 r^{n-1}$, where a_1 is the first term and r is the common ratio.

five number summary A way of summarizing the center and spread of a one-variable distribution of data. The five number summary includes the minimum, first quartile, median, third quartile, and maximum of the set of data. Also see *boxplot*.

form (of an association) The form of an association can be linear of non-linear. The form can contain cluster of data. A residual plot can help determine if a particular form is appropriate for modeling the relationship.

fraction The quotient of two quantities in the form $\frac{a}{b}$ where b is not equal to 0.

fractional exponents Raising a number to a fractional exponent indicates a power as well as a root. $x^{a/b} = \sqrt[b]{x^a} = (\sqrt[b]{x})^a$. (p. B36)

function A relationship in which for each input value there is one and only one output value. For example, the relationship $f(x) = x + 4$ is a function; for each input value (x) there is exactly one output value. In terms of ordered pairs (x, y), no two ordered pairs of a function have the same first member (x). See also *description of a function* and *function notation*. (p. 6)

function notation When a rule expressing a function is written using function notation, the function is given a name, most commonly "*f*," "*g*," or "*h*." The notation $f(x)$ represents the output of a function, named *f*, when *x* is the input. It is pronounced "*f* of *x*." For example, $g(2)$, pronounced "*g* of 2", represents the output of the function *g* when $x = 2$. If $g(x) = x^2 + 3$, then $g(2) = 7$. (p. 6)

Fundamental Theorem of Algebra The Fundamental Theorem of Algebra states that a polynomial of degree n with (real or) complex coefficients has exactly n roots, which may be real or complex. This also means that the polynomial has n linear factors since for every root a, $(x - a)$ is a linear factor.

general equation If $y = f(x)$ is a parent equation, then the general equation for that function is given by $y = af(x-h)+k$ where (h, k) is the point corresponding to $(0, 0)$ in the parent graph and, relative to the parent graph, the function has been: 1) vertically stretched if the absolute value of a is greater than 1; 2) vertically compressed if the absolute value of a is less than 1; and/or 3) reflected across the x-axis if a is less than 0. (p. 98)

generator The generator of a sequence tells what you do to each term to get the next term. Note that this is different from the function for the nth term of the sequence. The generator only tells you how to find the following term, when you already know one term. In an arithmetic sequence the generator is the common difference; in a geometric sequence it is the multiplier or common ratio. (p. A34)

generic rectangle A type of diagram used to visualize multiplying expressions without algebra tiles. Each expression to be multiplied forms a side length of the rectangle, and the product is the sum of the areas of the sections of the rectangle. For example, the generic rectangle at right can be used to multiply $(2x+5)$ by $(x+3)$.

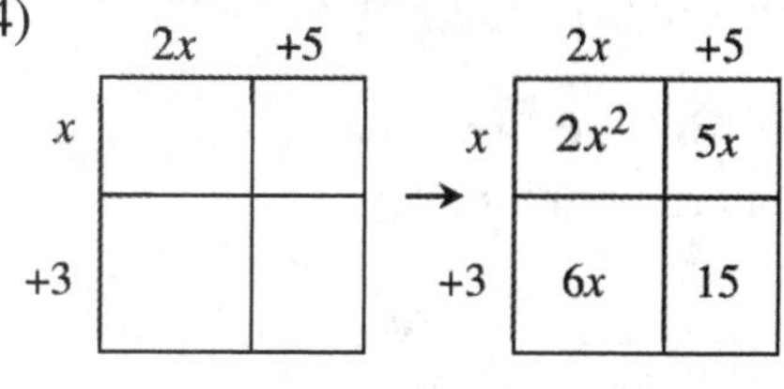

$(2x+5)(x+3) = 2x^2+11x+15$

area as a product area as a sum

geometric sequence A geometric sequence is a sequence that is generated by a multiplier. This means that each term of a geometric sequence can be found by multiplying the previous term by a constant. For example: 5, 15, 45… is the beginning of a geometric sequence with generator (common ratio) 3. In general a geometric sequence can be represented $a, ar, ar^2, ...+ar^{n-1}$. (p. A34)

geometric series The sum of a geometric sequence is a geometric series, for example: 5 + 15 + 45 + … The sum of the first n terms of a geometric sequence, $a+ar+ar^2+ar^3+\ldots+ar^{n-1}$ is given by the formula at right.

$$S = \frac{a(r^n - 1)}{r - 1}$$

Giant One A fraction that is equal to 1. Multiplying any fraction by a Giant One will create a new fraction equivalent to the original fraction. (p. 152)

$$\frac{x+2}{x-3} \cdot \frac{x-2}{x-2} = \frac{(x+2)^2}{(x-3)(x-2)}$$

graph The graph of an equation is the set of points representing the coordinates that make the equation true. The direction to "graph an equation" or "draw a graph" means use graph paper, scale your axes appropriately, label key points, and plot points accurately. This is different from *sketching* a graph. The equation $y = \frac{1}{3}(x-2)^2(x+3)$ is graphed at right.

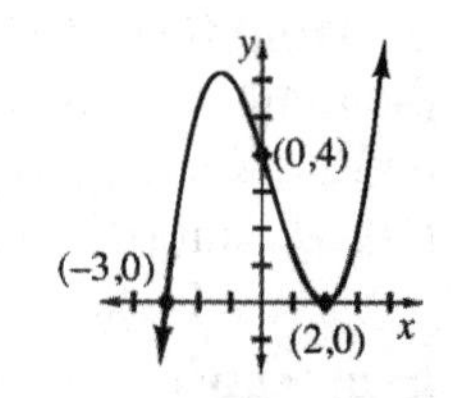

graphing form A form of the equation of a function or relation that clearly shows key information about the graph. For example, the graphing form for the general equation of a quadratic function (also called vertex form) is $y = a(x-h)^2 + k$. The vertex (h, k), orientation (whether a is positive or negative) and amount of stretch or compression based on $|a| > 1$ or $|a| < 1$ can be appear in the equation. (p. 68)

growth factor One way to analyze how the output value in a mathematical relation changes as the input value increases. Growth can be represented by constant addition, as the slope of a linear function or the constant difference in an arithmetic sequence, or by multiplication as the base of an exponential function or the multiplier in a geometric sequence. (p. 10)

(h, k) In this course h and k are used as parameters in general equations for families of functions $f(x) = af(x-h) + k$ and families of relations to represent the horizontal and vertical shifts of the parent graph. The point (h, k) represents location of a point that corresponds to $(0, 0)$ for parent graphs where $(0, 0)$ is on the graph.

half-life When material decays, the half-life is the time it takes until only half the material remains. (p. B19)

histogram A way of displaying one-variable data that is like a bar graph in that the height of the bars is proportional to the number of elements. However, a histogram is for numerical data. Each bin (bar) of a histogram represents the number of data elements in a range of values, such as the number of people who take from 15 minutes up to, but not including, 30 minutes to get to school. Each bin should the same width and the bins should touch each other. Also see *bar graph*.

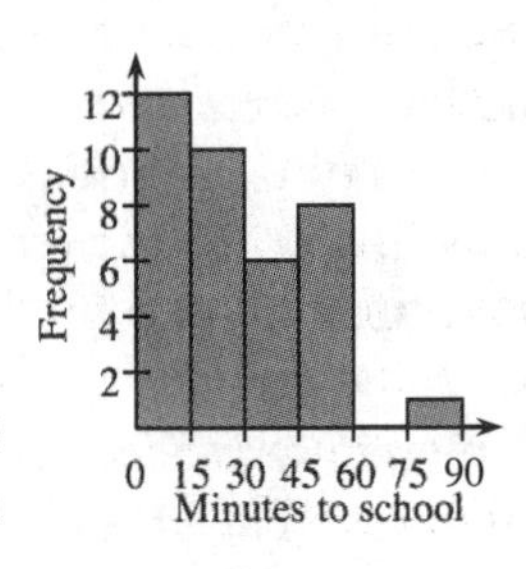

horizontal Parallel to the horizon. The x-axis of a coordinate graph is the horizontal axis.

horizontal lines Horizontal lines are "flat" and run left to right in the same direction as the x-axis. Horizontal lines have equations of the form $y = b$, where b can be any number. For example, the graph at right shows the horizontal line $y = 3$. The slope of any horizontal line is 0. The x-axis has the equation $y = 0$ because $y = 0$ everywhere on the x-axis.

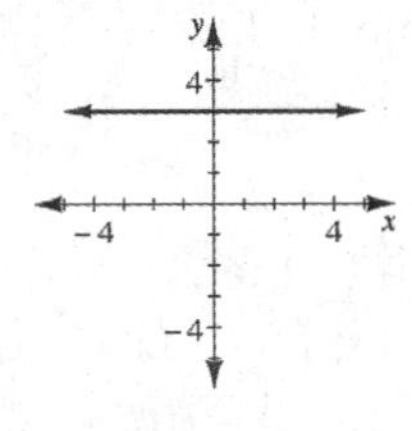

horizontal shift Used with parent graphs and general equations for functions and relations such as $y = a(x-h)^2 + k$. This type of transformation is a horizontal translation of a graph that moved left or right in relation to its parent graph. The horizontal shift will be h units to the right if h is positive, to the left if h is negative. (p. 66)

hypotenuse The longest side of a right triangle, the side opposite the right angle.

identity (trigonometric) Equations that are true for all values for which the functions are defined. For example $\sin^2 x + \cos^2 x = 1$ which is true for all values of x, or $\cot x = \frac{1}{\tan x}$ which is true whenever the tangent and cotangent are defined.

imaginary numbers The set of numbers that are solutions of equations of the form $x^2 =$ (a negative number) are called imaginary numbers. They are not positive, negative, or zero. The imaginary number i is a solution of the equation $x^2 = -1$, so $i^2 = -1$. In general, imaginary numbers follow the rules of real number arithmetic (e.g. $i + i = 2i$). Multiplying the imaginary number i by every possible real number yields all possible imaginary numbers.

independent variable When one quantity changes in a way that does not depend on the value of another quantity, the value that changes independently is represented with the independent variable. For example, we might relate the speed of a car to the amount of force you apply to the gas pedal. Here, the amount of force applied may be whatever the driver chooses, so it represents the independent variable. The independent variable appears as the input value in an $x \to y$ table, and is usually placed relative to the horizontal axis of a graph. We often use the letter x and the horizontal x-axis for the independent variable. When working with functions or relations, the independent variable represents the input value. In Statistics, the independent variable is often called the explanatory variable. Also see *dependent variable*. (p. 6)

index (plural indices) In summation notation, the indices are the numbers below and above the sigma that indicate which term to start with and which to end with. For a series they show the first and last replacement values for n. When the symbol above sigma is ∞ the series continues
without ending.

Example: $\sum_{n=1}^{8} 5n - 7 = -2 + 3 + 8 + ... + 33$.

inequality An inequality consists of two expressions on either side of an inequality symbol. For example, the inequality $7x + 4.2 < -8$ states that the expression $7x + 4.2$ has a value less than 8. (p. 197)

inequality symbols The symbol $\leq$ read from left to right means "less than or equal to." The symbol $\geq$ read from left to right means "greater than or equal to." The symbols $<$ and $>$ mean "less than" and "greater than," respectively. For example, "7<13" means that 7 is less than 13.

inequalities with absolute value If k is any positive number, an inequality of the form: $|f(x)| > k$ is equivalent to the statement $f(x) > k$ or $f(x) < -k$; and $|f(x)| < k$ is equivalent to the statement $-k < f(x) < k$. For example, you can solve the inequality, $|5x - 6| > 4$ by solving the two inequalities $5x - 6 > 4$ or $5x - 6 < -4$. (p. 193)

inference A statistical prediction.

infinite geometric series An infinite geometric series is a geometric series which never ends. The sum of such a series with an initial value a and common ratio r, with $-1 < r < 1$, is given by the formula at right.

$$S = \frac{a}{1-r}$$

infinity The concept that something is without limit or unending. The symbol for infinity is ∞. Note that infinity is an idea, not a number, even though it is often treated as such. (p. 18)

initial value The initial value of a sequence is the first term of the sequence. (p. 57)

input A replacement value for a variable in a function or relation. The first number in an ordered pair. The set of all possible input values is the domain of a function. (p. 26)

integer Any whole number or the opposite of a whole number: $\ldots -3, -2, -1, 0, 1, 2, 3, \ldots$

integral roots Roots (or zeros) of functions that are integers.

Integral Zero Theorem For any polynomial with integral coefficients, if an integer is a zero of the polynomial, it must be a factor of the constant term.

intercepts Points where a graph crosses the axes. x-intercepts are points at which the graph crosses the x axis and y-intercepts are points at which the graph crosses the y axis. On the graph at right the x-intercept is $(3, 0)$ and the y-intercept is $(0, 6)$. (p. 10)

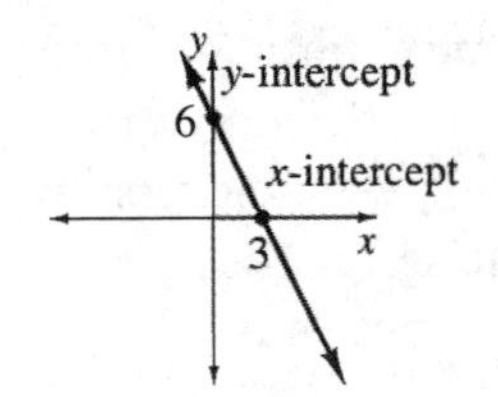

interest An amount paid which is a percentage of the principal. For example, a savings account may offer 4% annual interest rate, which means they will pay $4.00 in interest for a principal of $100 kept in the account for one year. (p. B15)

interquartile range (IQR) A way to measure the spread of data. It is calculated by subtracting the first quartile from the third quartile.

intersection A point of intersection is a point that the graphs of two or more equations have in common. Graphs may intersect in one, two, several, many or no points. The set of coordinates of a point of intersection are a solution to the equation for each graph. (p. 21)

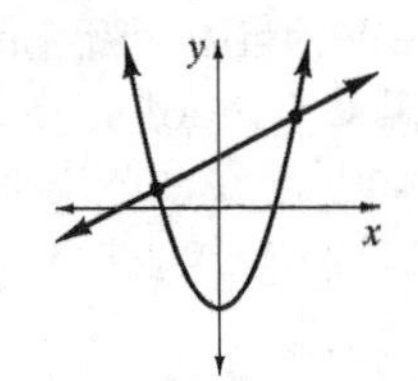

interval A set of numbers between two given numbers.

inverse circular functions See *inverse trigonometric functions*.

inverse function A function that "undoes" what the original function does. It can also be seen as the *x*-*y* interchange of the function. The inverse of a function performs in reverse order the inverse operation for each operation of the function. The graph of an inverse function is a reflection of the original function across the line $y = x$. For example, $y = x^3 + 2$ is equivalent to $x = \sqrt[3]{y-2}$, its inverse function is written $y = \sqrt[3]{x-2}$. (p. 216)

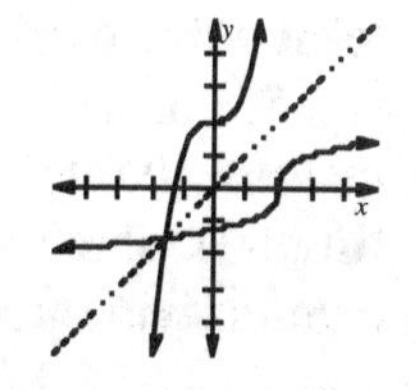

inverse operations Subtraction is the inverse operation for addition and vice versa, division for multiplication, square root for squaring, and more generally taking the nth root for raising to the nth power.

inverse trigonometric functions For each trigonometric function sin(*x*), cos(*x*), and tan(*x*), there is an inverse function written $\sin^{-1}(x)$, $\cos^{-1}(x)$, and $\tan^{-1}(x)$. Note: This symbol does not mean $\frac{1}{\sin(x)}$. It is a new function that "undoes" the original trig function, thus giving a specific angle measure when the input is $\sin x$, $\cos x$, or $\tan x$. For example: $\sin^{-1}(-\frac{1}{2}) = -\frac{\pi}{6}$. Note that the range of the inverse function is restricted to outputs for *y* such that $-\frac{\pi}{2} \le y \le \frac{\pi}{2}$ for $\sin x$, $-\frac{\pi}{2} < y < \frac{\pi}{2}$ for $\tan x$ and $0 \le y \le \pi$ for $\cos x$. Also see *cosine inverse*, *sine inverse*, and *tangent inverse*. (p. 629)

investigating a function To investigate a function means to make a complete graph of the function and to write down everything you know about the function. Some things to consider are: domain, range, intercepts, asymptotes, inverse, and symmetry. (p. 33)

irrational numbers The set of numbers that cannot be expressed in the form $\frac{a}{b}$, where *a* and *b* are integers and $b \ne 0$. For example, π and $\sqrt{2}$ are irrational numbers. (p. 389)

Law of Cosines For any ΔABC, $a^2 = b^2 + c^2 - 2bc\cos A$. (p. 29)

Law of Large Numbers A theorem stating that as the number of trials of a random process increases (for example, as the number of trials in a simulation increases), the results will approach the theoretical value closer. (p. 567)

Law of Sines For any ΔABC, $\frac{\sin A}{a} = \frac{\sin B}{b} = \frac{\sin C}{c}$. (p. 29)

laws of exponents The laws of exponents we study in this course are: (pp. B20, B36)

Law	Examples	
$x^m x^n = x^{m+n}$ for all x	$x^3 x^4 = x^{3+4} = x^7$	$2^5 \cdot 2^{-1} = 2^4$
$\frac{x^m}{x^n} = x^{m-n}$ for $x \ne 0$	$x^{10} \div x^4 = x^{10-4} = x^6$	$\frac{5^4}{5^7} = 5^{-3}$
$(x^m)^n = x^{mn}$ for all x	$(x^4)^3 = x^{4 \cdot 3} = x^{12}$	$(10^5)^6 = 10^{30}$
$x^0 = 1$ for $x \ne 0$	$\frac{y^2}{y^2} = y^0 = 1$	$9^0 = 1$
$x^{-1} = \frac{1}{x}$ for $x \ne 0$	$\frac{1}{x^2} = (\frac{1}{x})^2 = (x^{-1})^2 = x^{-2}$	$3^{-1} = \frac{1}{3}$
$x^{m/n} = \sqrt[n]{x^m}$ for $x \ge 0$	$\sqrt{k} = k^{1/2}$	$y^{2/3} = \sqrt[3]{y^2}$

least squares regression line (LSRL) A unique best-fit line that is found by making the squares of the residuals as small as possible.

line Graphed, a line is made up of an infinite number of points, is one-dimensional and extends without end in two directions. In two dimensions a line is the graph of an equation of the form $ax+by=c$.

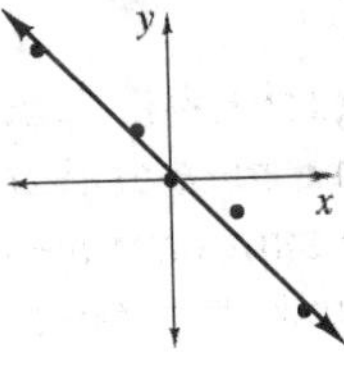

line of best fit A line that represents, in general, data on a scatterplot. The line of best fit is a model of numerical two-variable data that helps describe the data. It is also used to make predictions for other data. Also see *least square regression line*. (p. A9)

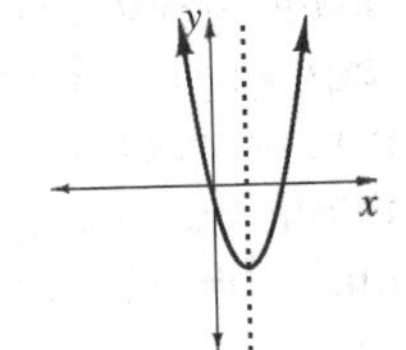

line of symmetry A line that divides a figure into two congruent shapes which are reflections of each other across the line. (p. 217)

linear equation An equation with at least one variable of degree one and no variables of degree greater than one. The graph of a linear equation of two variables is a line in the plane. $ax+by=c$ is the standard form of a linear equation. (p. 10)

linear factor A factor of the form $(ax + b)$.

linear function A polynomial function of degree one or zero, with general equation $f(x)=a(x-h)+k$. The graph of a linear function is a line. (p. 41)

linear inequality An inequality with a boundary line represented by a linear equation. (p. 197)

linear programming A method for solving a problem with several conditions or constraints that can be represented as linear equations or inequalities. (p. 195)

linear regression A method for finding a best- fit line through a set of points on a scatterplot. Also see *regression* and *least squares regression line*.

locator point A locator point is a point which gives the position of a graph with respect to the axes. For a parabola, the vertex is a locator point. (p. 82)

Log base 10 $\log_{10} m=n$ if $10^n=m$. See *common logarithm*.

Log-Power Property See *Power Property of Logs*.

Log-Product Property See *Product Property of Logs*.

Log-Quotient Property See *Quotient Property of Logs*.

logarithm The logarithm of a given number, x, with respect to a base, b, is the exponent to which b must be raised to give x. For example, since we know that $32 = 2^5$, it follows that 5 is the logarithm, base 2, of 32, or $\log_2 32 = 5$. (p. 233)

logarithmic and exponential notation $m = \log_b(n)$ is the logarithmic form of the exponential equation $b^m = n$ $(b > 0)$.

logarithmic functions Inverse exponential functions. The base of the logarithm is the same base as that of the exponential function. For instance $y = \log_2 x$ can be read as "y is the exponent needed for base 2 to get x," and is equivalent to $x = 2^y$. The short version is stated "log, base 2, of x," and written $\log_2 x$.

Looking Inside "Looking Inside" is a method of solving one-variable equations containing parentheses or an absolute value symbol. To use "looking inside," we first determine what the value of the entire expression inside the parentheses (or absolute value symbol) must be. We then use that fact to solve for the value of the variable. For example, to use "looking inside" to solve the equation $4(x+2) = 36$, we first determine that $x+2$ must equal 9. We then solve the equation $x+2=9$ to find that $x=7$. (p. 170)

lower control limit (LCL) See *control limit.*

lurking variable A hidden variable that was not part of the statistical study under investigation. Sometimes a lurking variable explains the true cause of an association between two other variables that are linked.

m When the equation of a line is expressed in $y = mx + b$ form, the parameter m gives the slope of the line. For example, the slope of the line $y = -\frac{1}{3}x + 7$ is $-\frac{1}{3}$.

margin of error Half of the spread between the upper and lower bounds of a statistical prediction. For example, if we predict weight is likely to be between an upper bound of 12 kg and lower bound of 18 kg, the margin of error is 3 kg, and we could write our prediction of the weight as 15 ± 3 kg.

maximize Make as large as possible. (p. 192)

maximum point The highest point on a graph. For example, the vertex of a downwardly oriented parabola.

maximum value The largest value in the range of a function. For example, the y-coordinate of the vertex of a downwardly oriented parabola.

mean The arithmetic mean, or average, of several numbers is one way of defining the "center" or "middle" or "typical value" of a set of numbers. The mean represents the center of a set of data well if the distribution of the data is symmetric and has no outliers. To find the mean of a numerical data set, add the values together then divide by the number of values in the set. For example, the mean of the numbers 1, 5, and 6 is $(1+5+6) \div 3 = 4$.

measure of central tendency Mean and median are measures of central tendency, representing the "center" or "middle" or "typical value" of a set of data. See *center (of a data distribution)*.

mean absolute deviation A way to measure the spread, or the amount of variability, in a set of data. The mean absolute deviation is the average of the distances to the mean, after the distances have been made positive with the absolute value. The standard deviation is a much more commonly used measure of spread than the mean absolute deviation.

median The middle number of a set of data which has been written in numerical order. If there is no distinct middle, then the mean of the two middle numbers is the median. The median is generally more representative of the "middle" or of a "typical value" than the mean if there are outliers or if the distribution of the data in not symmetric.

midline The horizontal axis of the graph of a trigonometric function. The midline is halfway between the maximum and minimum values of the function.

minimize Make as small as possible.

minimum point The lowest point on a graph. For example, the vertex of an upwardly oriented parabola.

minimum value The smallest value in the range of a function. For example, the y-coordinate of the vertex of an upwardly oriented parabola.

model A mathematical summary (often an equation) of a trend in data, after making assumptions and approximations to simplify a complicated situation. Models allow us to describe data to others, compare data more easily to other data, and allow us to make predictions. For example, mathematical models of weather patterns allow us to predict the weather. No model is perfect, but some models are better at describing trends than other models. Regressions are a type of model. Also see *regression*. (p. B13)

modified boxplot See *boxplot*.

monomial An expression with only one term. It can be a number, a variable, or the product of a number and one or more variables. For example, 7, $3x$, $-4ab$, and $3x^2y$ are each monomials.

multiple representations web An organizational tool we use to keep track of connections between the four representations of relationships between quantities emphasized in this course. In this course, we emphasize four different ways of representing a numerical relationship: with a graph, table, situation (pattern), or rule (equation or inequality). (p. 9)

table
graph equation
situation

multiplicative identity The number 1 is called the multiplicative identity because multiplying any number by 1 does not change the number. For example, $7(1) = 7$.

Multiplicative Identity Property The Multiplicative Identity Property states that multiplying any expression by 1 leaves the expression unchanged. That is, $a(1) = a$. For example, $437x \cdot 1 = 437x$.

multiplier In a geometric sequence the number multiplied times each term to get the next term is called the multiplier or the common ratio or generator. The multiplier is also the number you can multiply by in order to increase or decrease an amount by a given percentage in one step. For example, to increase a number by 4%, the multiplier is 1.04. We would multiply the number by 1.04. The multiplier for decreasing by 4% is 0.96. (p. A34)

natural logarithm A logarithm base e. Abbreviated "ln".

negative exponent Raising a number to a negative exponent is the same as taking the reciprocal of the number. $x^{-a} = \frac{1}{x^a}$ for $x \neq 0$. (p. B36)

non-function A relation that has more than one output for one or more of its inputs.

normal distribution A distribution of data that can be modeled with the normal probability density function. See *normal probability density function*.

normal probability density function A very specific function that is used to model single-peaked, symmetric, bell-shaped data.

observational study A study where data is collected by observing an existing situation without the researcher (or observer) imposing any type of change or treatment.

observed value An actual measurement, as opposed to a prediction made from a model.

odd function A function where $f(-x) = -f(x)$ for all values of x defined for the function. The graph of the function will be symmetric about the origin. (p. 108)

open question A question that allows respondents to offer any answer they like.

one-dimensional Not having any width or depth. Lines and curves are one-dimensional.

ordered pair A pair of numbers written (x, y) used to represent the coordinates of a point in an xy-plane where x represents the horizontal distance from 0 and y is the vertical. The input and output values of a function or relation can be represented as ordered pairs were x is the input, and y is the output.

ordered triple Three real numbers written in order (x, y, z) represent a point in space or replacement values for a situation involving three variables. See *3-dimensional coordinate system*.

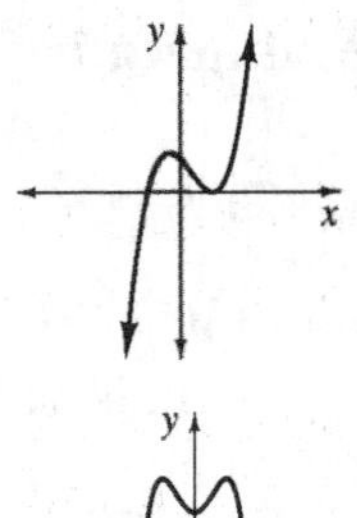

orientation Used informally in this course to describe some graphs. For example the direction a parabola opens might be referred to as its orientation. When describing the graph of a polynomial function, a positive orientation would mean the graph eventually continues upward as the value of x increases, as in the example above right. A negative orientation would mean it eventually heads downward as the value of x continues to increase, as in the example below right.

origin The point on a coordinate plane where the x- and y-axes intersect is called the origin. This point has coordinates $(0, 0)$. The point assigned to zero on a number line is also called the origin.

outlier A number in a set of data that is far away from the bulk of the data.

output Used to describe the result of applying a function or relationship rule to an input value. For the function $f(x) = x^2 - 73$ when the input is 10, the output is 27. Function notation shows how the function operates on the input to produce the output: $f(10) = 10^2 - 73 = 27$. (p. 26)

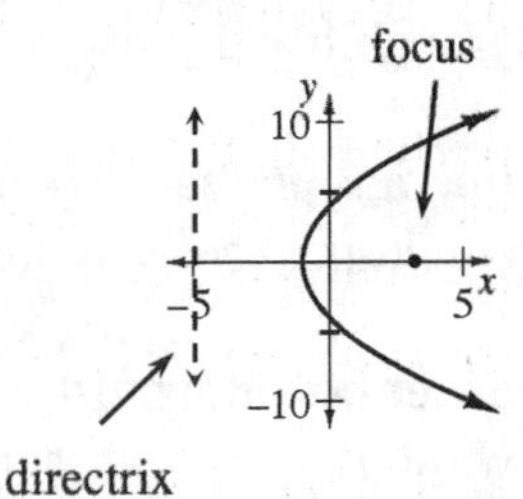

parabola The set of all points that are equidistant from a single point (the focus) and a line (the directrix). The general equation for a parabola that is a function (or a quadratic function) in graphing (or vertex) form, is $y = a(x - h)^2 + k$. The general equation of a quadratic function in standard form is $y = ax^2 + bx + c$. A general equation for parabolas that are not functions, "sleeping" parabolas, is $x - h = a(y - k)^2$. (p. 66)

parallel Two lines in a plane are parallel if they never intersect. Parallel lines have the same slope. Two line segments in a plane are parallel if the lines they lie on lines that never intersect. Two lines in space are parallel if they lie in the same plane and they do not intersect. There is a constant distance between parallel lines.

parameter In a general equations where x and y represent the inputs and outputs of the function, variables such as a, b, c, m, h, and k are often referred to as parameters, and they are often replaced with specific values. For example: in the equation $y = a(x - h)^2 + k$ representing all parabolas that are functions, the a, h, and k are (variable) parameters that give the shape and location, while x and y are the independent and dependent variables. (p. 41)

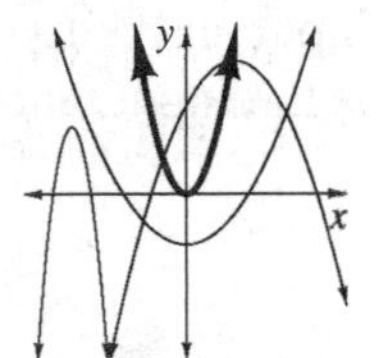

parent graph The simplest version of a family of graphs. For instance, the graph of $y = x^2$, is considered the parent graph for parabolas that are functions. (p. 98)

Pascal's Triangle The array of numbers at right. The triangular pattern continues downward. This array shows all the values of ${}_nC_r$ where n is the row number when the vertex is ${}_0C_0$. r is the number of places to the right in row n (when the counting begins with 0). For instance, ${}_5C_2$ is equal to 10.

1
1 1
1 2 1
1 3 3 1
1 4 6 4 1
1 5 10 10 5 1

percent A ratio that compares a number to 100. Percents are often written using the "%" symbol. For example, 0.75 is equal to $\frac{75}{100}$ or 75%.

percentile A percentile ranking indicates the percentage of scores which are below the score in question. For example, if you scored at the 90th percentile on a test, your score was higher than the scores of 90% of the other test takers.

perfect square Usually, a quadratic polynomial ax^2+bx+c that can be rewritten as the second power of a binomial, $(cx+d)^2$. For example, x^2-6x+9 is a perfect square that can be rewritten as $(x-3)^2$. Also, any polynomial of even degree that can be rewritten as the square of one polynomial factor. For numbers, a whole number that can be written as the second power of another whole number. For example, 1, 4, 9, 16, and 25 are perfect squares.

perfect square form A quadratic equation in the form $a(x+b)^2=c$, where a is nonzero, is said to be in perfect square form. For example, $3(x-12)^2=19$ is a quadratic equation in perfect square form. (p. 68)

perfect square trinomials Trinomials of the form $a^2x^2+2abx+b^2$, where a and b are nonzero real numbers, are known as perfect square trinomials and factor as $(ax+b)^2$. For example, the perfect square trinomial $9x^2-24x+16$ can be factored as $(3x-4)^2$.

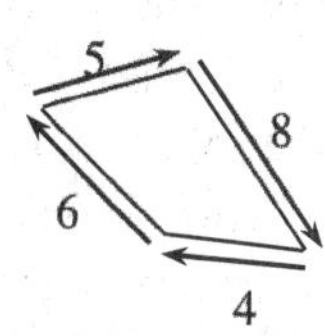

Perimeter = 5 + 8 + 4 + 6 = 23 units

perimeter The distance around a figure on a flat surface.

period The length of one cycle of a graph, as shown by the dashed line in the graph at right.

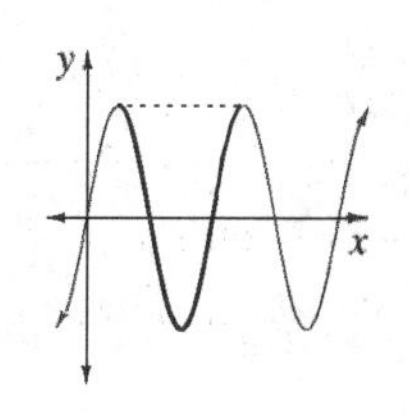

periodic function A function which has a repetitive section or cycle such as the sine, cosine and tangent functions. In a periodic function, the cyclic pattern continues forever both to the left and to the right.

permutation A permutation is an arrangement in which the order of selection matters. For example a batting line-up is a permutation because it is an ordered list of players. If each of five letters, A, B, C, D, E is printed on a card, the number of 3-letter sequences can you make by selecting three of the five cards is a permutation. Permutations can be represented with tree diagrams, decision charts, and their value calculated by using the formula for ${}_nP_r=\frac{n!}{(n-r)!}$. In the example given above, ${}_5P_3=\frac{5!}{2!}=\frac{5\cdot4\cdot3\cdot2\cdot1}{2\cdot1}=5\cdot4\cdot3=60$.

perpendicular Two lines, rays, or line segments that intersect to form a right angle. A line and a plane can also be perpendicular if the line does not lie in the plane, but intersects it and forms a right angle with every line in the plane that passes through the point of intersection.

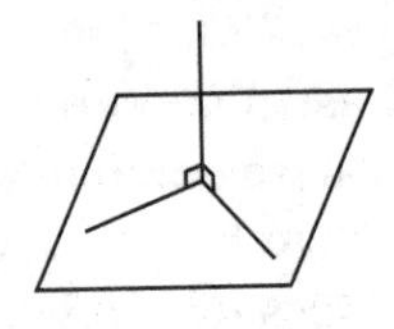

piecewise function A function composed of parts of two or more functions. Each part is usually consists of a function with a restricted (limited) domain. (p. 105)

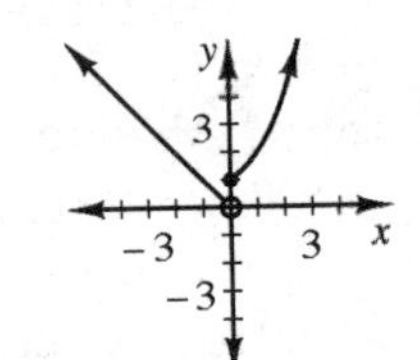

placebo A treatment with no effect. A placebo is sometimes used in experiments involving people so that the psychological effects of participating in an experiment are the same in all the treatment groups.

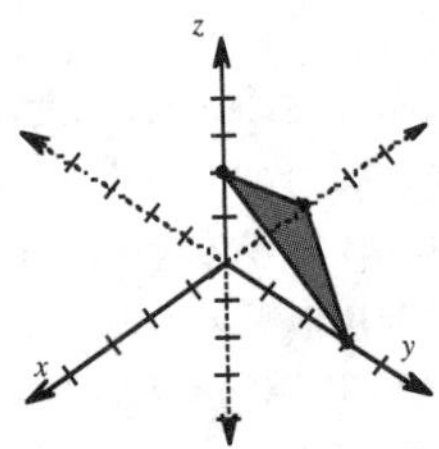

plane A plane is an undefined term in geometry. It is a two-dimensional flat surface that extends without end. It is made up of points and has no thickness. The part of a plane outlined by its *xy*-, *xz*- and *yz*-traces is often used to represent a plane on a 3-dimensional coordinate system.

point An undefined term in geometry. A point has no dimensions but can be located by its coordinates on a number line, in a plane, or in space.

Point-Slope form $y-k=m(x-h)$ is called the point slope form of a linear equation or function because it shows the slope m and a point (h, k) that is on the graph of the line. For example, given a line that has slope $\frac{5}{3}$ and contains the point with coordinates (3, –4) its equation can be written $y+4=\frac{5}{3}(x-3)$. (p. 92)

polynomial An algebraic expression that involves at most the operations of addition, subtraction, and multiplication. A polynomial in one variable is an expression that can be written as the sum of terms of the form: (any number) $\cdot$ $x^{\text{(whole number)}}$. These polynomials are usually arranged with the powers of x in order, starting with the highest, left to right. The numbers that multiply the powers of x are called the coefficients of the polynomial. See *degree of a polynomial* for an example. (p. 135)

population A collection of objects or group of people about whom information is gathered.

power A number or variable raised to an exponent in the form x^n. See *exponent.*

power model or power curve A best-fit curve of the form $y=ax^b$ that represents data on a scatterplot.

Power Property of Logs $\log_m(a^n)=n\log_m(a)$. For example, $\log_3 625=4\log_3 5$.

predicted value (of an association) The dependent (y-value) that is predicted for an independent (x-value) by the best-fit model for an association.

principal Initial investment or capital. An initial value.

probability The probability that an event A. with a finite number of equally likely outcomes, will occur is the number of outcomes for event A divided by the total number of equally likely outcomes. This can be written as $\frac{\text{number of outcomes for event A}}{\text{total number of possible outcomes}}$. A probability p is a ratio, $0 \le p \le 1$.

process control See *statistical process control.*

Product Property of Logs $\log_m(a \cdot b) = \log_m(a) + \log_m(b)$. For example, $\log_3 30 = \log_3 5 + \log_3 6$.

profit The amount of money after expenses have been accounted for.

proportion Equal ratios are described as a proportion. For example, the equation $\frac{x-8}{2x+1} = \frac{5}{6}$.

Pythagorean Identity For trigonometric functions, $\cos^2 x + \sin^2 x = 1$ for any value of x.

quadrants The coordinate plane is divided by its axes into four quadrants. The quadrants are numbered as shown in the first diagram at right. When graphing data that has no negative values, we sometimes use a graph showing only the first quadrant.

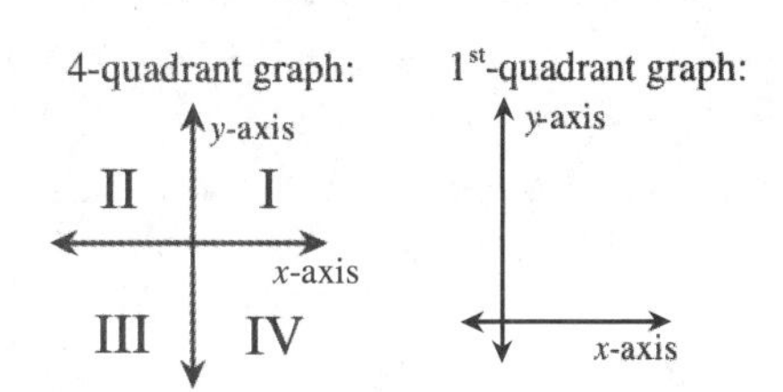

quadratic equation Any equation where at least one term has degree 2 and no term has degree higher than 2. The standard equation $Ax^2 + By^2 + Cxy + Dx + Ey + F = 0$ represents all quadratic relations in one or two variables. (p. 24)

quadratic expression An expression that can be written in the form $ax^2 + bx + c$, where a, b, and c are real numbers and a is nonzero. For example, $3x^2 - 4x + 7.5$ is a quadratic expression.

Quadratic Formula This formula gives you the solutions $x = \frac{-b \pm \sqrt{b^2 - 4ac}}{2a}$, for a quadratic equation in one variable that can be written in the standard form $ax^2 + bx + c = 0$. (p. 24)

quadratic function A quadratic equation that can be written $y = ax^2 + bx + c$ is also a quadratic function where x is the independent variable and y is the dependent variable. Its graph is a parabola with a vertical orientation. The graphing form of a quadratic function is $f(x) = a(x-h)^2 + k$.

quarterly Occurring four times a year. (p. B14)

quartile Along with the median, the quartiles divide a set of data into four groups of the same size. Also see *boxplot*.

quotient The result of a division problem is a quotient with a remainder (which could be 0). When a polynomial $p(x)$ is divided by a polynomial $d(x)$ the a polynomial $q(x)$ will be the quotient with a remainder $r(x)$. The product of $q(x)$ and $d(x)$ plus the remainder $r(x)$ will equal the original polynomial. $p(x) = d(x)q(x) + r(x)$.

Quotient Property of Logs $\log_m(\frac{a}{b}) = \log_m(a) - \log_m(b)$. For example, $\log_3 \frac{37}{5} = \log_3 37 - \log_3 5$.

***R*²** See *R*-squared.

radian measure An arc of a unit circle equal to the length of the radius of the circle is one radian. The central angle for this arc has measure one radian. 1 radian = $\frac{180}{\pi}$ degrees.

radical An expression in the form $\sqrt{a}$, where $\sqrt{a}$ is the positive square root of a. For example, $\sqrt{49} = 7$. Also see *square root*. (p. 68)

radicand The expression under a radical sign. For example, in the expression $3 + 2\sqrt{x-7}$, the radicand is $x - 7$.

random sample A sample which was chosen as a result of a random process. A random sample can represent the whole population well.

range (of a data set) The range of a set of data is the difference between the highest and lowest values.

range (of a function) The range of a function is the set of possible outputs for a function. It consists of all the values of the dependent variable, that is every number that y can represent for the function $f(x) = y$. (p. 18)

ratio The comparison of two quantities or expressions by division.

rational equation An equation that includes at least one rational expression. For example, $5 - \frac{x+2}{x} = 7$.

rational expression An expression in the form of a fraction in which the numerator and denominator are polynomials. For example, $\frac{x-7}{x^2+8x-9}$ is a rational expression. (p. 135)

rational function A function that contains at least one rational expression. For example, $f(x) = \frac{5}{x-3}$. (p. 138)

rational number A number that can be written as a fraction $\frac{a}{b}$ where a and b are integers and $b \neq 0$.

real numbers The set of all rational numbers and irrational numbers is referred to as the set of real numbers. Any real number can be represented by a point on a number line.

rebound height The height a ball reaches after a bounce.

rebound ratio The ratio of the height a ball bounces after one bounce to the height from which it dropped. (p. A8)

reciprocal The multiplicative inverse of a number or an expression.

reciprocal trigonometric functions The functions $y=\frac{1}{\sin x}=\csc x$, $y=\frac{1}{\cos x}=\sec x$, and $y=\frac{1}{\tan x}=\cot x$.

rectangular numbers The terms of the sequence 0, 2, 6, 12, 20, ... These numbers are called rectangular because they count the number of dots in rectangular arrays with the dimensions $n(n+1)$ where $n=0,1,2,3,4,\ldots$

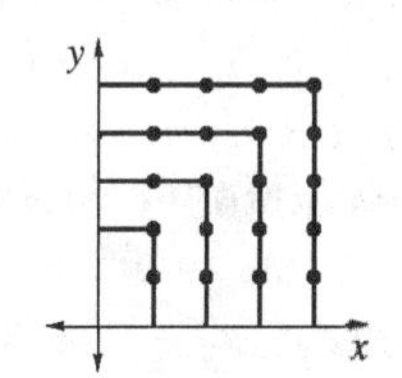

recursive equation (for a sequence) An equation for a term in a sequence that requires knowing other terms in the sequence first. For example, the equation for the Fibonacci sequence is recursive because you need to know the previous two terms to find any other term. The equation for the Fibonacci sequence is $t(n)=t(n-2)+t(n-1)$, $t(1)=1$, $t(2)=1$. Also see *explicit equation*. (p. A34)

recursive sequence A sequence which can be described by a recursive equation. See *recursive equation*. (p. A34)

reference angle For every angle of rotation in standard position, the reference angle is the angle in the first quadrant $0 \leq \theta \leq \frac{\pi}{2}$ whose cosine and sine have the same absolute values as the cosine and sine of the original angle.

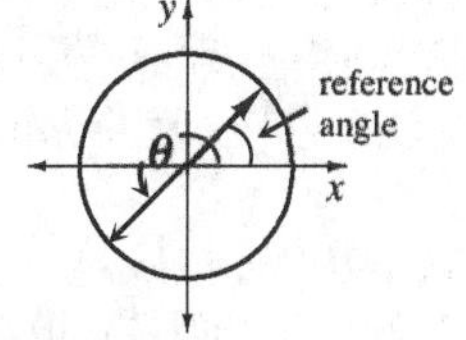

reflective symmetry A type of symmetry where one half of the image is a reflection across a line of the other half of the image. You can fold the image on the line of symmetry and have both halves match exactly. Also see *line of symmetry*.

regression A method for finding a best-fit line or curve through a set of points on a scatterplot. The most common type of regression is finding the least squares regression line. In this course we also do curved regressions: exponential regressions (fitting $y=a\cdot b^x$), quadratic regressions (fitting $y=ax^2+bx+c$) and power regressions (fitting $y=ax^b$).

relation Functions are also relations, but relations are not necessarily functions. The equations for parabolas, ellipses, hyperbolas, and circles are all relations but only the equations that describe vertically oriented parabolas are functions.

relative frequency A ratio or percent. If 60 people are asked, and 15 people prefer "red," the relative frequency of people preferring red is $\frac{15}{60} = 25\%$.

relative maximum (minimum) A function that has a "peak" (or "valley") at a point P is said to have a relative maximum (minimum) at the point P. This is the point where the function changes direction.

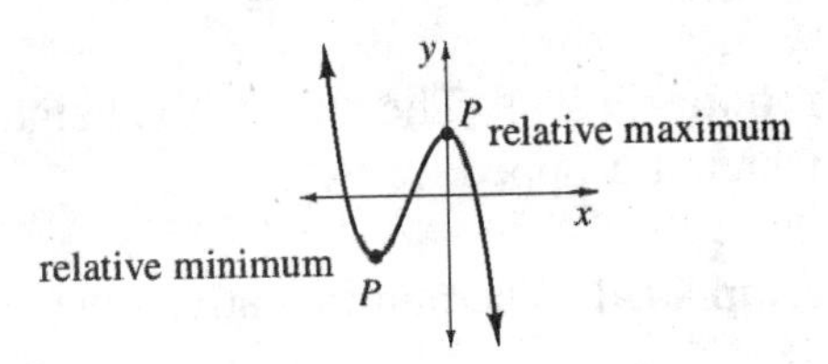

remainder When dividing polynomials in one variable, the remainder is what is left after the constant term of the quotient has been determined. The degree of the remainder must be less than the degree of the divisor. In the example below the remainder is $3x-3$.
$(x^4+3x^3-x^2+x-7)\div(x^2+x+1)=x^2+2x-4+\frac{3x-3}{x^2+x+1}$. Also see *quotient*.

Remainder Theorem For any number c, when a polynomial $p(x)$ is divided by $(x-c)$, the remainder is $p(c)$. For example, if the polynomial $p(x)=x^4-x^3+20x-48$ is divided by $(x-5)$, the remainder is $p(5) =$ 552.

y
triple root
x
double root

repeated root A root of a polynomial that occurs more than once. The root r will occur as many times as $(x-r)$ is a factor of the polynomial. See *double root* and *triple root*.

residual The distance a prediction is from the actual observed measurement in an association. The residual is the y-value predicted by the best-fit model subtracted from the actual observed y-value. A residual can be graphed with a vertical segment that extends from the observed point to the line or curve made by the best-fit model. It has the same units as the y-axis.

residual plot A display of the residuals of an association. A residual plot is created in order to analyze the appropriateness of a best-fit model. If a model fits the data well, no apparent pattern will be made by the residuals—the residuals will be randomly scattered.

rewrite To rewrite an equation or expression is to write an equivalent equation or expression. Rewriting could involve using the Distributive Property, following the Order of Operations, using properties of 0 or 1, substitution, inverse operations, Properties of Logarithms, or use of trigonometric identities. We usually rewrite in order to change expressions or equations into more useful forms or sometimes, just simpler forms. (p. 170)

right angle An angle with measure 90°.

right triangle A triangle with a right angle.

roots of a function The number r is a root (or zero) of the function $f(x)$ if $f(r)=0$. A root may be a real or a complex number. Real roots occur where the graph of the function $f(x)$ crosses the x-axis. Complex roots must be found algebraically.

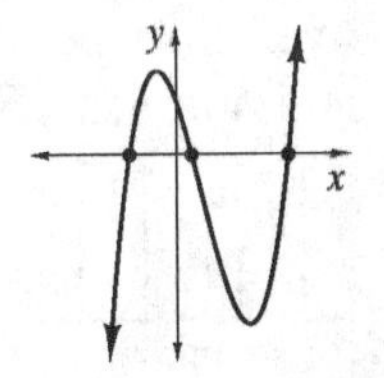

***R*-squared** The correlation coefficient squared, and usually expressed as a percent. R^2 is a measure of the strength of a linear relationship. Its interpretation is that R^2 % of the variability in the dependent variable can be explained by a linear relationship with the independent variable. The rest of the variability is explained by other variables not part of the study.

rule An algebraic representation or a written description of a mathematical relationship.

sample A subset (group) of a given population with the same characteristics as the whole population.

sample space With probability, all the possible outcomes.

scatter The variability in data. When the scatter of data forms a pattern, we can often describe and model the data. Random scatter has no discernable pattern. (Note that random scatter does not mean evenly scattered—randomly scattered data often forms clusters and gaps.) See *variability* and *spread*.

scatterplot A way of displaying two-variable numerical data where two measurements are taken for each subject (like height and forearm length, or surface area of cardboard and volume of cereal held in a cereal box). To create a scatterplot, the two values for each subject are written as coordinate pairs and graphed on a pair of coordinate axes (each axis representing a variable). Also see *association*.

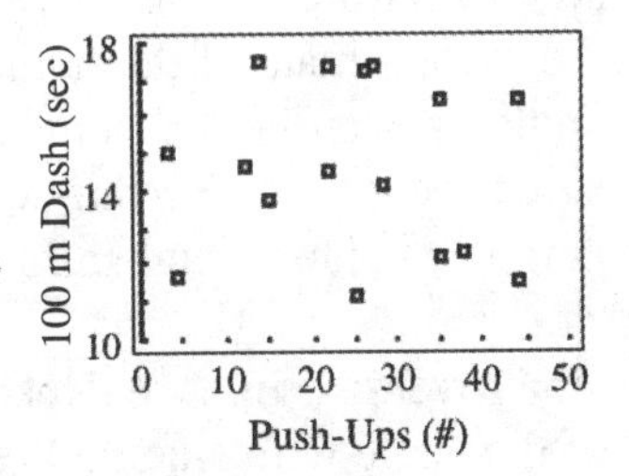

secant The reciprocal of the cosine.

sequence A function in which the independent variable is a positive integer (sometimes called the "term number"). The dependent variable is the term value. A sequence is usually written as a list of numbers. For example, the arithmetic sequence 5, 8, 11, ... (p. A34)

series The sum of the terms of a sequence.

set A collection of data or items. (p. 139)

shape (of a data distribution) Statisticians use the following words to describe the overall shape of a data distribution: symmetric, skewed, single-peaked, double-peaked, and uniform. Examples are shown below.

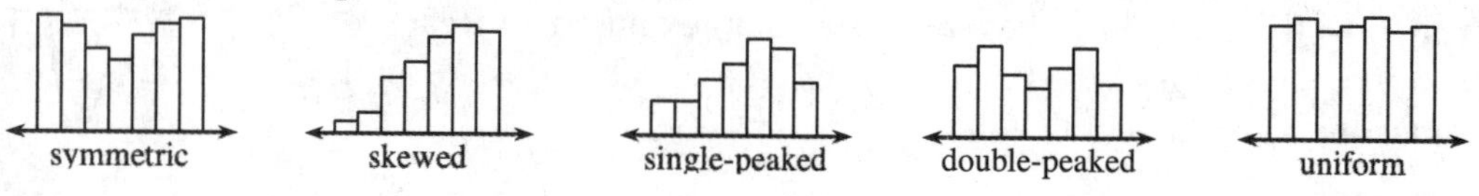

sigma The Greek letter Σ which is used to mean sum. Using Σ provides a way to write a short, compact mathematical representation for a series. See *summation notation.*

simple interest Interest paid on the principal alone. (p. B15)

simplify To rewrite an expression or equation as an equivalent expression or equation in a form that is considered to be simpler or less cumbersome than the original.

simulation (probability) When conducting an experiment with an event that is unrealistic to perform, a simulation can be used. A simulation is a similar experiment that has the same probabilities as the original experiment.

sine In a right triangle (as shown at right) the ratio $\frac{\text{opposite side}}{\text{hypotenuse}}$ is known as the sine of the acute angle. At right, $\sin B = \frac{b}{c}$ since the side length b is opposite angle B.

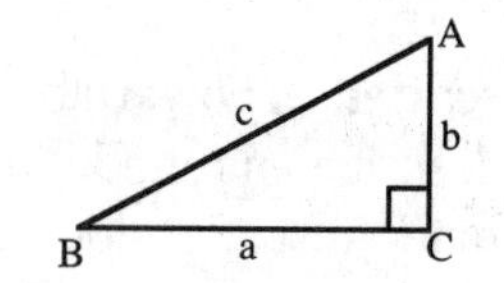

sine function For any real number θ, the sine of θ, denoted $\sin\theta$, is the y-coordinate of the point on the unit circle reached by a rotation angle of θ radians in standard position. The general equation for the sine function is $y = a\sin b(x-h)+k$. This function has amplitude a, period $\frac{2\pi}{b}$, horizontal shift h, and vertical shift k.

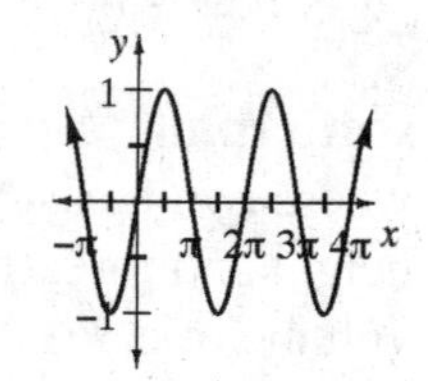

sine inverse ($\sin^{-1} x$) Read as the inverse of sine x, $\sin^{-1} x$ is the measure of the angle with sine x. We can also write $y = \arcsin x$. Note that the notation refers to the inverse of the sine function, *not* $\frac{1}{\sin x}$. Because $y = \sin^{-1} x$ is equivalent to $x = \sin y$ and there are infinitely many angles y such that $\sin y = x$, the inverse *function* is restricted to select the *principal* value of y such that $-\frac{\pi}{2} \le y \le \frac{\pi}{2}$. The graph of the inverse function, $y = \sin^{-1} x$ with $\frac{\pi}{2} \le y \le \frac{\pi}{2}$ is at right.

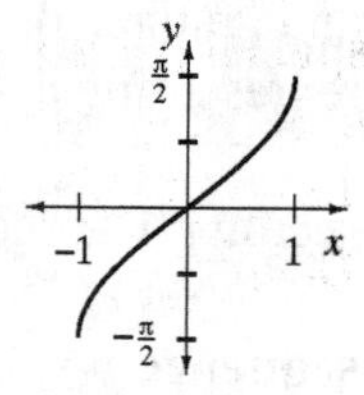

single-peaked See *shape (of a data display).*

sketch To sketch the graph of an equation means to show the approximate shape of the graph in the correct location with respect to the axes with key points clearly labeled.

skewed (data display) See *shape (of a data display).*

"sleeping" parabola A "sleeping" parabola is a parabola which opens to the left or right, rather than upward or downward. These parabolas are not the graphs of functions.

slope The ratio of the vertical change to the horizontal change between any two points on a line. For any two points (x_1, y_1) and (x_2, y_2) on a given line, the slope is $\frac{y_2 - y_1}{x_2 - x_1}$. For example, the slope of a line between points with coordinates $(3, -5)$ and $(-7, 2)$ is $\frac{2-(-5)}{-7-3} = -\frac{7}{10}$. (p. 10)

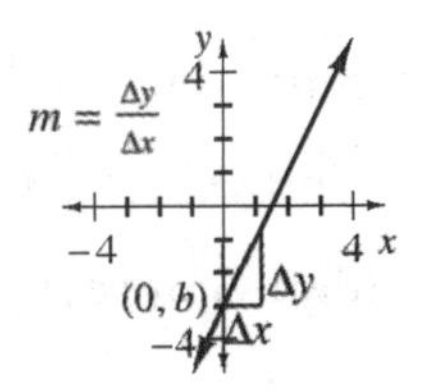

Slope-Intercept Form A linear equation written in the form $y = mx + b$ is written in slope-intercept form. In this form, m is the slope of the line and the point $(0, b)$ is the y-intercept. (p. 10)

solution Of an equation or inequality is a number or expression that makes the equation or inequality true when substituted for the variable. To find the numerical solution means to identify all the numbers that make a mathematical equation or inequality true. There may be any number of solutions for an equation or inequality, from 0 to infinitely many. Solutions to equations and inequalities in one variable are single numbers. For two variables they are ordered pairs, for three variables ordered triples. Equations with no solutions, such as $|x - 5| = -3$, are never true. Equations with one, several, or many solutions, such as $x(x+3)(x-7) = 0$ are sometimes true, and equations or identities such as $5(2x-4) = 10x - 20$ are always true. (p. 200)

solve (1) To find all the solutions to an equation or an inequality (or a system of equations or inequalities). For example, solving the equation $x^2 = 9$ gives the solutions $x = 3$ and $x = -3$. (2) Solving an equation for a variable gives an equivalent equation that expresses that variable in terms of other variables and constants. For example, solving $2y - 8x = 16$ for y gives $y = 4x + 8$. The equation $y = 4x + 8$ has the same solutions as $2y - 8x = 16$, but $y = 4x + 8$ expresses y in terms of x and some constants.

special right triangles A right triangle with particular notable features that can be used to solve problems. Sometimes, these triangles can be recognized by the angles, such as the 45°-45°-90° triangle (also known as an "isosceles right triangle") and a 30°-60°-90° triangle.

spread (of a data distribution) A measure of the amount of variability, or how "spread out" a set of data is. Some ways to measure spread are the range, the mean absolute deviation, the standard deviation, and the interquartile range. For symmetric distributions with no outliers, the standard deviation or the interquartile range can represent the spread of the data well. However, in the presence of outliers or non-symmetrical data distributions, the interquartile range may be a better measure. Also see *variability*.

square root A number a is a square root of b if $a^2 = b$. For example, the number 9 has two square roots, 3 and −3. A negative number has no real square roots; a positive number has two; and zero has just one square root, namely, itself. Other roots, such as cube root, will be studied in other courses. Also see *radical*. (p. 83)

standard deviation A way to measure the spread, or the amount of variability, in a set of data. The standard deviation is the square root of the average of the distances to the mean, after the distances have been made positive by squaring. The standard deviation represents the spread of a set of data well if the distribution of the data is symmetric and has no outliers.

Standard Form (linear function) A linear equation written in the form $Ax + By = C$ is written in standard form. For linear functions, $B \neq 0$. (p. 10)

Standard Form (quadratic function) The standard form for the equation of a quadratic function is $y = ax^2 + bx + c$ where $a \neq 0$. (p. 68)

Standard Form (quadratic relations in general) The standard for parabolas, ellipses, and hyperbolas with axes parallel to the *x*- or *y*-axes is $Ax^2 + By^2 + Cx + Dy + E = 0$.

standard position An angle is in standard position if its vertex is located at the origin and one ray is on the positive *x*-axis.

standard window The graphing window on a calculator set to show the *x*- and *y*-axes for values $-10 \leq x \leq 10$ and $-10 \leq y \leq 10$.

statistic A numerical fact or calculation that is formed from data. For example, a mean or a correlation coefficient is a statistic. With a capital "S," Statistics is the field of study which is concerned with summarizing data, and using probability to make predictions from data with natural variability.

statistical process control The process of checking whether manufacturing quality remains stable over time. A process is "in control" if critical measurements of quality remain within the upper control limit and lower control limit as expected.

statistical test A method of making decisions based on a statistical analysis of data.

step function A special kind of piecewise function (a function composed of parts of two or more functions). A step function has a graph that is a series of line segments that often looks like a set of steps. (p. B24)

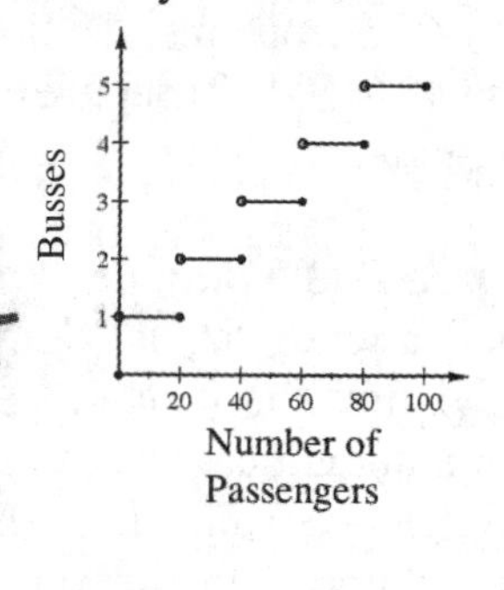

stoplight icon The icon (shown at right) will appear periodically throughout the text. Problems that display this icon contain errors of some type.

strength (of an association) A description of how much scatter there is in the data away from the line or curve of best fit. If an association is linear, the correlation coefficient, *r*, or *R*-squared can be used to numerically describe and interpret the strength.

streak Consecutive identical outcomes in a probabilistic situation. For example, if a baseball team wins four consecutive games, they have a winning streak of 4. (p. 572)

study See *observational study*. (p. 461)

stretch factor Used to describe the effect of a in the graphing form of a quadratic, cubic, absolute value, or exponential function. For $a > 1$ or $a < -1$ the outputs increase or decrease faster than the outputs for the parent functions, and the graphs are described as being stretched upwards or downwards in relation to the parent graph. (p. 66)

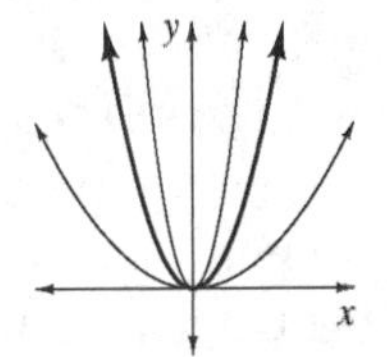

subjects The people or items being measured in a statistical study.

substitution Replacing a variable or expression with a number, another variable, or another expression. For example, when evaluating the function $f(x) = 5x - 1$, for $x = 3$, substitute 3 for x to get $f(3) = 5(3) - 1 = 14$.

Substitution Method A method for solving a system of equations by replacing one variable with an expression involving the remaining variable(s). For example, in the system of equations at right the first equation tells you that y is equal to $-3x + 5$. We can substitute $-3x + 5$ in for y in the second equation to get $2(-3x + 5) + 10x = 18$, then solve this equation to find x. Once we have x, we substitute that value back into either of the original equations to find the value of y.

$$y = -3x + 5$$
$$2y + 10x = 18$$

sum The result of adding two or more numbers. For example, the sum of 4 and 5 is 9.

sum of cubes A polynomial of the form $x^3 + y^3$. It can be factored as follows: $x^3 + y^3 = (x + y)(x^2 - xy + y^2)$. For example, the sum of cubes $27y^3 + 64$ can be factored as $(3y + 4)(9y^2 - 12y + 16)$. (p. 427)

summation notation A convenient way to represent a series is to use summation notation. The Greek letter sigma, Σ, indicates a sum.

For example, $\sum_{n=1}^{4} 3n = 3(1) + 3(2) + 3(3) + 3(4) = 30$. (p. 519)

The numbers below and above the sigma are called the indices. The index below, $n = 1$, tells us what value to start with for n. The top index tells us how high the value can go. In the example shown above, n starts at 1 and increases to 4.

symmetry A figure that appears not to change when reflected across a line is said to have reflection symmetry. A figure that appears not to change when rotated through an angle of less than 360° is described as having rotation symmetry.

system of equations A system of equations is a set of equations with more than one unknown or variable. The systems we solve most often in this course have two or three equations and two or three variables. Systems of equations are often solved using substitution or elimination to reduce the number of variables. A system of quadratic equations is shown at right. (p. 171)

$$y = x^2 + 8x - 4$$
$$y = 2x^2 + 5x - 8$$

system of inequalities A system of inequalities is a set of inequalities with the same variables. Solving a system of inequalities means finding one or more regions on the coordinate plane whose points represent solutions to each of the inequalities in the system. There may be zero, one, or several such regions for a system of inequalities. For example, the shaded region at right is a graph of the system of inequalities that appears below it. (p. 187)

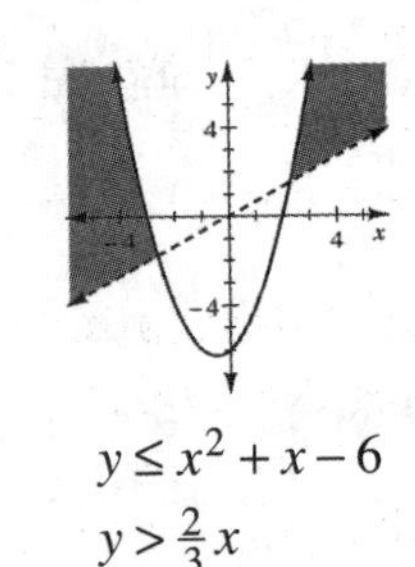

tangent In a right triangle (at right) the ratio $\frac{\text{opposite side}}{\text{adjacent side}}$ is known as the tangent of an acute angle. At right, $\tan B = \frac{b}{a}$ since the side of length b is opposite angle B and the side length a is adjacent to (or next to) angle B. The function $f(\theta) = \tan(\theta) = \frac{y}{x}$ where (x, y) are the coordinates of the point on the unit circle where the radius makes an angle of θ with the positive horizontal axis.

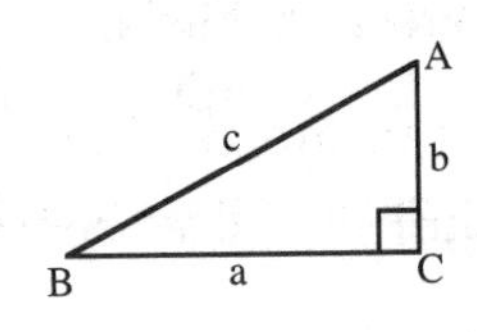

tangent function For any real number θ, the tangent of θ, denoted tan θ, is the slope of the line containing the ray which represents a rotation of θ radians in standard position. The general equation for the tangent function is $y = a \tan b(x - h) + k$. This function has period of $\frac{\pi}{b}$, vertical asymptotes at $\frac{\pi}{2b} + h \pm \frac{n\pi}{b}$ for $n = 1, 2, \ldots$, horizontal shift h, and vertical shift k.

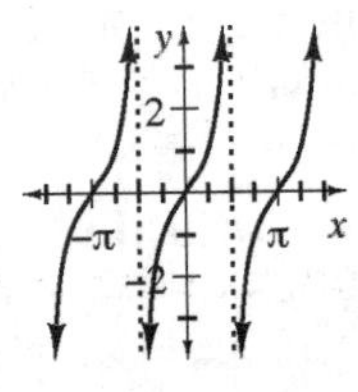

tangent inverse ($\tan^{-1} x$) Read as the inverse of tangent x, $\tan^{-1} x$ is the measure of the angle that has tangent x. We can also write $y = \arctan x$. Note that the notation refers to the inverse of the tangent function, *not* $\frac{1}{\tan x}$. Because $y = \tan^{-1} x$ is equivalent to $x = \tan y$ and there are infinitely many angles y such that $\tan y = x$, the inverse *function* is restricted to select the *principal* value of y such that $\frac{\pi}{2} < x < \frac{\pi}{2}$. The graph of the inverse tangent function is at right.

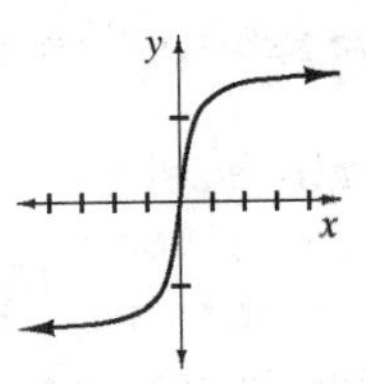

term A single number, variable, or product of numbers and variables. A monomial is a term. Also a component of a sequence. (p. 135)

term number In a sequence, a number that gives the position of a term in the sequence. A replacement value for the independent variable in a function that determines the sequence. See *sequence*. (p. A18)

theoretical probability A probability calculation based on counting possible outcomes.

third quartile (Q3) The median of the upper half of a set of data which has been written in numerical order

three-dimensional An object that has height, width, and depth.

transcendental number A number that is not the root of *any* polynomial equation with rational coefficients. Transcendental numbers are very common. The most prominent examples of transcendental numbers are π and e.

transformation (of a function) The conversion of a function to a corresponding function, often by a factor of constant k. Transformations often slide, reflect, stretch, and/or compress graphs of functions. For example, the transformation of $f(x) + k$ moves the graph of the function up or down by an amount k. The transformation $f(-x)$ reflects the graph of the function across the y-axis.

translation The result of moving a graph horizontally, vertically, or both but without changing its orientation.

treatment Some type of change imposed on one or more groups in an experiment so that a direct comparison can be made.

trend line Another name for a line of best fit. See *line of best fit*.

trigonometric identities The different trigonometric functions are related by many different equations, termed identities. A few examples of these identities are: $\cos(x) = \cos(-x)$ and $\sin(-x) = -\sin(x)$.

trigonometric ratios See *sine*, *cosine*, *tangent*, *secant*, *cosecant*, and *cotangent*.

trinomial A polynomial that is the sum or difference of exactly three terms, each of which is a monomial. For example, $x^2 + 6x + 9$ is a trinomial.

triple root A root of a function that occurs exactly three times. If an expression of the form $(x-a)^3$ is a factor of a polynomial, then the polynomial has a triple root at $x = a$. The graph of the polynomial has an inflection point at $x = a$.

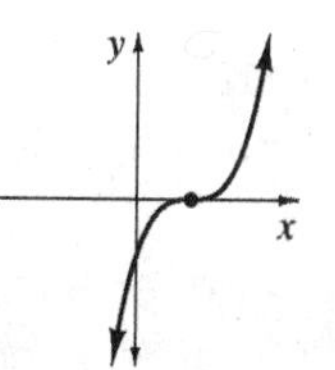

two-dimensional An object having length and width.

Undoing Using inverse operations and reversing the order of operations to solve an equation in one variable or to "undo" a function rule in order to write its inverse. For example, in the equation $y = x^3 - 7$, add y and write the cube root. (p. 170)

uniform See *shape (of a data display)*.

unit circle A circle with a radius of one unit is called a unit circle.

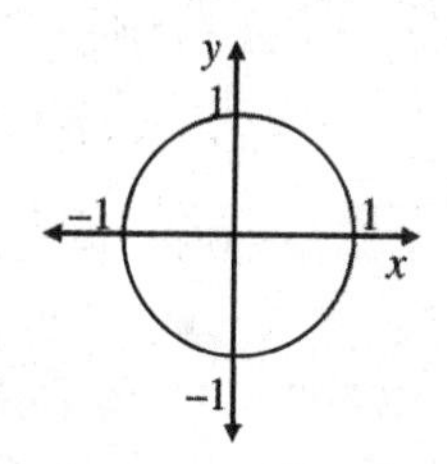

upper control limit (UCL) See *control limit*.

variable A symbol used to represent one or more numbers. In this course, letters of the English alphabet are used as variables. For example, in the expression $3x-(8.6xy+z)$, the variables are x, y, and z. (p. 41)

variability The inconsistency in measured data. Variability comes from two sources. Measurement error is the inconsistency in measurement of the same element repeated times and/or by different people. Element variability is the natural variation of the elements themselves. For example, even though in general people with larger shoe sizes are taller, not all people with the same shoe size have the same height. That is element variability. See *spread*.

vertex (of a parabola) The vertex of a parabola is the highest or lowest point on the parabola (depending on the parabola's orientation). See *parabola*. (p. 60)

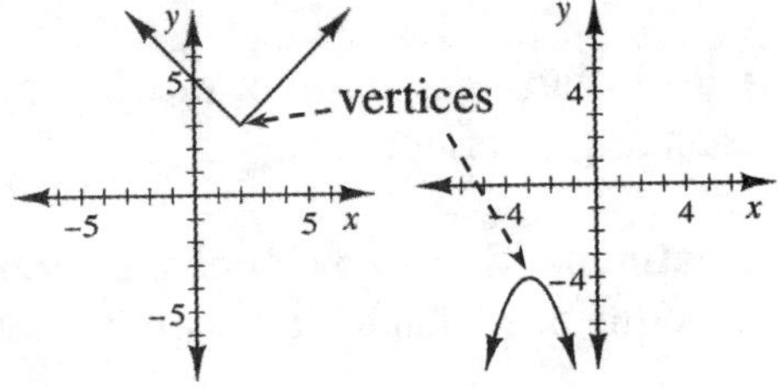

vertex form The vertex form for the equation of a quadratic function (also called graphing form) is written $y=a(x-h)^2+k$. (p. 68)

vertical shift Used to describe the location of a graph in relation to its parent graph, the shift is the vertical distance (up or down) of each point on the graph from the corresponding point on the parent graph. This type of transformation is a vertical translation. For example, each point on the graph of $y=x^2+2$ is two units higher that its corresponding point on $y=x^2$. In a general equation such as $y=a(x-h)^2+k$ the vertical shift is represented by k. (p. 66)

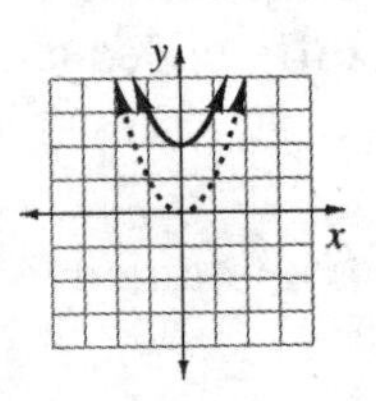

volume For a three-dimensional figure the number of non-overlapping cubic units that will fit inside.

x-bar process control chart A plot of the mean measurement of samples over time. x-bar process control charts are used to monitor whether a manufacturing process is proceeding within limits as expected.

x-intercept A point where a graph intersects the x-axis. In two dimensions, the coordinates of the x-intercept are $(x, 0)$. In three dimensions they are $(x, 0, 0)$. See *intercept*. (p. 10)

x-y interchange The result of exchanging the x and y variables and then solving for y. The resulting equation is the inverse of the original function.

$x \rightarrow y$ table A table that represents pairs of related values. The input value x appears in the first row or column, and the output value, y, appears in the second. The $x \rightarrow y$ table at right contains input and output pairs for the equation $y=x^2-3$.

x	y
−3	6
−2	1
−1	−2
0	−3
1	−2
2	1

y-intercept A point where a graph intersects the y-axis. In two dimensions the coordinates of the y-intercept are $(0, y)$. In three dimensions, the coordinates are $(0, y, 0)$. See *intercept*. (p. 10)

z-score A z-score indicates how many standard deviations a data value is from the mean. More formally, $z = \frac{\text{data value} - \text{mean}}{\text{standard deviation}}$.

zero factorial Zero factorial is 1, $0! = 1$.

zero power The result of raising any number (except zero) to the zero power is 1. $x^0 = 1$ for any number $x \neq 0$. (p. B36)

Zero Product Property When the product of two or more factors is zero, at least one of the factors must equal zero. Used to solve equations in factored form. For example, given the equation $(x-4)(x+5)=0$ you can see that 4 and –5 are solutions and that they are the only possible solutions because there are no other numbers that make either factor zero. (p. 24)

zeros of a function The roots of a function or the values of x for which the function value $y = 0$. The x-intercepts of the graph of a function in the real plane are zeros. These are also called the roots of the function. A function can have complex zeros. These complex zeros cause $y = 0$, but they are not x-intercepts since they do not exist in the real plane. See *roots of a function*.

Index

Student Version, Volume 1

Many of the pages referenced here contain a definition or an example of the topic listed, often within the body of a Math Notes box. Others contain problems that develop or demonstrate the topic. It may be necessary to read the text on several pages to fully understand the topic. Also, some problems listed here are good examples of the topic and may not offer any explanation. The page numbers below reflect the pages in the Student Version. References to Math Notes boxes are bolded.

G

H

I

J

K

L

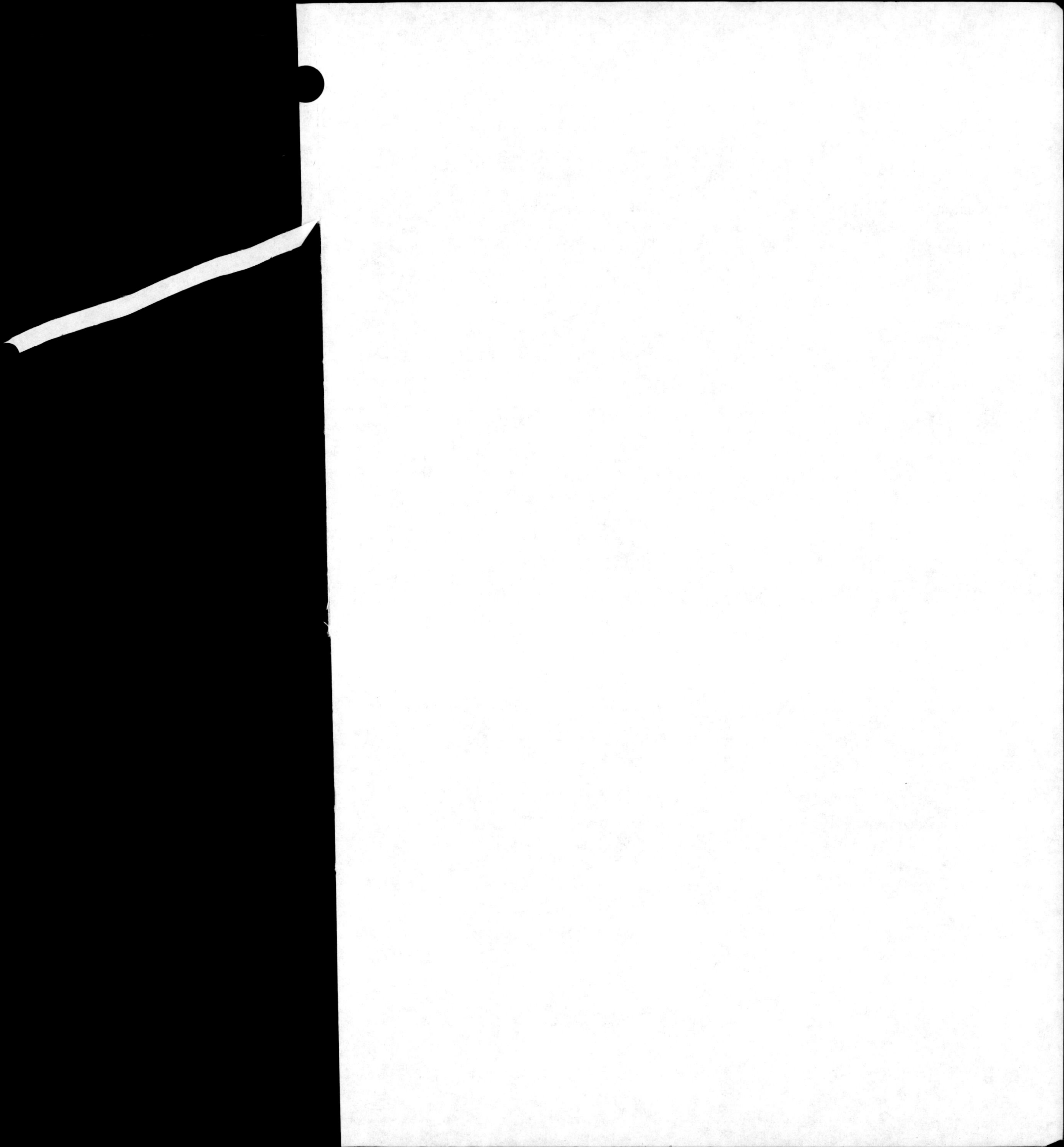

THIS BOOK IS THE PROPERTY OF:

Book No.__________

ISSUED TO	*Year Used*	*CONDITION*	
		ISSUED	*RETURNED*

PUPILS to whom this texbook is issued must not write on any part of it in any way, unless otherwise instructed by the teacher.